THE PANTHER'S FEAST

THE PANTHER'S FEAST

ROBERT ASPREY

Carroll & Graf Publishers, Inc.
New York

Published by arrangement with the author.

First Carroll & Graf edition 1986

Carroll & Graf Publishers, Inc.
260 Fifth Avenue
New York, NY 10001

ISBN: 0-88184-239-7

Manufactured in the United States of America

This book is dedicated to my parents.

It was like feasting with panthers;
the danger was half the excitement.
—*Oscar Wilde*

Prologue

Room Number One of the Hotel Klomser could have been rented in a dozen Vienna hotels: a large, semiluxurious room with pale green walls rising high to a white, ornamented ceiling, two double beds covered with white embroidered spreads, above them framed pictures of the Emperor and Empress of Austria, beside them bed tables holding ash trays and reading lamps, a wardrobe with mirror door, a bureau, two upholstered divans, an armchair and a desk—heavy furniture whose mahogany veneer shimmered in the light of the white globe suspended from the center of the ceiling. A thick brown carpet covered the floor, massive red drapery closed across the three front windows.

Two expensive suitcases, a briefcase and some disorder challenged the impersonal character of the room. An empty champagne bottle lolled in its bucket which had sweated through to the bureau doily further stained by a spilled glass. Ash trays on the bureau and desk overflowed their stubbed holdings. A copy of the *Neue Freie Presse,* a Vienna daily, lay scattered across one bed. On the other bed was a carelessly thrown military blouse. This was a General Staff blouse. Its choke collar of gold showed the three-star insigne of full colonel; its left breast bore a row of colored decorations.

The blouse belonged to the man slumped in the armchair: Colonel Alfred Victor Redl of the General Staff Corps. He was a small man; the top of his clipped blond hair just showed over the back of the chair. He sat quite still but an involuntary twitch of his left hand and the dullness of his overbright eyes staring at the red drapery contradicted his seeming calm. Once he raised a hand to stroke the fine hair of his blond mustache. Once he moved forward, cupped both hands around his head as if it hurt. Once he cleared his throat with what might have been a sob. But as the chimes of Parliament Clock filtered through the windows and the red drapery of Room Number One, as the large metal hands pointed to the hour of one thirty A.M., May 25, 1913 . . . the figure in the chair sat motionless, its puffy, oval face impenetrable.

This face and its expression were known to a large number of people in the Austro-Hungarian Empire and to a few outside it. If a few hours earlier some of these persons had been asked about Colonel Redl, the answers would have been illuminating, most of them complimentary. General Conrad von Hötzendorf, Chief of the Imperial and Royal Army General Staff, would have put down the brandy he was sipping in a swank salon of the Grand Hotel and said, "Colonel Redl is General Staff Chief of the Eighth Prague Corps. I have known him for eight years as an outstanding General Staff officer, and that is why I assigned him to this important and sensitive post. In case of war, incidentally, I shall probably appoint him Chief of my Intelligence Bureau."

Doctor Viktor Pollak, a kindly man in his early fifties who was the Government's leading prosecuting attorney, would have said, "I am just on my way to meet Alfred for dinner. He is one of my oldest friends. We have worked together for years on espionage cases. He is the best counterintelligence officer in the Dual Monarchy."

Colonel of the General Staff August Urbanski von Ostrymiecz, Chief of the Intelligence Bureau, who was having a quiet dinner with his wife, would have said, "Colonel Redl was my deputy for two years. When I was away on official business, which was often, he was in charge of the Intelligence Bureau. Personally we are not close, but I admire and respect his professional ability. He is an exceptionally able individual. As I wrote on his fitness report in 1910: 'A very educated, excellent General Staff officer who will fully qualify for any post.'"

Also at home with his wife, Major of the General Staff Maximilian Ronge, Chief of the Counterintelligence Section in the Intelligence Bureau, would have said, "The most brilliant man I have ever known. I was his protégé in the Bureau for four years—he taught me everything. Altogether Colonel Redl served nine years in Intelligence—come to think of it, he was the Intelligence Bureau."

A famous Viennese surgeon, Arthur Schnitzel, would not have liked the question. "Yes, yes, I knew Redl, vaguely, years ago. I was a medical aid man in the Army, up in Lemberg in Galicia, that was 1891, I believe. I saw him a few times in Vienna later—have not seen him in years. He is a sick man."

Out in Stockerau, a small village twenty-five miles from Vienna, a dashing young cavalry lieutenant in the 7th Ulan Regiment named Stefan Hromodka would have turned his pretty face away from a girl to whom he was making love. "Uncle Alfred? I have known him for nine years. He is a wonderful, brilliant man and he has given me everything including this apartment and my horses and automobile. Still, he does have some strange ideas. That is why I saw him this afternoon. We had another argument."

Outside of Vienna, in Prague, old General Baron von Giesl, commanding Eighth Corps, would have said, "Alfred Redl joined the Intelligence Bureau in 1900 when I was its chief. He was a captain then, obviously a brilliant young officer. I gave him a free hand and it was not long before he furnished the results I desired. I do not know how many spies he uncovered and sent to jail but the number is impressive. I do not believe that it would be an exaggeration to say that our splendid internal security is due in large part to his making. Last year I was very fortunate to secure him as my General Staff Chief. He has proved outstanding in this billet and I am the first to admit that he is running my Corps. Immensely popular with my officers. He lives quietly but very well—came into some money several years ago and bought an Austro-Daimler automobile. Goes to Vienna quite often for the weekends. I would too if I were still a young bachelor. He is in Vienna this weekend taking care of some trouble with his nephew."

In Russian Poland, in the city of Warsaw, Colonel Batjuschin of the Czar's Army would have stared out the window of his large office overlooking Sachsenplatz and would have smiled: "Oh, yes. Redl, Alfred Victor. Born in Lemberg, Galicia, March 14, 1864. Son of a railroad—" He would have stopped, then said: "You must not talk too much in my business. Yes, I know

Redl. First heard the name back in the 'eighties. A clever man, very cunning. He sent a lot of my agents to jail—but I sent a lot of his agents to jail. Oh, he has weaknesses—every man has." Then he would have chuckled. Colonel Batjuschin was Chief of Russian Army Intelligence in Warsaw.

Of the many officers and civilians who knew Alfred Redl, some knew only the name, others the name and face. But none, none at all, knew the man. The man did not even know himself. That was why he now sat in the armchair, staring at the red drapery, hoping to see through and beyond and somehow find himself. He would do this, but not quite yet and not from the night.

The night was important though. It had already passed a sentence and offered an escape. Its emissaries—Urbanski and Ronge and a General von Höfer and a Judge Advocate named Wenzel Vorlicek—had come to Redl an hour ago. They had been sent by the Chief of the General Staff. They had brought a sentence and they delivered it with an exclamation point which they left on the desk between two sealed letters. The exclamation point was a small, black, 6.35 mm. Browning pistol.

But neither a sentence nor an escape is a real answer to one's existence. And for the first time in his forty-nine years of life, Alfred Redl demanded the real answer. So he sat slumped in this chair to pick his mind like he might pick the flea-infested coat of a mongrel dog. With each flea went some of the maddening irritation, but he had to get all of them before relief was to come. The trouble was, there were so many fleas of thought burrowed in the mind of Alfred Redl.

Part I

THE REHEARSAL

1.

EVEN among the rows of uniforms and the shining long bay-
onets, the musicians, the sparkling instruments, even among
the pomp and color of an Imperial and Royal infantry regiment on parade, the young cadet stood out. His name was
Alfred Victor Redl. At twenty-three years of age, he was short,
just over five feet three inches, and he was small in frame. His
body was trim, neatly proportioned for its height, his shoulders
wide, hips slim. He carried himself straight and when he stood
at ease his shoulders were back, his head up and his uniform
gloved him as if he stood at attention. His face that morning
bore its normal serious stamp: a slightly oval face, straight nose,
small even mouth, each feature dominated by the bright blue
eyes that gained in luster from blond eyebrows and hair and tan
skin. Many said this soldier was handsome, all agreed that he
was military.

He stood with his regiment on the long wide drill field of
the Lemberg garrison, a field that was green and sunny and
happy with people that morning of May 1, 1887. On the reviewing stand the Corps Commander chatted easily with the Governor of Galicia while deputies and aides intermingled smart,
scarlet uniforms with black morning coats and top hats in a
temporary truce of the military-civil enmity common to Empire
provinces. On uncomfortable benches flanking the stand civilians from the town of Lemberg and from surrounding farms
sat in starched primness to whisper of the dignitaries above
them or to discuss the crops or to exchange town gossip.

Sudden music turned all eyes toward the white-uniformed
band followed now by the marching soldiers of the 9th Galician
Infantry Regiment. As the regiment passed in review the spectators stood to complement the saluting officers serious in their
respect to the black and yellow flag of Empire and to the regimental standard whose faded and scarred battle flags bragged of
survival in an age of defeat. With its passing, the Corps Com-

17

mander_and his officers tucked away their stiff salutes, the Governor and his aides replaced their top hats, the spectators sat down. Then they watched the band and the soldiers square the large field, halt and face about.

Though at ease the regiment sacrificed nothing of its parade neatness. Each platoon and company and battalion stood fronted by its commanding officer; in the center of the field the red-bloused solitary regimental Adjutant poised, ready to catalyze the units into a whole. Suddenly the Adjutant straightened to attention, the verdant stillness of the field was broken by his powerful voice: "REG-I-MENT," and his word was caught and respected by other voices warning: "BATT-AL-ION," "COM-PA-NY," "PLA-TOON," and again the Adjutant: "ATTEN-SHUN!" Fourteen hundred heels snapped together with the explosion of a howitzer shell, the Adjutant about-faced to await the Colonel of the Regiment who, followed by his aides, walked slowly onto the field, and across the springy turf. The Adjutant saluted: "Sir, the Regiment stands ready, all present and accounted for."

Colonel Friedrick Pranton returned the salute. "Thank you, Major. Order the cadets forward, if you please."

Once again the Adjutant about-faced. "The following cadet officer deputies will come forward on command: Carl von Anders, Thomas Kustrón, Felix Mreule, Eduard Peter, Alfred Redl, Johann Tischler. Cadet officer deputies: FOR-WARD MARCH."

From the ranks stepped the six young men who that day were to be commissioned as officers in the Imperial and Royal Army of the Austro-Hungarian Empire. Marching stiffly, they converged in line before the Colonel of the Regiment, saluted and remained at attention.

"There he is, Ma," a boy excitedly said, "there, Ma, see, there he is."

The woman, dumpy and cheaply dressed, her body sagged and her high-cheekboned face lined far beyond the due of her years, adjusted her bonnet and squinted across the field. "My, don't he look nice, now," she said. She raised her hand and waved.

"Ma, stop that," a young woman on her left said. "People are watching you."

"Never you mind, Ernestine Johanna. You got so proper since you been teachin' in school that a body can't move any—"

"Ma, make Marion quit," a girl's voice interrupted.

"Marion, stop it," the woman said automatically. She looked quickly at the younger children. "You, Adolphine Maria, stop your whinin' now. Natalia, straighten your sister's bow. Heinrich, give your brother's ear a pull if he don't quit with Maria." Lending them a final scowl while oblivious to simultaneous scowls of neighboring spectators, the woman tugged at the sleeves of her dress and turned again to the drill field, squinting so that she could see her son, Alfred.

The field grew quiet as Colonel Pranton faced the six cadets, his eyes resting for a moment on each face. Then he ordered, "Raise your right hands, and repeat after me: Before God Almighty . . ."

"Before God Almighty," Alfred Redl swore, his mouth forming the noble words slowly, his eyes riveted on the collar insignia of Colonel Pranton,

"we solemnly swear to His Apostolic Majesty, our Most Supreme Prince and Master . . . Francis Joseph the First, by God's Grace the Emperor of Austria, the King of Bohemia and the Apostolic King of Hungary . . . to be loyal and obedient, to obey his generals, our superiors and seniors . . . to respect them and to defend them . . . to carry out their commands and orders in every instance, against any enemy, whoever it may be . . . and wherever it will serve the Will of His Imperial and Royal Majesty . . . on water and on land, by day and by night, in battles, assaults, engagements and actions of any kind . . . in short, to fight bravely and valiantly at any place and at any time . . . never to forsake our comrades, colors, standards and arms . . . never to make mutual understanding with the enemy . . . always to conduct ourselves in accordance with the rules of war as befits good soldiers . . . and in these ways to live and to die in Honor. So Help Us God. Amen." *

* The contrast between Habsburg and Prussian authoritarianism is clear from the speech made by Emperor William the Second to his recruits at Potsdam on November 23, 1891:

PART I

His mother was the first to kiss him. She held him tightly
and while she cried and patted his back, the younger brothers
and sisters pulled at his uniform and everyone was excited and
talking all at once. When he had slipped from his mother's
embrace, he heard her voice saying over the rest, "If his father
could only have seen him he would have been a proud man.
My Franz was an officer, God rest his soul"—this to a few
friends—" 'fore we married and a fine-looking man, too, in his
uniform. Franz always loved the Army, he always said he
should never have left it to marry—'course he never meant it,
bless him—but he said it often enough Oskar and Alfred don't
remember much else of their father, do you boys? Why I
remember once . . ." and she went on while Alfred embraced
his older sisters and shook hands with the friends. Such was the
talk and the excitement, no one seemed to pay him much attention after a few minutes, no one seemed to notice that the
blue eyes were no longer openly alert and alive, that he held
them half-closed and distant, and when he quietly excused
himself no one seemed to heed him or to mind except his oldest
sister who told him to be sure he was on time for the dinner
later.

He walked by himself across the empty drill field. Behind
him he could hear the babble easily, he could hear his mother's
voice and he thought to himself, *Ever since I can remember, I
have heard those voices.* Aloud he said, "Damn them," and
quickened his pace toward the barracks.

Alfred was sitting half-undressed on his bunk when Carl
came in to change. Carl was smiling and excited. He pounded
Alfred on the back and called him lieutenant. *"Mein lieber
Gott,* Fredl," he finally said, "after five years I never thought
we would do it. I am excited. Aren't you excited, Fredl?"

"Recruits: Before the altar and before the ministers of God you have sworn
the oath of fealty to me. You are too young fully to understand the significance
of what has been said. Your first duty is to obey every order and every command blindly. You have sworn fealty to me. You are the men of my Guard
and my soldiers. You have committed yourselves to me body and soul. There
can be but one enemy for you, and that is whoever shall be my enemy. Owing
to the present machinations of the Socialists it may happen that I shall order
you to fire on your own relatives, on your brothers and on your fathers—God
grant it may not be—and in that case you are bound to obey my orders blindly."

20

Alfred smiled. "It is wonderful, Carl, of course." Then his smile vanished, his blue eyes looked coldly into the air past Carl and he said in a promise to himself, "But this is only the beginning."

No augury like a bolt of lightning or a falling comet or a new star accompanied the birth of Alfred Redl. It happened in a crowded dwelling in Lemberg, an event whose force had long since been dissipated by habit. To Franz and Mathilde Redl, having babies was another consequence of night no more profound than washing faces or combing hair. When they had moved to this city two weeks earlier, Mathilde's time was close and she no sooner had the furniture arranged and the eight children divided in the few beds than she herself took to bed. The baby was born on March 14, 1864. Several days later a Roman Catholic priest christened it Alfred Victor Redl.

Other than forcing its father to borrow one hundred gulden* the new baby in no way disturbed the routine of the Redl household. As he had done for so many years, Franz Redl continued to rise early, dress his small body in a heavy woolen uniform that was at once threadbare and greasy, eat a *Würstl* with black bread and drink a cup of coffee, and then grump his way to the freight office of the Lemberg railroad station where he worked for the Carl Ludwig Railroad. At forty-five years of age he held the job of *Expeditor* Second Class—a minor freight clerk—and he was paid altogether 1700 gulden a year for filling it. After a day of writing bills of lading—the crabbed hand testifying to his six years of elementary schooling—and of checking and filing invoices, he would return to his family, eat supper and smoke a pipe of cheap tobacco. If he were in a good humor, which was rare, he sometimes told the children a story or two before sending them to bed. More often he simply told them to shut up and then, in revolt against the hopeless air of dirty babies and cabbage soup, sought the better atmosphere of Wilkowski's *Stüberl* which smelled of bad cigars and good beer. Sometimes Franz would go to bed early, sometimes late, but when he felt the desire of his loins neither time

* One Austrian gulden or florin equaled approximately forty-five cents in U. S. money.

nor the reaction of his wife interfered. Wordlessly, with no attempt to gratify his mate, he would climb onto her, relieve himself, roll off, turn over, go to sleep, snore, and swear when he learned she was pregnant again.

As she had done for so many years, Mathilde Redl also continued to rise early and, in alliance with a young Polish girl servant, to get the older children dressed and fed and off to school, to feed and change the babies, to shop for enough of the cheapest of anything to fill twelve stomachs for another day, to gossip a spell in the bustling Lemberg market, to light a candle in church, to cook the noon and evening meals and finally to pack the children off to bed and, exhausted, to follow them soon after. Younger than her husband, the years of childbearing had already sagged her body, lined her face and sapped her strength. Cherishing the not uncommon belief that piety is synonymous with suffering, she crossed herself frequently, prayed constantly for her husband and found her greatest joy on Saturdays when she led the children to confession and on Sundays to two masses and service, occasions on which she clucked over them as if she were a mother hen leading her chicks to corns of goodness.

Nothing short of an earthquake could have interfered with this schedule. It had begun in 1851 when Franz Redl, not without misgiving, had left eleven years of service as a lieutenant in the Army in favor of marriage and a job with the state railroad at a starting annual wage of 500 gulden. Seven years later he had four children and was earning 700 gulden. When the Carl Ludwig Railroad, a private company, offered him 900 gulden a year and free living quarters, he took the job and moved his family to a Galician town called Wieliczka. During the next five years the ever-increasing family was transferred throughout Galicia until the company finally brought it to Lemberg where it was to remain.

The Lemberg of Alfred Redl's childhood—the Lwow of today—was a bustling trade town of thirty-five thousand inhabitants consisting of Poles, Ruthenes, Germans, Italians, Bulgarians, Greeks, Mohammedans and Jews—people altogether remarkable only in their variety. Situated in a narrow basin surrounded by hills, the town was denied a natural perspective and this in part accounted for the failure of parks and gardens to soften its compressed air that was subject to the soot from the locomotives in the busy railroad terminus and to the smoke from the town's numerous iron foundries. Still another quality permeated this air, an unhealthy compound in which discontent and melancholy were at once discernible. But this quality was not unique to Lemberg, nor even to the harsh, monotonous landscape of Galicia. Rather it permeated the entire Austro-Hungarian Empire and because it was to play an essential role in Alfred Redl's life, its origins must be briefly examined.

Sixteen years before the birth of Alfred Redl, Austria had been gripped by widespread revolution. In 1848 this had caused the idiot Emperor Ferdinand to abdicate in favor of his eighteen-year-old nephew, Francis Joseph. Backed by his Army, the young ruler had restored order to his land and had then inaugurated a decade of imperial autocracy under ministers like Schwarzenberg and Bach, men devoted to the Habsburg belief that absolutism was "the natural constitution of the Monarchy." Prosperity did not result. An internal economic crisis in 1857 was followed by external defeat two years later when the Austrian Army went down to the French at Solferino. This setback caused Francis Joseph the loss of his Italian province, Lombardy, and forced him as well to begin an internal rule best described in brief as that of constitutional as opposed to imperial absolutism. He next proceeded into conflict with his powerful German rival, Prussia. Francis Joseph's defeat at the Battle of Königgrätz (or Sadowa)—fought in 1866 when Alfred Redl was two years old—marked the real turning point for ill of Habsburg fortunes. Not only did it cost Francis Joseph the loss of Venetia, the last of his Italian lands, but it also, and far worse, forced him to yield leadership of the cultural-political hegemony over central Europe which the House of Habsburg had exercised for centuries. To regain it meant a second and successful war against Prussia, and to prepare for that he had to strengthen himself internally, a complicated process that involved raising the recalcitrant Magyars of Hungary to a nearly

equal partnership in empire with Austria. In 1867 the Dual
Monarchy of Austria-Hungary was formally created.

The political abortion of the Dual Monarchy insured a lasting infection that was to ooze the corruption of dissolution until
the body of State died. A victory of Magyar separatists over
German-Austrian nationalists, it also served as a signal for other
Empire races, particularly the Bohemian Czechs, the Galician
Poles, and the Galician-Bukowina Ruthenes or "little Russians," to release their own autonomous demands to a Vienna
soon turned into a smoldering volcano of dissension by the
constant conflict of national claims.

The case of Galicia was typical only in its complexity. Of the
Empire's thirty-six millions, nearly six million lived in this
large northeastern province. In theory about 58 per cent of the
inhabitants were Polish, slightly over 40 per cent Ruthenian
and just over 1 per cent German. In fact the population was
composed of numerous nationalities, including a Jewish ele-
ment perhaps as high as 10 per cent of the whole; further,
numerous segments, each with contrary demands, existed in
the major national groups. Polish and Ruthenian were the languages of the land with German recognized as "a customary
language" used for central administration and military matters.
The wealth, indeed the real power of Galicia, rested in the
hands of the conservative Poles who for the most part were
wealthy, aristocratic landowners. It was with this group that
Francis Joseph contracted in 1867. The relationship was essentially negative, a convenience designed to settle rather than to
solve. In return for their support, the Emperor granted the
Poles a large measure of internal autonomy in their administration of the province. Because this was reactionary in the
extreme, it meant a continuation of the terrible poverty
throughout Galicia; because it was Polish in spirit, it meant a
continuation of a governing attitude that was fundamentally
non-Austrian. By 1869—Alfred Redl was then five years old—
a visitor to Lemberg could write:

The Imperial Governor at the time was Count Goluchowski.
He was very rich and felt himself more an Imperial Satrap than
Governor—more an assistant King than a high official. Under
such auspices the Polish influence became strongly dominant and

the German upper-class society as well as the Ruthenian lower-class society was soon completely pushed to the side. *

This was the air of one portion of Empire—dissident voices protesting in dissident tongues, a heavy oppressed air of discontent and melancholy, of furtive revolutionaries plotting in smoke-filled cellars, of police and army units seeking them out, of citizen's peace suddenly broken by violent acts of political terrorism. This was the Lemberg of Alfred Redl's youth, but it could have been Cracow, Prague, Budapest. An atmosphere that defies precise definition, it was negative and destructive, a powerful and tragic mood of pervasive and hopeless hatred:

There are fearful excitements on any side.
Any side can accuse the other
And feel virtuous without the hardships of virtue.
When pride of race has been pent up
In a tyrannous disregard, and valued liberties
Have been lost for long enough, what comes in the way
Of dignity's free and natural flowing
Is nothing but rocks to be blasted. I envy them
Their certainty. Each private man
Has a public cause to elucidate him,
And a reasonable sense of having been wronged.
If you like you can call this man your enemy;
It's what he expects.**

"Too proud to beg, too honest to steal,
So we belong to the shabby genteel."

The most singular characteristic of Alfred Redl's homelife was its povertied anonymity. When he was born his father earned 1700 gulden a year. When he was eight years old, when his birth had been followed by five more, his father's annual income had increased to 2400 gulden. This economic fact insured a restricted table with heavy reliance on cabbage soup and beans; the biological fact insured that the ninth child would occupy no particular spot in the family sun. Still, he was dressed and he did eat and in the evenings he sat with the rest

* Auffenberg-Komarów, Moritz von, *Aus Österreichs Höhe und Niedergang.*
** Christopher Fry. *The Dark Is Light Enough,* Oxford University Press, 1954.

of the children in the main room that was heated; he read by the feeble candlelight or he joined the childish games or he listened to his father tell exaggerated stories of his army days. With his brothers and sisters and the other children of the poor neighborhood, he took his lunch pail each day to walk the cobblestone streets up the Ringplatz, past the barns of Lemberg's horse-drawn streetcar system, past the post office and bank and courthouse and the Renaissance and baroque façades of the little stores to the small, uncomfortable, elementary school, the *Volksschule*. On holidays he went with his family on outings in the hills that surrounded this old fortified city, on weekends he was herded to the wicker confessional of the church and to the masses and service. At first glance this little boy in patched knickerbockers and darned sweater seemed remarkably well adapted to the motto of the family Redl, remarkably like the eight brothers and sisters who had come before him, like the five who followed him. He was a small boy, almost frail, but he was a nice-looking lad, a blond with clear, blue eyes and white, even teeth. He was quieter than the others but he went about the same life, did the same things, spoke the same Polish and Ruthenian languages, studied the same German grammar, sat on the same hard bench in the *Volksschule*, seemed to fit just as well in the pattern of the days as anyone else in the Redl family, as anyone else in the town of Lemberg.

And yet he was different. The spawn of ignorance and apathy, he should have reflected and respected his heritage. He did neither. Because he was intelligent and sensitive, he recognized it for what it was, a useless existence of monotony. He began to escape from it at an early age and he used the only weapon available to him: his mind. To this boy, home was a challenge, a small world where survival with the least pain was the gain of him who trod it softly and quietly, who stayed out of the way as some people manage to do through a lifetime to die with no assurance of a better future except that nothing could be worse. Anonymity in a dwelling crowded with two adults and a dozen children is not difficult if one remains silent and when caught in some impish perversity shifts the blame by deceit and trickery to one of the noisier and thus more likely bodies. By the time he was eight years old, Alfred had learned the wiles of survival. He could lie, cheat and swindle with as little effort as it took him to stare with his open blue eyes, and with a great deal of effect because he was a quiet and a good boy.

School was something else again, a place of more positive rewards. If the brain were used properly, he discovered, it could furnish correct answers, and correct answers were profitable because they often drew the comfort of pedagogic kudos. Correct answers were great levelers of society; they furnished their donor a certain position among his contemporaries that transcended the shame of hand-me-down clothes and the poverty of the lunch pail. These rewards alone were sufficient to cause the small boy to work his quick and able mind, to keep it furnishing the correct answers. Deep within him, too, lay a dim discernment that the mind owned still greater power, that the mind could ultimately transport him from shabby mediocrity to a world that presently existed only in his dreams.

Here was Alfred's real escape. Through his cunning he could mitigate some of the misery of the home and through his mental agility compensate for some of the loneliness and insecurity that he felt. But he had to escape to something, and it was in the dream that he found something. When he was young, very young, he practiced one favorite dream. He was the only son of one of the rich houses on the other side of town. He awakened in a bed so large that he could roll across it five times and the bed was in a room so large that a carriage and a team of four could fit into it. A servant helped him wash and dress and another servant brought him breakfast and he rushed down the wide, carpeted staircase to the chandeliered dining room of morning sun and a mother who hugged and kissed him and a father who patted his head and gave him a kreuzer to spend later in the day. He stood in the warmth of the morning sun and his mother's arms to wave the father good-bye in the large carriage with the coachmen on top and liveried footmen in the rear. He was always happy in this dream until one day in a rare burst of confidence he had told an older sister—later he tried to remember, it was either Ernestine or Helena—and she had laughed and said it was silly and that had ruined it for him.

27

By then it didn't matter so much. He was growing tired of the dream or he would never have shared it with anyone. He was not quite certain when he made his new dream, but it was probably before his father died. Each year his father took him and Oskar and Heinrich to watch the army corps maneuver, a grand show of hissing rockets and cannonading and long white columns assaulting to the tune of the Radetzky March. He worked on this dream until in it he sat astride a giant white stallion to wave his marshal's baton at the generals and aides on the field and he always held the field and broke the enemy, and later he knelt before the Emperor who hung still another decoration on his chest and thanked him for saving the Empire.

He had other dreams too, one for nearly every circumstance, but of course a dream never altered anything. He could sit in the noisy room or lie in the crowded bed and project himself to a mansion or a battlefield, but sooner or later he had to accept the crowded bed and he had to obey the orders of his older and bigger brothers and sisters. When he was eleven years old and his father lay dying, he could dream that he was a famous surgeon summoned to save the life of this man, but he had to awaken to the real smell of burning incense and a priest administering final rites, to long services in the dark, cold church, the crying, hysterical mother who had already begun to canonize the departed one, the final words and prayers in a cold rain of a March day in the year 1875. Dream as he would around life, he was forever pulled back to its reality.

And this reality was harsh and growing harsher because the sum and substance of Franz Redl's last will and testament was a bequeathment of the poverty into which he had been born, which he had successfully propagated and which he had escaped at the age of fifty-five years by the expediency of death. Whatever petty cash was on hand had been claimed by his sickness and funeral expenses of 300 gulden. A month after his death Mathilde was awarded 666 gulden a year pension plus another thousand gulden for the annual support of the ten children still under eighteen years of age. That autumn Alfred left elementary school for *Realschule,* a junior school that emphasized mathematics and engineering. For the next three years of his life the cabbage soup was to come more often on the table, the clothes more often to the darning needle, the weary complaints of his mother more often to his ears. For three more years he would be dominated by his sisters, sixteen-year-old Ernestine Johanna, fifteen-year-old Helena Emilia, thirteen-year-old Ottilia Adela.

But now the one dream was not so foolish. The Lemberg garrison was active in these years, the Imperial and Royal Army was expanding. In 1877 his older brother, Oskar, left home for Cadet School. Perhaps it was his uniform, perhaps the glowing stories of army life that intrigued his younger brother. Alfred took the entrance examinations in 1879 when he was fourteen years old. He passed them with no difficulty, nor did anyone in the family object to his entering Karthaus Cadet School in Lemberg that autumn. Franz Redl had been an officer; the Cadet School was free.

2.

WHEN Alfred Redl was seventeen years old he chose a military career. This choice was almost automatic to the boy obsessively determined to break from his past and everything it represented, and when on March 14, 1881, he joined the regular Army he sealed this determination by pledging himself to five additional reserve and two Home Guard years, a total service far greater than that demanded by law. The Commandant of Karthaus Cadet School swore him in and the Adjutant paid him three gulden *Handgeld*—literally, "hand money," a payment originated in the Thirty Years' War to enable a recruit to buy toilet articles at the time of his enlistment. With this act Alfred became an *infanterist*, a private soldier earning six kreuzer a day.*

From the moment he entered Karthaus to be pigeonholed in the manner of a stray blanket or a pair of shorts, Alfred liked it. Karthaus was the bugle and the schedule: you will drill now,

---

* One gulden contained one hundred kreuzer, therefore his pay was less than $.03 a day.

you will eat now, you will go to the toilet now, you will think now, you will sleep now. Like a small prison Karthaus ran with its own rules, its own code, its own way of doing things. But prison offered new clothes, the first he had ever owned, a gray uniform that began to cloak him from his past as though he were a thousand, not two miles away from home. Prison gave him healthy food, not good food, but food that put meat and muscle on his small frame, that furnished the energy for him to swim and tumble and fence and drill. Like the food the curriculum, too, was healthy, at least to a future officer. Not all of this nonsense about learning to think but rather the practical business of learning to calculate. Formulae, rules, graphs, distances, charts—these were the military's meat and Alfred chewed them and savored them and when called upon spat them back to the instructor in the form of solutions that were rarely wrong. Yes, life in Karthaus was a good thing. Alfred liked every aspect of it. He even liked its secrets.

"Ssshhh, be quiet, Fredl," Hans told him. Alfred opened his eyes, oriented himself to the dark sleeping dormitory, made out the face of his friend. "Come on, Fredl," Hans said. "The storeroom."

Alfred crept from his warm bed to follow Hans through the tiers of bunks down a passageway. Hans knocked lightly on a door which opened to admit the two boys into a room dimly lighted by candle. This was the mattress room and one of the stacks had been plundered to carpet the stone floor. Alfred recognized several friends lying on the mattresses, laughing at the antics of Fritz Witzleben who stood naked, his plump buttocks thrust out in imitation of an affected junior officer on the staff.

Hans pulled Alfred down beside him on an empty mattress and the two boys lay on their stomachs next to each other's warmth and laughed with the rest at Fritz's continued obscenities. Then someone blew out the candle, someone called, "Help, I'm blind," and Alfred laughed even while he felt the warm hands of Hans lift his nightgown and slide up his body to stroke his buttocks and roll him over and tickle the light growth of hair. When Hans' soft hand took it and pressed it Alfred could stand no more and he threw his arms around Hans and pressed wet kisses on him and pulled the body tight to him and worked his hands over that body and they did this until they panted and stiffened and clutched and slowly fell away. Then they lay in the darkness, Hans holding Alfred who felt a million miles from his world, felt cared for and wanted and safe and comfortable. When all the boys finished, they straightened the storeroom, crept back to their beds. For the rest of the night Alfred dreamed about Hans.

Believing that physical exercise would subordinate sexual desire, the Karthaus staff did not imagine the existence of such sessions. But it is a mistake of elders to hang tired maturity on the prominent peg of the young. The young do not want to subordinate sexual desire. And as on that night when the Commandant slept in a far corner of his marital bed (sexual desire having absented itself several years earlier, physical exercise or no), and a small storeroom seemed itself to writhe with the twistings of the young bodies on the mattress-covered floor, so on many nights the old officer and the rest of the Karthaus cadre slept while these passions found release.

Alfred liked it best when Hans came alone to his bed. Very quietly he would come, silently pull back the covers, slip in beside him, and then in the night they would consummate the love drive with the same urgency they showed on the fencing floor, the same intensity with which they bent over a difficult math problem. And with effects no more lasting. Sometimes during the day Alfred would look at Hans and try to recapture the spirit of one of their nights and realize, finally and a trifle sadly, that he could not do this, that the excitement had vanished with the act and that he might as well try to recapture the thrill of a last week's *touché* against a fencer better than himself. Even the anticipation of Hans escaped him. Sometimes when he finished a problem early and knew it was correct, he would lean back and look at Hans scribbling and erasing and frowning, he would think him stupid and even ugly and then would forget him in favor of looking again at his answer which he knew would gain the instructor's approbation.

Whether the problem was Hans or mathematics or drill, when Alfred faced it, that was everything, away from it, that was nothing. He compartmented problems as if a portion of his brain were stuck with a little flag labeled *Hans* and other portions labeled *mathematics* or *fencing* or *history*. To the immediate problem went his entire attention. As he anticipated it, worked on it, solved it, he was freed from those maddening little side thoughts that can intrude like the visit of an unwanted relative, free to bask in the enjoyment and exploit the success of a correct answer. Having already learned that overt emotional display was not military, Alfred taught himself to accept an instructor's compliments with no more than a quick, shy smile, a winning smile that he had practiced in a mirror, before looking away in feigned embarrassment. Because of this his teachers and friends called him modest.

Failure, however, worked a far more complicated process in his mind. Because he masked it with a brief frown and silence his teachers and friends tagged him a good sport. Because he tried to convert it to his own advantage and because he often did salvage profit from the transaction his teachers called him industrious. No one sensed the hot wrath that failure invariably aroused in him, the frantic searching for an external force to bear the blame of a particular shortcoming, the cold fury that possessed him when he could find none.

Once in fencing class he made an improper parry. "What is the matter, Redl?" the instructor demanded.

Alfred reddened. "I . . . I slipped, sir. The floor . . . the floor caused me to slip."

The instructor looked coldly at him. "You slipped, lad, because you were careless."

Alfred frowned slightly, said nothing. He repeated the parry, mastered it, fenced for another year under the same master. He never forgave the man, never ceased hating him when he saw him, but no one, not even Hans, ever divined this.

Hans did know about the one night. Alfred awakened that night thinking to have heard Hans but Hans did not appear. Alfred got up, stole swiftly to Hans' bunk, found it empty. He climbed in it anyway, he fell asleep. He was shaken roughly awake by a merciless Hans who told him to get out and go back to his own bunk. He did as he was told. He knew that he was suddenly out of favor, that his lover had gone to someone else. In the dark, in his own bed, he frowned. But no one could see him now and he had no need of swallowing injustice and being a good sport and so in the dark and alone he cried and finally slept. He never spoke to Hans again.

These were two failures, essentially important ones. But important failures do not often compete well against superficial successes—to a boy the glare of feeble victory easily dims the brilliance of vital defeat. And in his next two years Alfred Redl built himself a shining record of feeble victories. When he graduated from Karthaus in August, 1882, his four-year effort was marked with an over-all "very good," the next to the top grade. He was posted as an acting noncommissioned officer to Infantry Regiment Number 9 in Lemberg.

Both by tradition and constitution the Imperial and Royal Army was an instrument of dynasty. Its leadership and organization were the exclusive concern of the Emperor to whom its officers swore their oaths. Like the Empire it was to protect, the Army looked simple and efficient on paper. In reality it was complicated and cumbrous.

In 1882 it numbered 22,000 officers and 321,000 men. Its core was one hundred and two infantry regiments which, together with artillery, cavalry, engineer and supply units, formed the brigades and divisions of fifteen corps, each located at a strategic point in the Empire. This was the territorial system basis with each corps command responsible for administration, supply and operations in a given area, an arrangement designed to expedite mobilization in case of war. The corps commands were tied together administratively by a Ministry of War in Vienna, operationally by a General Staff in Vienna with its representatives at brigade, division and corps level.

But a significant portion of the Empire's military strength lay if not remote at least compartmented from the Imperial and Royal Army. In order to create the Dual Monarchy in 1867, Emperor Francis Joseph had to grant Hungary permission to establish her own army, the *Honvéd*, not a Home Guard organization but a national army, albeit limited to infantry and cavalry, with its own units, its own conscription, its own budget, its own reserve formations—an army run by a Hungarian

Ministry of Defense responsible to a Hungarian Parliament although operationally subject to Francis Joseph. This concession had to be countered by establishing a purely Austrian army, the *Landwehr,* again a national army of infantry and cavalry run by an Austrian Ministry of Defense responsible to an Austrian Parliament and operationally subject to Francis Joseph. Each year the two Parliaments had to draw up and wangle and finally vote on appropriations of men and money for two armies: their own and the joint Imperial and Royal Army. In view of the extremist attitude of many influential Magyars who wanted to separate entirely from the Empire the position could not but deteriorate, and indeed it eventually forced Francis Joseph to sit with the precariousness of a Damocles at his own military councils.

To further complicate matters all regiments were generally provincial in make-up, which meant that the troops of any one regiment could speak German or Czech or Polish or Ruthenian, Hungarian, Italian, Serbo-Croat, or a mixture of all of these with a dialect of any. German was the "official" language of command and service, but the "regimental" language of instruction conformed to the speech of its soldiers. In a mixed regiment any minority over 20 per cent of the total personnel strength had the right to receive instruction in its own tongue, and as a rule every effort was made to instruct in each tongue represented.

The unifying force of the Imperial and Royal Army as well as its adjuncts, the *Landwehr* and *Honvéd,* was an officer corps whose members, by tradition and oath, were *kaisertreu*—they swore their support to the Emperor, not to the State. But in such a complicated military organism the officer corps alone could not remain simple, nor did it. It held three basic careers —the royal, the traditional, the ordinary—and the early stages of each are best illustrated by three men who followed them.

Archduke Francis Ferdinand von Este, whose assassination at Sarajevo in 1914 touched off World War I, was the son of the Emperor's brother, Archduke Carl Ludwig. Francis Ferdinand was fourteen years old when his emperor-uncle appointed him a second lieutenant in Infantry Regiment Number 32. The rank did not intrude upon his private studies, but one summer holiday he briefly held platoon and company commands so that he could be promoted by his uncle to captain and given command of a cavalry squadron. When he was twenty-five years old he was advanced to major and assigned to Infantry Regiment Number 102 in Prague as a staff officer. This was the royal road of military nepotism.

August Urbanski von Ostrymiecz took the traditional road. He was the son of a professional army officer, but for career purposes he could also have been the son of a lesser aristocrat or of a wealthy civilian. When he had completed three years of elementary school—when he was nine years old—August was adopted by the Ministry of War in Vienna which sent him to a military prep school for four years followed by three years in a military cadet school. Faced either with the Infantry-Cavalry Academy at Wiener Neustadt or the Artillery-Engineering Academy in Vienna, he chose the latter and three years later, when he was eighteen years old, was commissioned a second lieutenant. This was the beginning of a true professional career. It did not guarantee later membership in the General Staff or assignment to the best billets or eventual general officer rank, but it was a definite help toward these goals and it was more than coincidence that officers with this background generally attained them.

Alfred Redl faced an ordinary career. After a year as acting noncommissioned officer in Infantry Regiment Number 9, he passed a difficult practical examination and was appointed Cadet Number 58 in the Army, an appointment followed six months later by that to Cadet Officer Deputy. For the next three years he wore the cadet rank of a gold stripe with three small stars, earned 35 kreuzer a day plus 7 gulden a month allowances, performed subordinate platoon duties in various of the sixteen infantry companies located in Lemberg, Stryj and Jaroslaw, spent six months at Infantry Equitation School, passed a series of final examinations and on a May morning in 1887 stood on the Lemberg drill field to swear his oath of duty to his Emperor. When a few days later he reported for duty to the Commanding Officer of the 4th Battalion at Stryj, he was assigned to command an infantry platoon in one of the four companies. Thus began what to all outward appearances

was an uncomplicated Army career of garrison duty: if he
worked hard, ran his unit to the dictates of the book rather
than the head or heart, if he avoided an excess of liquor, cards,
women, if he had any luck at all he could one day become a
colonel "with gout and a pension."

Here were the early stages of three careers in the officer
corps. By the time twenty-three-year-old Alfred Redl was commissioned, twenty-four-year-old Francis Ferdinand was a major,
twenty-two-year-old August Urbanski was adjutant of an artillery battery and was studying for the War College entrance
examinations. By all the rules of tradition, Alfred Redl's subsequent career should never have brushed against either of the
other two. Had Alfred been as ordinary as his early life out-
wardly indicated—as ordinary as his older brother Oskar who
was to follow a simple military career—he would not have
brushed against them. But he was not ordinary. Before he was
finished, Alfred Redl would intrude into Francis Ferdinand's
life, he would nearly ruin August Urbanski's life and he would
shake the Imperial and Royal officer corps to the very roots of
its traditionally honorable existence.

The 9th Galician Infantry Regiment was a typical border
regiment of the Imperial and Royal Army. A colonel commanded it and 132 officers and 1360 troops maintained a regimental staff in Lemberg, four regular field battalions in Lemberg, Jaroslaw, Stryj and Radymno, a cadre of the *ersatz* or
reserve battalion that would form in case of mobilization, and
a quartermaster depot at Stryj. The bulk of the officers had
spent years with the regiment, the bulk of the men were Ruthenian and Polish peasant lads called up for two years military
service. Most of the officers spoke Ruthenian and Polish "sufficient for service needs," which is to say they spoke very little;
most of the troops understood no German.

A common ground existed between officers and men and
between the 9th Infantry Regiment and the other regiments
that garrisoned the fortresses and strong points of the Empire's borders. The common ground was monotony. Referring
to a fortress garrison of the day August Urbanski later wrote:

Alcoholic excesses in the miserable inns and whorehouses of Karlsburg, useless card games, gypsy music, sharp quarrels and other discords framed the ordinary horizon of single officers. The service became neglected by discontent, vexation and uneasiness; punishments could not procure a change. It became a matter of incessant abuse, whisperings and grumblings, each noble impulse was choked, each attempt to eliminate the vices of this fortress rot through advice and encouragement was in vain. The remaining better elements among the junior officers found their salvation in flight: to the military-geographic institute, to a cadet school as teacher, to gymnastic- and fencing- instructor courses, and if such efforts were frustrated, then in the devil's name— to the Hungarian *Honvéd.*

Border garrisons echoed the cry. "It is of no importance," said the lieutenant in one of Stefan Zweig's novels,

"whether I call the little town by its right name or not, for two buttons on a uniform could not more closely resemble each other than does one Austrian provincial garrison town another. In one as in the other the same military establishments: barracks, a riding-school, a parade-ground, an officers' mess, and in addition three hotels, two cafés, a *patisserie,* a wine-bar, a dingy music-hall with faded soubrettes who, as a sideline, most obligingly divide their attentions between the regular officers and the volunteers. Everywhere soldiering entails the same busily empty monotony; hour after hour is mapped out in accordance with inflexible, antediluvian regulations, and even one's leisure does not seem to offer much in the way of variety. In the officers' mess the same faces, the same conversation; at the café the same games of cards and billiards . . ."

Sordid surroundings here, perhaps even hopeless. But surroundings are relative and these were no more sordid, no more hopeless than the small, crowded apartment with its cabbage-soup air, no more restricted than the minute life of Karthaus Cadet School. Further they were new surroundings, they offered a challenge. Before they could pall they had to be learned. To the neat, blond cadet they were a being, an actuality to cock the head at, to study for personal gain. He knew something about them, of course—how to dress for them, how to polish

and shine and walk and march for them. And because he did
all of these things well he produced the maximum impact of
himself on them. As they opened to him, as he learned to know
them, they slowly turned into what all surroundings really are:
small groups of people thrown together by forces of circumstance. In five years he learned to know his comrades: the weak
and the strong, the leaders and the followers, the good and the
bad, the clever and the stupid, the sensitive and the brutish. He
served under them, over them, with them; ate, slept, drank,
talked and laughed in their constant presence. Because he was
young and clean and neat and smart and eager and quiet and respectful the majority liked him and trusted him and went out
of their way to help him.

He sat one night in an officers' mess with an artillery officer
named Paulus Holzlofer. Paulus was not a young man: he was
forty-two years old and he was still a lieutenant because he was
an artillery officer and because the refrain of the song being
sung at the next table was true:

> "Two old men marched through the land,
> A first and second lieutenant;
> Captains now they never will be,
> For both are from the artillery."

After dinner Paulus had gotten quite drunk and now he
shouted the last two lines of the verse, laughed with the other
officers, drank from a large crock of beer, belched and continued
his somewhat maudlin speech to Alfred.

"I used to think," he said, "that if you did your job well
and stayed out of trouble you would make out in this man's
army. So I did my job and kept my nose clean and still the
promotions never came. But habit, Fredl—habit is a monster
that devours and so I did my job well and stayed out of trouble
and habit ate the years up." He signaled for more beer. "There
was a kid who joined my battery as a youngster out of the
Academy. Three years later they made him a first lieutenant,
two years after that he went off to War College and today he
is a goddamn General Staff major. I was a first lieutenant then
and I am still a first lieutenant." Paulus suddenly cocked his

ear to a new song the officers had begun. "You know that song, Fredl?"

Alfred said he did not.

"It is an artillery song," Paulus said, "a Czech song. It tells about a hero of Sadowa, Franz Javurek, an artilleryman with the 'Battery of the Dead.' After his head was torn off by a Prussian shell he stood by his cannon and kept on firing. The last words are, '*A u kanonu stal a furt jen ladoval*'—'he stands by the cannon and goes on loading.' " Paulus laughed wryly. "That is the way with all of us. They tear out our brains to leave us by the cannon where we go on loading. That is the way you will end, too, my friend—unless you get to War College."

Alfred chuckled. "I am not even an officer and you talk about War College."

"But you will be an officer soon."

"Not Academy," Alfred objected.

"Goddamn it, who said you would be? Not being Academy does make it difficult, perhaps impossible. But if you work, if you have any luck . . . well, if you do not make it, so you do not make it—then get out, marry some rich Jew's daughter and run his factory for him. If you make it? You have seen them. The General Staffers—the *flaschen-grünen* boys; they strut around in their glass-green uniforms like God's own peacocks. They get the best jobs, the fast promotions, the important decorations. They sit on their fat asses in the staff billets and live to tell how important they were in the last battle."

"You do not make it sound pleasant," Alfred said.

"I am not trying to. But it is the system." Paulus leaned over the table, his thin face serious. "I am trying to show you, my friend, how a man wastes his life. Look at me. I was young once, like you, and smart, like you. I could have worked—perhaps I would have if some broken-down lieutenant had sat in a forlorn mess to tell me the facts of the army I was in. But I missed, I am stuck with it. Another ten years I make captain, possibly major, and I retire. That is my concern. But I am telling you, Fredl, learn from me. Work, work hard. Read all the manuals, study them, learn every stupid line in them.

Keep off the booze, stay away from the whores. Ask for extra duties—learn everything you can. Kiss any ass whenever you have to. Do anything—to hell with what the others say—do anything in the world to get there. And if you do not get there, then for the love of God get out before it is too late." Paulus took a final drink from the stein. "Come on," he said tiredly, "let's hit the sack."

They all had their stories, these officers, and Alfred heard most of them. They all had their tricks and he learned those, too. He missed many advantages by not going to the Academy, but one he gained, one that no Academy in the world could offer: the study of men in all man's variance. Here was the opportunity of those five years and in between the drilling and polishing and saluting he took advantage of it. He listened and questioned and applied what he learned. It was like learning to play a stringed instrument. The strings were vanity, the song his own success.

3.

Three incorrigibles;
Three incorrigible traitors, can't help it:
The heart, that's one, the brain, that's the second,
And the will, old will power, deserters to the death.
—Christopher Fry

A FEW days after he was commissioned, Alfred reported for duty to the commanding officer of the 4th Battalion at Stryj. As a second lieutenant in the Imperial and Royal Army he was paid fifty gulden a month plus quarters allowance sufficient to rent a couple of rooms in a private home which the Army furnished with two chests, two tables, four chairs, one bed, one mirror, one bed table, one coat rack and one washstand. The Army also gave him a personal servant—a private soldier—to empty the slop buckets, shine shoes, polish brass and press uniforms. Thus squared away, he took command of an infantry platoon.

When a week earlier Alfred had sat on his bunk to answer

Carl von Anders' exuberance with five words, "This is only the beginning," he had already rejected these surroundings and the career they implied. He did not know how to escape, only that he was to escape. Since the night with Paulus Holzlofer he had transformed his nebulous notions of glory into a single, fixed goal. He believed Paulus. His goal was the General Staff, and he was prepared to use any artifice and make almost any sacrifice to attain it. His confidence was like an arrow winging straight to a target. It was born from insecurity, nurtured on the weakness of others and launched in personal ambition, but that eliminated neither the straightness of its aim nor the power of its flight.

Right from the start Alfred worked hard to make his platoon the best one in the battalion. Because he spoke Ruthenian and Polish better than he did German and because he had already spent five years with the troops and could apply the numerous lessons he had learned, he succeeded. Seeing the excellent effect Redl exercised on his first platoon, the company commander, Captain Salzmann, shrewdly transferred him to his weaker platoons, his pleasure increasing as Redl's successes continued. The captain spoke less Ruthenian and Polish than most and soon introduced Redl into his inner councils to repair this deficiency. Delighted with finding himself at last in communication with his own men, Captain Salzmann began referring to Redl as "a damn fine officer" and followed that by singing his praises to the battalion commander. Lieutenant Colonel Sypneski generally remained sober enough for Saturday morning inspections and he, too, began to notice Redl, began to summon him to the front office where Redl performed the extra duties with his customary thoroughness and excellence. Like Captain Salzmann, Colonel Sypneski was soon converted and when he referred to Redl he inevitably added the tag "a damn fine officer." In Stryj, a small town that absorbed mediocrity like a sponge, talent stood out as if it were an isolated case of plague. In not many months Colonel Hoffmann, commanding the Quartermaster Depot, heard about Redl.

Colonel Hoffmann's quartermaster function involved daily intercourse with Galician peasant farmers because most of the regiment's food and fodder for the horses was procured on the spot. In addition the quartermaster had to inventory and classify the transport of each town and village since in event of general mobilization this had to be requisitioned—the Army could not go to war without it. To the individual peasant these officers correctly appeared as a distinct threat to his capital holdings of one horse, one cart and a cellar full of grain. He did not like these officers and he chose, when forced to speak with them, a language of grunts that to the officers seemed unintelligible. When Colonel Hoffmann was told that Lieutenant Redl possessed the uncanny ability to understand such grunts, he reasoned that here at least would be a beginning. His request to Regiment was honored: Redl was assigned to him for additional duty. This in turn broadened Redl's sphere of activity in that quartermaster duties now took him to the other battalions at Jaroslaw, Radymno and Lemberg. Before he had served two years in the regiment, Alfred Redl was asscciated in the minds of several majors, lieutenant colonels and colonels with the words "a damn fine officer." Inevitably the tag was to land in Regimental Headquarters.

The young lieutenant knocked on the door of the Adjutant's office.

"Eh?" The major looked up, adjusted his *pince-nez*. "Well, come in, come in."

The lieutenant walked smartly across the office, halted three paces in front of the desk, saluted: "Lieutenant Redl respectfully asks permission to report."

"Ah, there you are, Redl," the Adjutant said. "Not a minute late. Splendid. Well now, we have been hearing good things about you. Suspect that is why the Colonel wants to see you." He nodded knowingly.

"Thank you, sir," Redl said.

The Adjutant rose stiffly from his chair, tapped on a paneled door, opened it and disappeared. A second later he returned, motioned Redl in and closed the door behind him.

"Sit down," Colonel Pranton ordered. "Smoke? Cigarette? Cigar?"

"Cigar, sir, if I may," Redl said.

"Quite right," the Colonel said, biting an end off his cigar.

42

"The officer's proper smoke. Don't hold any brief with these cigarettes. You use them?"

"Never, sir."

Colonel Pranton lighted his cigar, vigorously puffed as if to create a cloud on which to float his thoughts. Alfred studied his leonine head, wondered if the scar on his right cheek was from an early duel.

"You are down in Stryj, Redl?"

"Yes, sir. Fourth Battalion, Lieutenant Colonel Sypneski commanding, sir."

"Good old Sypneski. How is he?"

Alfred thought for a moment of Colonel Sypneski, tried to remember when he had last seen him sober. "Very good, sir. Colonel Sypneski asks to be respectfully remembered to the Colonel. Colonel Sypneski wishes it reported that the 4th Battalion is prepared to uphold the honor of the Regiment in the forthcoming maneuver and that he will march as scheduled."

"Yes, of course," the Colonel said. "Good old Sypneski. Y'know, we soldiered together as lieutenants down in Herzegowina. Suspect that is before your time, eh?"

Alfred chuckled. "It was, sir." His eyes fell on the ribbons of the Colonel's blouse and remained until their look was noted. Raising his eyes, Redl said, "Pardon my frankness, sir, but I believe the Colonel was awarded the Military Service Cross for his participation in the Battle of Korita. Was that not in January, 1882, sir, a short time before Captain Pomankowski won the battle of Prabac Plains?"

The Colonel was obviously pleased. "*Lieber* Redl," he said, "either Sypneski talks too much or you study too hard. But that is correct." His fingers touched the decoration. "Tell me, son," he asked more seriously, "how are you coming along in Stryj?"

"Very well, sir, I believe. I have been very fortunate to have enjoyed such close contact with Colonel Sypneski, sir. As the Colonel knows, he is a very experienced officer and he has seen fit to take an interest in me."

"Fine, splendid," Colonel Pranton said. "I can tell you, Redl, that Colonel Sypneski is extremely satisfied with your performance of duty. Nor has our quartermaster remained silent on the subject."

43

Redl ducked the compliment. "I have truly enjoyed my duty with Colonel Hoffmann, sir. I had no idea of the complexity of staff procedure, although, of course," he added hastily, "I have read Von Clausewitz and Jomini on the subject."

"Yes, each army must have its paper and desks," the Colonel said. "Good lesson for a young officer, too. Speaking of staff work, Redl, have you been doing any thinking about the future?"

"Well, no, sir, not exact—"

"I mean War College," the Colonel interrupted. "The General Staff?"

"The *flaschen-grünen corps*?" Alfred's tone expressed his amazement, the derogatory term the correct contempt for a troop officer to display. "No, sir, I have not."

"I know, Redl, the green-uniformed seers who are never wrong. In my day the General Staff did not mean so much, but today"—he sighed a prelude to the old soldier's lament—"the Army is different. The General Staff runs it and has run it for a decade. The General Staff—best assignments, decorations, rapid promotions."

"I understand that, sir, but I do not have the schooling and it would mean leaving the Regiment and the troops."

"A soldier always has to leave his regiment and his troops," the old officer said. "The education? Sypneski and Hoffmann think you have it and I think you are going to get it if you already haven't. Colonel Sypneski proposes making you Battalion Adjutant as of 1 May and I agree."

Alfred remained silent.

"Did you hear me? As of 1 May you will be Battalion Adjutant."

"Yes, sir," Redl said. He cast his eyes to the floor. "I hope . . . I do not know what to say, sir."

Colonel Pranton rose from his chair, came around the desk to tower over his lieutenant. "Nothing to say, Redl. You have earned this honor by hard work and outstanding performance." He walked with the young officer to the door. "I want to see you the next time you come to Lemberg."

Outside, well away from the headquarters building, Alfred smiled, nodded his head slightly. Then he pulled a silver case

44

from his tunic, selected and tamped a cigarette and lighted it. He turned slowly, stared at the building in the distance. He exhaled a cloud of smoke and walked down the street.

The post of Battalion Adjutant was normally reserved for the senior first lieutenant of the battalion. A post of honor, it was also an exacting billet since the adjutant was the go-between of the battalion commander and his officers. When Alfred Redl was assigned to this billet in the spring of 1889, no one in the 9th Galician Regiment was surprised, and no one was surprised, least of all Alfred Redl, when in a few months time it became obvious that he was doing an excellent job.

He had prepared for the job and he continued to prepare for bigger jobs that he hoped lay ahead. While he spent most of the night studying the manuals, he spent most of the day studying man. To Redl man was a challenge, a walking problem to be solved by fixed formulae exactly the way one masters an algebraic complexity with the proper equation. Redl's face and speech composed his formulae for man's solution: he dressed them for each man as carefully as he dressed his body for each weather. And he largely succeeded, a success of calculation made the more terrifying because he accomplished it despite a lacuna of the heart.

In man, as in everything else, Alfred Redl missed the point, and he missed the point because he never learned about the heart. Perhaps he was born not to learn and could not learn, or perhaps some perverse fate melded the complexities of his environment into a permanent shield against humanism. He always got the facts, never the idea. He read, studied, memorized and glibly quoted Part One of Service Regulations. But had he been asked to explain the paragraph:

> *Esprit de corps* has its roots in the feeling of solidarity and in knowledge of the necessity to subordinate personal interests to the good of the whole. It engenders the standing conviction that spurs one on to stricter, more devoted fulfillment of duty and it demands the highest military virtues. It is through *esprit de corps* that each alone finds his honor in the honor of the whole,

he would have had to repeat its words in explanation. As a youngster when he went to church he had genuflected properly,

45

learned the sacraments, whispered some of his secrets to the priest, performed lip penance for his sins, enjoyed the drama of liturgic mass and missed the slightest notion of the meaning of the whole. In school and in the military he studied his own Empire, could discuss each province, its population, its agricultural and industrial significance, and those things to him were the beginning and the end of the Empire. As with Army, Church and Empire, he missed the idea of life itself. Perhaps if he had studied Humanities instead of Sciences—if formulae and equations had been replaced by Plato and Aristotle and Cicero and Sappho—he would have learned that some of man's actions must be a material waste if a happy, creative life is to be gained. Perhaps if his own childhood had not been so barren . . . but no matter the way he missed it, he did miss it. Not once in a thousand years could Alfred Redl have spent an afternoon slouched on a stream's bank, his naked toes dunked in the rushing water, his body stretched in an air warmed nearly as much by the heart as by the sun overhead. No, if Redl came on the stream he would have seen a problem, would have cocked his good-looking blond head to one side, assimilated it with his blue eyes and active mind and somehow have dammed it to his own profit. He could never give, he had always to take. His heart never, not once in forty-nine years, ruled his actions. Yet in those forty-nine years he lived and worked with many people who did know about the heart but who failed to sense Redl's lack of heart, failed to see through this latter-day Janus. That is terrifying.

It is also understandable. Man likes to dominate physically. Redl was small and quiet, boyish in appearance—physically no threat at all and therefore offering no challenge by mere presence. Man's ego demands ministration. Redl attended man because that was part of controlling man; he saw man for the individual, not the species, and he knew and exercised the power of personal attention and sympathy, qualities more peculiar to the female than to the male and qualities virtually non-existent in a military society. Man also likes excellent performance by man. Because Redl made the officers his friends they did not denigrate his professional abilities, rather they were proud to associate with talent, and they felt even superior when as seers they slapped the stein to the table and said of him, "He's a damn fine officer."

Redl's acting ability grew as his professional talents enlarged and his reputation spread. He perfected the knack of driving home in a sentence what others failed to extend by paragraphs. A comrade once asked him, "Why do you study so much, Fredl?" Alfred cocked his head, pondered the question until he had won the attention of his audience, then fixed his blue eyes on the questioner to answer with that fraudulent force gained by the words of those who never say much: "It will make me a better officer."

There is the hallmark of Alfred Redl's success. He forever gave the answer that people could not refute, and one they often wished they themselves had made. Had he said petulantly, "I like to," or "It is interesting," or "Because I will become a General Staff officer," he would have appeared selfish, insulting and grasping. Instead he gave an answer that people wanted, hoped for and rarely received: a feathery answer that tickled the ego while its lightness and obscurity passed unnoticed through the vale of conceit. *Vanitas vanitatum*—Alfred Redl was the manipulator whose mental divining rod found wells in the most barren deserts.

"It will make me a better officer." No one bothered to ask what kind of an officer, or the purpose of becoming a better officer or why it would make him a better officer. Seven simple words in answer to a complex question and with them he imparted humility, lofty ambition, duty, loyalty and honor.

By the time Alfred Redl was twenty-five years old he was in the process of becoming a great actor. It was just as well for him—he already had something to hide.

The first of Alfred Redl's two secrets was shared by most junior officers and a few senior officers in the Imperial and Royal Army: finances. The Army did not pay its officers a large income but it nonetheless expected them to live well, a disparity met in the case of fortunate officers by private allowances from sympathetic families. An officer from a substantial middle-class background might receive fifty or one hundred gulden a month from home while an aristocrat in a smart cav-

alry regiment might receive ten thousand. Numerous officers,
however, had no allowances and faced the monthly effort of
trying to spread fifty gulden over mess, tailor and bootmaker
bills with a "few kreuzer left for carousing in that paradise of
a café."

Coming as he did from poverty, living for years as he had
on a cadet's pay of thirty-five kreuzer a day, Alfred should have
handled his income with respect. He did the reverse: he spent it
and more. He always had to have the best uniforms, the finest
accessories, the most expensive boots. He had to run the largest
mess bills, pick up the tab on the parties in Lemberg. He forever sought to be the good fellow; part of the title he bought.

He got the extra money from the common source of impoverished junior officers: by small loans from Jewish moneylenders
who covered Galician garrisons like so many locusts. An officer
borrowed on his signature, paid usurious interest, returned the
principal as he advanced in rank or, as many did, made a
wealthy marriage. Among junior officers debt was more a
matter of pride than a subject of shame. Seniors must not know,
however, and juniors formed protective associations to keep it
from them. Most senior officers did not press too closely into
the financial affairs of their subordinates. Many a colonel had
himself been saved from exposure in "the beautiful wild days"
of his lieutenancy by fellow officers filling the pot to pay a
pressing debt. Several allegations exist that Redl was saved
once or twice from exposure by his fellow officers and in all
probability this was the case. Much more definite is the fact
of his debt which at the time of his entrance into War College
ran to several thousand gulden.

Redl's second secret was known to few, yet centered on a
subject common to all: passion. The Austro-Hungarian officer
without private means faced a dilemma forced upon him by
the Army. A lieutenant earning 600 gulden a year could scarcely
maintain himself, much less a wife, in the style demanded by
the Army. To insure that way of life, an officer was required
to post a marriage bond or *Kaution* previous to marriage. In
the case of a lieutenant this amounted to about 45,000 gulden,
an enormous sum usually posted by his own or his fiancée's
family. The annual interest from the gilt-edged bonds in which

48

the money was invested allowed the desired standard of living. The *Kaution* could not be touched by the officer until he retired.

An officer without private means wishing to marry a girl without private means was forced to leave the Army as Alfred's father, Franz, had done in 1852. To marry and remain in the Army most often meant a marriage founded first on economics, second on love. But one had to find a wealthy woman before one could rationalize emotion, and in the provinces this was not easy. True, there were daughters of *nouveau riche* Jewish industrialists who, although not acceptable socially, were often taken (and help to account for the mixed blood often found in Vienna today). But the choice finds, the wealthy *and* socially respectable, were usually the daughters of local nobility whose country estates were not open to Imperial and Royal Army officers. Writing of Lemberg in 1894, August Urbanski later complained that:

> the Commanding General tried to eliminate the latent tension between military and civil authority. He found no support from the Governor, Count Kasimir Badeni, who as direct representative of the Monarchy believed himself superior to everyone and this conceit carried over to his exclusively Polish staff. As in Karlsburg, so in Lemberg: the off-duty activities of officers were confined solely to military circles, especially since on principle the Polish nobility would not speak German and visibly exerted themselves to have no contact with the Officer Corps. One had the feeling of being not in Austria, but in enemy land.

As a final hindrance, even if an officer possessed private means, a fiancée and the inclination, he could not have married were he to go to War College, nor, if he were appointed to the General Staff upon graduation from War College, could he marry until attaining the rank of captain five years later. Numerous officers, therefore, faced a celibate life with sexual opportunities limited to "nice girls" who were generally daughters of older officers or to "faded soubrettes" of the local music hall. Since chastity is said to appeal to only priests and the impotent, and since "nice girls" could not often risk going to private apartments, this left the local prostitutes. It also left the Imperial and Royal Army officer corps with a high incidence of venereal disease. But it was an outlet that in official eyes was no particular sin. Some of the garrison outposts, however, lacking even whores, threw men to each other for company, for mental stimuli, for laughter . . . and for sex. Though not a rarity in the Army, the final outlet of homosexuality was a sin, one of the worst.

The sexual introduction of young aristocrats was very often placed in the hands of professional hostesses, perhaps the most exclusive of whom was Anna Sacher of the famed Sacher Hotel in Vienna. Anna, a cigar-smoking *kaistertreu* patriot and a woman of great discretion, could at the drop of a hundred-gulden note arrange a *chambre séparée* into a charming scene of intimacy: a table of linen, crystal, silver and candle, a gourmet's menu and, for more practical purposes, a young dinner companion whose charm was exceeded only by her experience. And here the virgin prince or archduke or count would come to be wined, dined and seduced, a tasteful and practical procedure with exact minutes recorded and a full report sent off with the bill to the *pater familias*.

Though not so carefully handled, most Academy officers also managed to join the world of men at a proper time. The majority finished the Academy, lieutenants at nineteen or twenty years of age, and left the dormitory nights in favor of gliding waltzes, tripping quadrilles and leaping galops. These were the "beautiful wild days" of a young, single officer who neglected neither gambling casinos nor bordellos.

Redl, on the other hand, left Cadet School when he was eighteen years old. For five years he was paid 35 kreuzer a day, an annual sum that would have bought one night in a *chambre séparée* furnished à la Sacher. During the years when young officers in smart regiments were learning about women, Cadet Officer Deputy Alfred Redl lighted another candle or trimmed the wick of a kerosene lamp and turned once more to Part One, Service Regulations, so that he would finally become an officer in any regiment. By the time he was commissioned, the walls of an all-male environment had pressed even closer upon him. Like Stefan Zweig's lieutenant, he had to say:

> . . . I had lived continuously in a masculine, a male environment. From morning till night, from night till morning, in the

dormitory . . . in camp, in barracks, in the mess and on the march, in the riding-school and in the classroom, always and always I had breathed an air that reeked of the male, first of boys, then of grown lads, but always of men, men; I had grown used to their virile gestures, their firm, noisy tread, their guttural voices, their tobacco-y smell, their free and easy ways and sometimes coarseness.

The difference was, Alfred liked it. Until he entered Cadet School he had spent his life surrounded by women, and after his father died he had been completely under their thumb, dominated by their outlook, their shrieking voices and nagging persistence. More unconsciously he identified them with the poverty he detested, with the rancid odors of his childhood in a dwelling crowded with youngsters, of a worn, bleating mother seemingly always fat and cross with child. As an officer, Alfred on occasion had to mix socially with women. When the daughters of regimental officers arranged a ball he had to go and he did not mind going because there was purpose. He dressed in his best uniform, brought flowers to the hostess, drank lemonade, waltzed when he should. He was always polite, even charming . . . and he loathed it. Deadly bored, he composed his face into a suitable reservoir to receive the platitudinous streams poured by his dancing partners, smiled when he was supposed to, and always left at the proper hour. Although he would not admit it, perhaps did not even know it, he was frightened. No one noticed that his eyes frequently darted to the girl's abdomen and if a girl did notice she would have flattered herself that he was looking at her bosom. For these reasons Alfred succeeded in the Lemberg social spheres. Many a daughter upon reviewing the ball would come mentally to the small, graceful figure of the blond lieutenant and say to her father, *"Herr Leutnant* Redl is very sweet, isn't he, Papa? Quiet, but oh, so charming." And Papa would draw on his cigar, pat his daughter's hand, agree with his daughter, clear his throat and add, "He is a damn fine officer, too."

Because "a damn fine officer" thought it politic to be popular with his fellow officers by joining their stag parties, Alfred's experience with women had soon extended from the genteel circle of military society. He had never forgotten the night it

51

first happened. They were all lieutenants sitting in the wine
Stüberl singing their songs and telling stories and relaxing in
the pleasant bath of drunkenness.

"We must eat," Fritz Witzleben shouted.

"Good, to the Pole's," Kurt Schneider said.

"We shall pay and be off," Georg Ganshausen commanded.
"Herr Ober, zahlen."

Alfred took the bill, paid it. He felt nervous. He had heard
about the Pole's.

The front of the Pole's was a small restaurant where the
laughing officers now hurriedly spooned their soup. Before they
had finished, a wizened old woman appeared from the back to
greet them in Polish and invite them to another room for coffee.
They filed past small tables to push through a beaded entrance,
cross a small pantry, then through another door into the parlor.
Alfred watched the old woman lock this door after them. He
suddenly felt trapped and afraid. Turning to the room he saw
overstuffed chairs, allowed himself to be sunk into one, allowed
the brunette sitting on the floor beside his chair to remove his
shoes and place his feet on a small footstool. Now she stood,
placed her buttocks on one arm of the chair, snaked her arms
around Alfred, said, "I am Helene," and kissed him, her right
hand gently rubbing the hollow of his neck. He jerked away,
looked quickly around the room. The scene mollified his fear of
being joked at: he saw his comrades in poses like his own, saw
their hands seeking pleasure from fat breasts and buttocks.

The Polish girl laughed softly, nuzzled his ear to whisper,
"It is so crowded here; come, we go where we will be alone."
She led him up the stairs and down a corridor to a room. Hesi-
tating before the door, he cocked his head, looked at the girl,
her small body, her well-formed breasts. He followed her into
the room.

The room smelled of disinfectant and closeness and woman.
He reeled slightly, stumbled. Helene led him to the bed, pushed
him down on it. On the bed in the dark it was better. He lay
still, tried to relax his tight stomach. He heard the girl in another part of the room, listened to the splash of water in a
basin and wondered what she was doing. He heard her cross the
room, place the basin on a night table. The bed shifted as she

lay down beside him. He flinched when her arm wormed its way beneath his neck and her warm wet lips found his own. Her kiss pleased him and he relaxed while her hand played down his body, caressing and drawing him to her. She was naked. His hand touched her small back, lingered in the warmth, moved to the fleshy softness of her large buttocks. Suddenly she tugged at his uniform and together they undressed him. Her nipples now pressed hard against his bare chest and he heard himself breathing faster and felt his body responding to the persistent play of her fingers. Swallowing hard he whispered, "I don't know how," and she squeezed him and said, "I will show you." He felt himself raised in a cloud of warmth, felt the woman wiggle beneath him, the cross resting between her breasts scratching him. Then he felt her fingers expertly guiding, felt himself entering the wet hot cave from which men come, to which they return.

It was quickly over. He lay on the bed waiting for the feeling that other men had told him would come, the feeling he himself had known with men. Instead of fatigued satisfaction his body grew coldly nervous and into his mind swirled a picture of a pregnant whining woman and he smelled cabbage soup. It turned his stomach. He was afraid, very afraid, and he covered his genitals with one hand, then moved quickly to the bed table where he began to retch over the basin. Helene held his head, laid him down after the spasms and washed him. She said he would feel better after the second time but he wished no second time and he got up in a little while and dressed.

Outside in the cold night air he did feel better and by the time his comrades joined him he felt fine. He walked home with his friends, even swaggered in the knowledge of his act.

"How was she, Fredl?" Fritz Witzleben demanded.

"Like always," Alfred said. "She wanted to pay me."

The others laughed. Alfred smiled and thought of the two gulden—it did not cost much to be a good fellow.

It did not cost much to be a good fellow; that was one consideration. The other consideration was the notion if not the legend of sexual prowess that affixed itself to the minds of the young officers when they thought of Alfred Redl. That was

53

priceless and not altogether false. When Alfred was with them and they went to the Pole's he went along. He always took Helene. Helene never mentioned the night he was ill nor did she question when sometimes he said he was tired and they would sit in the room and keep their clothes on and talk. They told each other a lot on these nights. They would sit and drink beer and tell of their childhoods and the poverty; kindred souls feeling very sorry for themselves. Alfred liked the girl, the quiet and docile girl who even at times appealed to him physically, and he would welcome the tugging fingers and the wiggling body and the cave, but the cave forever cast shadows upon his departure, forever denied the mind the satisfaction so seemingly promised by the entrance of the body. He resented that but it was secondary to maintaining a virile reputation in the regiment. He had to maintain a virile reputation at any price because it was the best answer to his second secret: he could not find the fulfillment in Helene that he had already found from persons of his own sex.

The indulgence of his secret passion presented no great difficulty of accomplishment. He soon had grown to recognize the special, the different ones, the officer like Christoph Jungermann, a new lieutenant in the battalion, a handsome chap whose eyes and words carried currents no less powerful for their invisibility, who caught Alfred's own currents until one night in the mess Alfred's leg brushed carelessly against Christoph's. That night they walked into Stryj by themselves. On the dusty road tanned by a harvest moon their hands touched, their bodies drew closer and without stopping and in a careless voice Alfred said, "Shall we?" If the currents had been wrong Christoph could have answered, "Shall we what?" to signal Alfred's hand away from his body. But the currents were not wrong, they rarely were. Christoph took his hand, held it against his own thigh, nodded his head and their feet quickened toward a sanctuary of darkness, toward a single bed and a passion that to Alfred was the best of any passion because with it he felt safe and unafraid, wanted and loved, no longer alone.

But not after it was over, and because of that it was a secret that he did not like. He knew its danger, and if it were delicious at the time, later it proved a worry. It was a demon

54

that he could not calculate as he could his other actions. He would think he had stifled it, even killed it, but then the demon would assert itself with a power seemingly strengthened by respite. He fought it always. Sometimes he won. Often he succumbed to its vicious and dangerous grasp.

4.

THE black-bearded, beady-eyed captain finished the report, smoothed its pages, placed a pencil on them, stuck out his lower lip and turned his glance to the young lieutenant sitting before his desk.

"Ah, good, now," he said. His heavy voice was sarcastic. "You have made the rare discovery of one who owes money. And now you wish to develop him. Is that correct?"

Lieutenant Pawlow nodded. "Yes, sir—as is recommended."

"I know what is recommended, don't you worry. But you tell me, what do you intend to learn? Tell me what you intend to learn, please," the captain said.

Pawlow answered carefully. He knew this tone of voice and this type of conference. "Considering his function in the regiment, sir . . ."

"Bah! Could he tell us anything of importance that we do not already know? Could he add one scrap of information to the two thousand reports from Galicia each month?"

"Probably not, sir," the lieutenant admitted.

"And what is going to happen to this officer? Where is he going? Do you know where he is going?"

"No, sir."

"You must think out these things. He is going far in the Army. Read the report: '. . . twenty-five years old, very popular with his comrades, adjutant of the battalion, additional duties in quartermaster and recruiting.' Does this sound like we have an idiot?"

"No, sir."

"And what is the debt, anyway?" He leafed through the report to answer his own question. "A couple of thousand

gulden. That is little enough. If his seniors did learn about
it he would receive a reprimand, not a discharge."

The lieutenant looked crestfallen. Captain Batjuschin of
the Russian Imperial General Staff stared at him a moment,
walked to the buffet across the room and filled two glasses with
vodka. He gave Pawlow one. Drinking his own as if it were
water he said, "Listen to me. One day you will become a fine
Intelligence officer. But please learn that we must exercise
patience in our business. We are spiders in our webs and
sometimes a spider must wait and wait and wait. A spider
waits more than a spider acts. We must have patience even
when our General Staff is impatient. They want to know
about this Austria-Hungary because they will fight and destroy
this Austria-Hungary. But they will not fight tomorrow or
the year after tomorrow. Russia must wait until Russia is
strong, until the Orient is gained. Then Russia strikes south.
Meanwhile Russia prepares. And you—you and I, my dear
Pawlow—we prepare by patience. What does this lieutenant
know now that he won't know more of as a captain? What is
a couple of thousand gulden when his own desires will build
his debt to ten times ten thousand gulden? Let us wait. Let
us wait while he helps us build our web. It costs us nothing
to watch."

"No," the lieutenant agreed, "it costs nothing."

"But we shall help him, too. See to it that this officer is
pressed for payment but pressed not too hard. See to it that
he is allowed to continue borrowing at the same time. For
now, he will borrow to pay. In the future, perhaps—he will
pay for having borrowed."

"Very well, sir."

"Then that is all this afternoon." Captain Batjuschin
picked up the report and handed it to Pawlow. The Cyrillic
letters on its cover read: *Redl, Alfred. Lieutenant of the Imperial and Royal Army, 9th Galician Infantry Regiment,
Lemberg.*

Alfred left the party early to walk alone through the quiet,
dark night and breathe the crisp autumn air that cleared the
champagne from his head to firm his steps. He passed the

wordless plea of a beggar, answered it with a coin, nodded to the effusive gratitude that followed him. A young couple arm-in-arm hurried by. He moved from their path, listened to their Polish words. His steps automatically led toward his lodgings and when he realized where he was going he stopped. He did not want the bleak rooms or the Gothic print of the multitudinous regulations.

Hearing carnival music, he turned his steps in its direction, heard it grow louder, reached lights and tents and a crowd, read large signs that proclaimed a four-day visit of a traveling circus. Colored posters showed acrobats and lion tamers and jugglers surrounding an immense white stallion and on its back a small, lithe brunette. *Ten separate acts,* Alfred read, *from ten European lands. Featuring the world's greatest acrobatic rider, Maria Montessi.*

Alfred bought a ticket and entered the tent. In the box he looked carefully around him. He had never before smelled the sawdust air of circus and as he looked at the nets and rigging and heard the music and watched the clowns and listened to young laughter he suddenly felt as heady as from the earlier champagne, felt a wonderful glow of ease engulf him, bought a package of hot chestnuts and leaned back to watch the acts. After some bears lumbered through a comedy with two clowns, the tent darkened, drums rolled and a spotlight found a tall ringmaster. "Ladies and gentlemen, the sensation of five continents, the greatest acrobatic equestrienne in the history of the world: Maria Montessi." And with the trumpet's blare a brute of a white stallion charged from a side entrance to canter easily around the ring, a small woman in satin tights standing on the broad, powerful back gracefully waving to the audience's applause, twice, three times around the ring. "But she will fall, she will fall," Alfred told himself.

The girl did not fall. With a sudden almost imperceptible movement she straightened, sprang up and back from the horse, turned once and lighted easily on the ground. Simultaneously the horse circled tightly, pranced to her side and bowed with her to the audience's delight. Swiftly the ringmaster cracked his long whip to jump Maria again to the horse's back. Alfred sat entranced with the small figure convoluting on a patch of white, her narrow hips swaying expertly with each movement, her slim legs controlling so finally the pawing thousand pounds of force. He applauded frantically each bow, sat tensely waiting for each new maneuver.

"Ladies and gentlemen," the ringmaster announced, "you will now witness a performance that has been viewed by every crowned head in Europe. Because of the extreme danger that is involved, you are requested to maintain silence during the next few minutes. I give you: Maria Montessi."

She rode the lead of five white horses that cantered into the ring. Noses to rumps they circled it once, twice. As they entered the third lap Maria stood effortlessly, poised smiling until her horse approached the ring's exit, flipped suddenly backward to land on the back of the second horse while the first horse left the ring, instantly flipped from the second to the third horse while the second left the ring, from the third to the fourth to the fifth with a final double flip to land lightly and alone in the empty ring.

The audience howled its delight, the canvas fairly shook with stamping feet. Alfred's arms grew leaden from his applause. He was flushed and excited and when fifteen minutes later Maria Montessi emerged from her dressing room he was waiting for her. In poor French he invited her to a late supper. Her bright alert eyes scanned the resplendent uniform that cloaked his small graceful body. She looked at his young, eager face and in excellent German accepted his invitation. With a little laugh at his surprise she took his arm and they strolled from the circus grounds.

Alfred awakened, stretched himself in the afternoon sun. He looked at Maria still asleep, her short hair tousled, one cheek of her soft face resting on a small hand. Excepting the nightly hour of her performance they had been together nearly three days and nights. This is the way it should be, he thought. Love with Maria did not bring unpleasant pictures to his mind. Love with Maria brought a wonderful fulfillment, a lazy fatigue compatible to the telling of his inner thoughts. After the first time they had made love, he was delighted to find himself content, delighted to lie with her in the darkness, her arms around him. "I do not understand," he told her, "your riding . . . I hate riding." She had kissed him and asked him why, and suddenly he told her easily what he had never told before. "I learned to ride as a cadet. Infantry Equitation School. There were fourteen of us. They had all ridden as boys but I never had a chance to. The first day we sat at one end of an inside ring, a large ring. The air was close and the day was still dark—we started at four each morning—and the smell of horses and manure made me feel sick. The hall was still dark and rain fell on the tin roof. I remember watching a leak in the roof. I should have been watching the sergeant explain the horse to us but about three feet away from this horse there was a leak and all I could watch was the splash of each drop and I saw this wet patch getting bigger and bigger. I failed to hear the sergeant call me to mount and the lieutenant reprimanded me for not paying attention. I had to mount the horse—a stallion about seventeen hands—and I was awkward, the others laughed at me. The sergeant had him on a lead rein and I had to ride bareback. I fell, I do not know how many times that first morning. I fell the first time right in that damn wet patch. It was strange because when I first saw the patch and watched the rain drip I knew I was going to fall in it. I hurt myself the first time I fell but they make you remount and ride until you stay on. Right from the first the lieutenant disliked me and that day he gave me four hours' extra duty. I was the worst—I always drew extra duty. The others had ridden before but I never had."

"You learned, though."

"Oh, yes, I learned to ride. The course lasted over six months. We had to ride very well. One thing they did, they put cigarette papers between your knees and the horse's flank and if the papers escaped you got six hours' stable duty. I always got that. We had to learn all about a horse. Its anatomy, feed, how to forage in the field, how to fight mounted, how to jump and swim it, plan marches, shoeing them, all their tack. Finally they assigned you your own mount to take in the field. Mine was named Maria." He laughed and kissed her. "She was a chestnut mare about sixteen hands. A mean horse —that is why they gave her to me. I tried to get a quieter one

59

but by then I could not get anything. One morning in the
field we rode a snap-shooting problem. We simulated a scouting party—what a cavalry troop would normally do in a field
campaign—and the idea was to meet an enemy scouting party
and open fire. I rode over this small knoll, spotted a target,
halted Maria, swung my carbine to my shoulder and hunched
down the way you are taught. Just as I fired, Maria threw up
her head and I blew it half off. She fell instantly and hurt
my leg and I nearly was given a court-martial. It certainly
was not my fault, but I still had to pay for the horse."

"How terrible, Alfred," Maria said.

"No, I did not care. I hated that horse. Once she kicked
me. She used to bite. She hated me because she knew I was
afraid. All I wanted was to finish the course. I finally did. I
got the lowest grade, 'satisfactory.' The lieutenant told me I
was the worst horseman he had ever seen. I did not care. I
hate them."

"But you ride?"

"Yes, you have to. Besides, the General Staff is always
mounted."

"Are you General Staff?"

"No," Alfred said. He hesitated. "I will be one day soon.
I . . . marriage is out of the question until then. Until five
years after that, you know."

That part of the conversation came up later. Maria had
told him they could wait. Then he explained the money bond
required for marriage and she had laughed and kissed him
and said she did not think he wanted to marry her, he was
making so many objections. She quieted his quick protest by
kissing him again and pointing out that she was making good
money and her family in Trieste was well off and if they
would wait everything would work out. Alfred had tried to
believe her because this girl was something different for him,
offering as she did what Helene and Hans and Christoph and
his own loneliness could never have offered. She would be
good for him, he knew. He had taken her out several times to
show her off to his comrades. She fitted with the crowd and his
friends loved her. She would be a fine wife. He had given her
the gold bracelet she wore now and thought how pleased she

would be when he gave her the small diamond he had bought for her going-away present. Her going away made him frown. She was departing early the next morning to leave him with . . . with a lot of bills, he admitted. Maria was expensive—he did not know how much he had borrowed during the last two days, only that it was plenty and now she was going away and he knew, really, there would never be a someday for them.

The thought did not particularly annoy him and he wondered why. There in the sun, his body wonderfully stretched, it did not seem to make a damn bit of difference. It struck him even as pleasant though he felt sad and because of that he chased it away and chased away the rest of his past and turned to look at her again, to study the soft gentle face he could talk into and the small mouth that forever said the right thing. When she was sleeping he could see the minute lines by her eyes—she was older than he.

Only a sheet covered them and now in the warm sunlight of late afternoon he gently sneaked this away. He could not satiate himself with her body: the small neck and chest, an acrobat's tiny breasts, flat stomach, almost no hips to contour the long, flat thighs that led to slim, hard legs, tiny feet. Alfred's eyes pored over the body, watched a flicking muscle protest sleep; he thought of the giant stallion that brought this ninety pounds into worming undulation of grace, of himself who brought it to passion pitched beyond mortal dream. He looked from her body to his own, nearly as slim and muscular. For a moment he watched the sun gild his own hair. Staring at his masculinity, he thought, *It is good to be a man, to be in love.*

Very gently he placed his hand on Maria's shoulder, moved it lightly over her tiny breast, pressed the little bloom of nipple. When she stirred he leaned to her ear, kissed it lightly and curled his tongue in its contour. Her arm reached over him, found the small of his back, slid against the hollow of his neck to press his lips to her breast. His kisses stirred her small body to a minute tremor that grew as she snuggled her other arm beneath him and played her hands on his smooth back, her fingers reaching down and down finally to press his but-

61

tocks, to move the magnificent hardness of man close to her, all the time the tremor through her body communicating to him, bringing him closer to it, and then she was trembling and kissing and holding and neither had known such as this and fought to prolong it and fought to have it and finally granted its birth and death with luxurious shudder to lie back in the golden sun clasped in each other's arms wanting no words, wanting only time to be born and to die again.

Doctor Eduard Hartmann listened patiently to the halting words of the blond lieutenant. "Well," he said finally, "possibly a strain, perhaps too much wine, but let me take a look." He closed the office door. "Pull down your trousers."

Alfred noticed that his fingers trembled when he unbuttoned his tight uniform trousers. Doctor Hartmann put on rubber gloves and sat on a stool. He pushed back the foreskin, tightened his fingers and brought them forward on the soft flesh to evoke a light discharge which he caught on a glass slide. "You can dress," he told Alfred.

At his desk, Doctor Hartmann examined the slide under a microscope, shook his head, stared again and leaned back. From a bookcase he pulled a heavy tome, consulted its index and leafed through the thick pages. "Ah," he said. He studied the drawing briefly, turned back to the microscope. He did this twice, leaned back, sucked air through his teeth and said, "You have a case of gonorrhea. With whom have you had contact the last week?"

Alfred leaned against the rounded edge of the examination table, saw the swaying form of Maria on the white stallion, heard the audience applaud, saw her naked body burnished by the sun, felt her warmth, tasted her final kisses at the early-morning train. The doctor caught him before he fell, laid him back on the table and made him breathe from a cut-glass tube of white crystals. Alfred opened his eyes and focused them on the collar of Doctor Hartmann's coat. He wanted to say, "Her name was Maria Montessi and she was the loveliest girl I have ever known. She was small and soft and warm and smelled like a fresh breeze that caressed and soothed and loved." Instead he moved his eyes to a cherub that sprang from the Renaissance ceiling and said, "She was a circus rider. Evidently a rotten little whore."

"Yes," the doctor said, "most of them are."

"Will it keep me from War College, Doctor?"

A spontaneous laugh relieved him. "Good heavens, no. About ten to fifteen per cent of our comrades have it. As a matter of fact, it won't even go in your record. If you had syphilis—that is a different matter. No," he shook his head, "you just have to worry about getting rid of it."

"What is gonorrhea exactly?"

"A disease caused by a germ, gonococcus, which Doctor Neisser isolated twelve years ago." He drew briefly on a scratch pad: ◖◗. Handing it to Alfred, he said, "It looks like a microscopic *Semel,* the Viennese breakfast roll. Your symptoms are standard: burning during urination, discharge a few days after contact."

"Can it be cured?"

"It is very difficult to cure. At least we make it quiescent and harmless for, uh, practical purposes. Now if you will undress we shall start the treatment."

While Alfred undressed, Doctor Hartmann filled a small syringe with a dark silvery liquid, greased its tip and laid it on the examination table. "Sit there and straddle the table," he told Redl. "Hold on tight," he said quietly, "there will be pain."

Nothing in the world could have compared to the searing torture of the first day, but once the initial shock had passed, the sessions that were held three times daily became less of a hell. And the cure seemed to be working; the burning was not so noticeable, the discharge lessening. After two weeks of the silver nitrate and copper sulphate injections Alfred reported only once a day. His relations with Doctor Hartmann paralleled each notable improvement until he accepted the appointments with sufficient equanimity to enable him to laugh at the doctor's poor jokes. Too, a distinct benefit resulted from the disease. The word that passed among the officers of the regiment: "Fredl, poor boy, has a *Kavalierschnupfen*—a cold of a gentleman," actually completed the hallmark of

Redl's virility, even made him a momentary hero among his comrades.

"All right, my boy," Doctor Hartmann said one morning. He placed the syringe on the table and donned rubber gloves. "We shall get this out of the way and then perhaps you would join me for coffee."

Alfred was straddling the sheeted table. "Thank you, Surgeon. I would like to."

"Now," the doctor said, "just a look. No doubt about it, inflammation almost cleared up."

Alfred braced himself for the fierce burn of medicament. Instead of the pain came the doctor's startled voice: "When did this appear?"

Redl looked down at the coin-sized brown spot whose hard contour the doctor's fingers gently probed. Something in the tone of the doctor's voice erased the easy quality of Alfred's answer: "I noticed it last night in the bath. What is it?"

"Lie down," Doctor Hartmann ordered.

Alfred felt the firm fingers press the sides of his groin. "Hurt?" "No," Alfred said. The doctor continued to probe the lymph glands which were swollen and hard. "All right, son. I am going to inject you now."

The doctor sat silently behind his desk until Alfred had dressed. "Come over here and sit down," he said. They lighted cigarettes, exhaled the smoke into the rays of morning sun. "I am sorry to have to tell you, Redl," the older man said, "but you have syphilis."

Alfred stared at him. "Is that when you go blind and crazy?"

"Not necessarily," the doctor said. "It is serious, but we are having quite good success with the present treatment. Indeed, prognosis is excellent. But only if the treatment is faithfully adhered to."

"Will it . . . the War College . . ."

"No, if you respond to treatment it will not render you ineligible for War College. I must officially enter it in your record, however. You are not alone in this illness, you know. It has been the scourge of all ages. At least five per cent of the Officer Corps have it, a much larger percentage of our civil population."

64

"Did it come from Maria?"

"Undoubtedly," Doctor Hartmann said. "Gonorrhea symptomizes itself within three days to a week after contact, syphilis within three to four weeks. It is not uncommon for a carrier to hold both diseases."

Redl looked at the floor. "What next, then?"

"I am entering you in the hospital this afternoon. We shall keep you for at least six weeks. I can almost promise you that if you co-operate you will be able to take your examinations and will be sufficiently cured to enter War College next year."

"This afternoon." He choked down further words and stood up.

"Report at two P.M.," the doctor said.

Not until Alfred was halfway to the barracks did he remember that they had not drunk any coffee.

He was given a private room and a male nurse. "They call me Schnitzel, sir. I come from Vienna and, sir, I would appreciate it not to be called Wiener Schnitzel."

Alfred looked at the small soldier, noted his neat appearance in the white smock, his intelligent, clean face now serious in its request. "All right, Schnitzel," he said, "I won't call you that."

"Sir," Schnitzel said, "we are going to be together for some time. Anything the lieutenant wants, I am here to get it for him." As he talked he measured a few drops of brown liquid into a glass, and filled it with water. "This is iodine, sir. Tastes awful but you will get used to it. Eight glasses a day, sir."

Alfred waited until the boy left the room. Closing his nose against the acrid liquid, he took a swallow and gagged. He left the bed, walked swiftly to the window and threw the mixture to the ground.

A few minutes later Schnitzel returned. Going to the window, he looked out, nodded, poured several drops of brown liquid into a fresh glass, added water and wordlessly handed it to Alfred who looked scathingly at him. "They all do that," Schnitzel explained. "Then they get used to it and drink it like beer."

Under Schnitzel's scrutiny Alfred forced himself to drain

65

the glass. He burped, felt nausea enclose him. "You will feel better in a moment, sir. Just lie back." The boy dampened a towel and applied it gently to his patient's forehead.

An hour later Schnitzel draped a sheet under Alfred's head and shoulders. "Just lie still, sir, and I won't cut you." Deftly he sheared through the short blond hair, lathered the entire head and shaved it with a straight-edge razor. He stood up to admire his own handiwork by a little smile. "You won't be wanting a mirror for a few weeks, *Herr Leutnant,* nor visitors either. Well, good. Now we begin."

Schnitzel sat on the bed and dug his fingers into a large vessel of dark, greasy ointment. Starting at the top of Alfred's head he expertly massaged the ointment into the scalp, the back of the neck, the upper portions of the throat and finally onto the face carefully ringing the eyes. He spent over an hour before he was satisfied. "Try not to rub it off, sir," he gently admonished. "It is for your own good." Then, briskly, "Time for another iodine."

As the iodized water brought instant nausea, the mercuric salve brought prolonged nausea. His head ached, his appetite ceased and in two days his gums began to bleed. "The mercury does that," Doctor Hartmann told him. "It is a toxic or it would not kill the syphilis. Your body will gradually build resistance to it."

Doctor Hartmann stopped by each morning but besides Schnitzel there were no other visitors, nor did Alfred want any. During the day Schnitzel was never long from his side and when sickness got too bad Schnitzel would fix him a headache potion or place cold towels on his forehead and later administer gentle back rubs. Alfred held the nights for hating, the long nights when in the darkness he lay and could not sleep. He would bring the image of Maria to his mind, sometimes for hours, and his mind did not fail to conjure pins for the sticking. He retraced each step of the night he had met her: he cursed his friends and the party, the fair weather that drew him to wander through the streets, the beggar to whom he had given a coin and the arm-in-arm lovers who had passed him. Then he thought of his debts, swore at the filthy, greasy

66

moneylenders and his own comrades, cursed the poverty of his heritage, shuddered at the image of his dead father, the small house, the mother wringing her coarse, red hands, filling the air with monotonous droning. It was a cycle of hate and he ran through it forwards and backwards until he had to look at the clock, see the early hour, realize that his comrades were sitting in a tavern and soon would move to the Pole's. Then he would think of the War College examinations, visualize the manuals he still must master, groan, roll over, try to ease his aching head.

Alfred thought he would have gone mad without Schnitzel. He soon welcomed even the times for iodine and the rubbings for they were something that offered a voice to listen to. Schnitzel always talked to him while he massaged the mercury into his flesh. He would tell him about his childhood in Vienna or his plans to study medicine at the university when he could afford it or of the cases he had seen. "Women?" he would say. "You can have them all, Lieutenant. They kill more men than bullets ever. Compared to the average dose, you don't have anything, Lieutenant. You should see some of them: chancres as big as a fist, suppurative ulcers the size of a plate. No," he would say, his soft fingers endlessly massaging, "if that is the price of women, here is one person who will never pay it." Alfred listened without saying anything. Sometimes, he thought, Schnitzel sounded like a very wise man.

On the seventh day of his treatment Alfred was given a sweat bath followed by a day's rest from the rubbings. The treatment then recommenced with Schnitzel shaving his armpits and for a week rubbing the ointment into his arms and shoulders and upper chest. Alfred began to feel better at this stage. Although swelling had spread to all of the lymph glands and to his throat, there was almost no pain. The headaches eased, the nausea lessened, and before the week was up he had sent Schnitzel for his manuals. After another bath and rest Schnitzel shaved his chest to concentrate on the thorax and back and during the fourth week the abdomen and hips were treated.

"Don't be nervous, sir," Schnitzel told him as he lathered

the groin. "I have never slipped yet." He honed the razor expertly, rested his arm on Alfred's abdomen, whisked the razor through the first patch of hair.

"Have you done this so often, then?" Alfred asked.

Schnitzel whisked a second stroke. "Yes, sir. Every time there is an abdominal operation and of course for these rubbings." He laughed. "We shave for crabs, too, and there sure are plenty of those around the Army."

"Must be awful," Alfred said.

"It is not so bad," Schnitzel said.

Alfred looked quickly at him. Schnitzel continued to shave him. The side of his face, however, was flushed.

"It has gone," Alfred told Doctor Hartmann. "Look."

The chancre had vanished leaving only a slight discoloration of the skin. "And the swelling," Alfred went on, running his fingers along either side of his groin, along his throat and under his shoulders. "Practically gone."

"Yes," the doctor said. "The first stage is nearly ended—remarkably good time, too. But we don't know if that means a cure or not. It is now more important than ever to continue treatment."

Alfred scowled. "What do you mean, first stage?"

"This disease can occur in three stages unless it is cured at the beginning. In fact, under current regulations I can and will certify you cured to make you eligible for the War College examinations in January. If it is not halted, in about three or four months an exanthema, a slight rash, will emerge." He calculated on his fingers. "That will be about March, but you will be back here for another series of rubbings and baths in any event."

Doctor Hartmann removed his coat and turned to the medication tray Schnitzel had brought in. Inserting the syringe, he frowned as he squeezed the bulb and saw a trickle of liquid flow back into the basin. "Had any trouble pissing recently, Redl?"

"Some," Alfred said, "I was going to tell you."

Doctor Hartmann laid aside the syringe, probed with his fingers. "Schnitzel, fetch me a *Dittelstift*." To Alfred's questioning look he said, "The gonococci invariably inflame the urethral glands which swell to obstruct the canal. It usually happens early."

Schnitzel returned with a small tray from which Doctor Hartmann took a metal stick about six inches long and coated its surface with jelly. As he pushed it into the urethra, Alfred screamed and Schnitzel leaned on his chest to hold him down. Oblivious to his patient, the doctor worked the wicked instrument back and forth like a pipe cleaner until he was satisfied.

As he left the small room he heard his patient moan, "God, oh my God, I hate her . . . I hate her . . ."

"I shall be seeing you in my office, of course," Doctor Hartmann told Redl the day he was to leave the hospital. "But I want to impress a few things on you now. Your leaving here in no way ends the treatment for syphilis. No matter where you go, remember that it must continue for two years. I know the rubbings are unpleasant, but they are the only treatment we have. Under no circumstances put yourself into the hands of some quack practitioner who promises a painless cure—there is no such thing. Remember, too, you must avoid sexual intercourse or masturbation, you must drink very lightly and avoid rich foods. If you do these things, I would give you an excellent prognosis. If you do not"—he shrugged—"you will one day become a very sick man."

5.

IN January, 1892, Alfred Redl traveled to Corps Headquarters in Lemberg where he sat for a general examination simultaneously taken by several hundred officers throughout the Imperial and Royal Army who hoped to enter War College the next autumn. These officers had been carefully screened by unit commanders; each possessed or was believed to possess certain qualifications: single, under thirty years of age, orderly financial condition, knowledge of a national language besides German, very good physical condition, satisfactory riding ability, at least three years commissioned service with troops of which two years was with a company or battery and, finally, excellent fitness reports. About one-third of the aspirants were eliminated by this examination. The survivors, Redl among them, were called to a preliminary examination in February, a long test that covered mathematics (arithmetic, algebra, geometry, spherical trigonometry), weapons, pioneer service, field and permanent fortresses, fortress warfare, international law and geography. The results of the preliminary examination eliminated all but one hundred officers from a final examination, the dreaded eighteen-day *Hauptprüfung* to be given that October in Vienna. Among the fortunate names was that of Alfred.

In order to determine the results of the final examination the commission composed of the War College Commandant and the General Staff faculty officers had been in session since early morning. Now, as the Adjutant read the next name, the officers around the table forced their tired attention to his words: "Redl, Alfred, 9th Galician Infantry Regiment." Each officer took a neat folder from a stack to his front, opened it to read the past of Alfred Redl. "Karthaus Cadet School," the Adjutant read aloud, "final grade: very good. Infantry Equitation School, Lemberg, final grade: satisfactory. Results of this examination: private work over a theme of—"

"Just a moment," General von Bilabruck interrupted, "did Redl not attend the Academy?"

"No, sir," the Adjutant replied.

"Very well. Carry on."

"Private work over a theme of general knowledge for judgment of style: very good; French language: satisfactory; history: good; army organization: very good; drill regulations of the three chief weapons, Part Two, Service Regulations: very good; tactical problem: good; terrain doctrine and appreciation: good plus; terrain and situation sketches: good; findings of the examiners over the total success and in consequence for admission into War College: suitable."

"It is my opinion," the Commandant said, "that this is quite a remarkable case. Here is a lad with"—he consulted the folder—"three years of *Realschule* and four years of Cadet School and somehow he turns out to be one of the brightest young officers in the Imperial and Royal Army." General von Bilabruck turned to Redl's most recent fitness report. "I would read an entry or two, gentlemen," he said. "Colonel Grivičić has judged Redl to have a 'strong, staunch character, quiet, good-natured, many capabilities, quick and accurate comprehension.' Under 'service attitude' he says: 'very zealous and industrious with best success, strives for higher education.' His conduct officially is 'respectful, conscientiously frank.' Private conduct: 'friendly, tactful, very popularly regarded comrade, co-operative, modest.' Colonel Grivičić writes in summary that he is a 'very fine and able officer.' Gentlemen, those of you who know Colonel Grivičić will agree that he is not an easy man to please." General von Bilabruck smiled and read further. " 'Health: since 2 October sick with syphilis.' I would say, gentlemen, that First Lieutenant Redl had not confined himself entirely to study."

After the laughter Major von Brügel said, "Pardon me, sir, but when I was with Second Corps two years ago Redl was pointed out to me on maneuver. Colonel Pranton, his regimental commander at the time, spoke of him as 'a damn fine officer' and after watching him closely I had to agree. He was then Battalion Adjutant—very alert, extremely co-operative and courteous, even under pressure, and obviously most popular with the other officers."

"He certainly caught my attention during the examination," Colonel Kochmann added. "He knows his Clausewitz and Jomini word perfect and he handled the Franco-Prussian War as if he had been there himself. Very mature performance, all the way."

"I believe his showing here precludes any question as to his suitability," General von Bilabruck pronounced. He questioned the other officers with his eyes, found no dissenters. "What is his tentative entrance grade?" he asked the Adjutant.

"Number seventeen, sir."

"I move, then, gentlemen, that Lieutenant Redl be admitted

into War College as Number Seventeen of forty-five admissions."

Approval was unanimous.

The special education of Imperial and Royal Army officers for high leadership began during the Napoleonic Wars. Mainly under the impetus of the famed Marshal Radetzky, a *Kriegsschule*, or War College, was opened in 1852 to furnish an annual quota of graduates trained for ultimate General Staff duty. This two-year course placed the highest physical and mental demands on its students. A harsh school, it deliberately subjected the student to a spartan routine that daily began before sunrise and ended long after sundown. In the field noon meals were not served "because in front of the enemy there is no noon hour." Variable weather was welcomed by the faculty "because in war no one can select the weather." Perfection in all activities was demanded—poor spelling and unclear handwriting were punished as strongly as more serious errors. The academic mortality rate was high, and more than one student committed suicide under the strain. Of the professional military schools in Europe, the Imperial and Royal *Kriegsschule* rated at the top, and the Austro-Hungarian General Staff officer at this time was considered in military circles to be professionally superior to his Prussian opposite.

The faculty of the War College comprised sixteen staff officers ranging in rank from full colonel to captain together with a few civilian professors. The two-year curriculum embraced thirteen subjects: military geography, weapons, General Staff administration and operations, war history and strategy, tactics, army organization, terrain appreciation, natural science, fortresses and fortress warfare, cultural history, state and international law, French, and riding. The most important subjects of the first year were strategy, tactics, General Staff administration and operations. A War College contemporary of Redl, Doctor Karl Bardolff—their paths were later to cross—recalled that Lieutenant Colonel Karl Pflanzer "taught General Staff operations or how to carry out the strategic concept in the technique of movement to and from battle and to provide the logistic requirements for a campaigning army over a period of time." Free of pedantry, Colonel Pflanzer's lectures "were thrilling . . . and his critical discussions of various solutions were educational in the highest sense of the word." Artillery instruction was equally superior, but the highest teaching demands came from strategy and tactics. "The scholastic treatment of both subjects warded off the danger of placing too much emphasis on imagination and thus sacrificing the real ground of possibility." Fortification theory was well taught by two engineering officers, but higher army techniques and natural sciences were passed over lightly. "Riding instruction was very worth while and, as was nearly always the case in old Austria, was excellently conducted."

Each day began with early morning riding drill followed by classes throughout the day. After supper an hour of Russian language instruction was given with students then retiring for private study to prepare the material assigned for the next day's classes. One day a week was devoted to a classroom tactical project; Saturdays were held for field exercises. The first year ended with a mapping exercise to which the highest importance was attached. On this examination Alfred Redl received the second highest grade of "very good"; the same report noted that his mapping training and ability were "very good" and that he was "very industrious." For his first year's work he was graded "very good" on tactics, "satisfactory" in French and horsemanship, and "good" in the remaining subjects. He was returned to the second year as Number Five in his class.

Even more rigorous was the second year which culminated in a two-month tactical field trip that was "either work or marching daily from sunup to sundown including Sundays and holidays . . . only one meal a day late in the evening after the solution of the last problem." For this exercise the students were divided into groups of ten. Alfred Redl's group leader, Lieutenant Colonel von Hortstein, judged him as follows:

Diligence: Excellent.
Success: Very good.
Remarks: Strong, manly character; even, quiet temperament
           and disposition.

73

Very well qualified with quick, certain, pertinent comprehension and independent, determined resolution.

Works tirelessly, very thoroughly and always strikingly neat; hence his reports are completely suitable in content and form.

Socially always courteous with good, if somewhat stiff manners.

Very respectful to superiors, frank and of unmistakable loyalty.

Very friendly to contemporaries; as oldest officer of his section enjoys the full confidence of his younger class comrades upon whom he exercises good influence.

Firm to juniors, at the same time very thoughtful.

During the last eight days of the exercise unable to serve on account of a boil, otherwise equal to all physical demands.

In general: a precise, very industrious officer, who thinks independently, works reliably and neatly.

Especially suitable for service in the General Staff.

The last line of this report was the supreme encomium available to a reporting senior. The entire report was endorsed by the Commandant:

I agree. As soon as the articular rheumatism from which he suffers and which also adversely affects his riding is removed by a suitable mineral spa cure, he promises on the basis of natural talent, zeal and thoroughness to become a very able General Staff officer.

A short holiday followed the final tactical exercise, the students then returning for an oral graduation examination held under the supervision of the Chief of the General Staff, General Beck, for the main purpose of determining the best disposition of the new General Staff blood.

On October 30, 1894, First Lieutenant Alfred Redl was formally graduated from the War College as Number Twenty-eight in his class with an over-all grade of "very good." A day later he was ordered to duty with the Railroad Bureau of the General Staff in Vienna. Upon his departure from War College he wore the coveted double gold braid from his right shoulder to his left hip—he had been temporarily assigned to the General Staff.

To the fun-loving Viennese, *Fasching* was the most fun of all. Exploding between January and Shrovetide of each year, it blew the citizenry into singing and dancing and drinking throngs that jammed Ringstrasse of the Inner City, the immense boulevard lined with elegant shops and town houses of the wealthy, each festooned and lighted and pouring its own gliding waltzes and frantic czardas into the convivial mélange below. A holiday from reality, a release from care; husbands temporarily separated from wives, lovers from sweethearts: each night a million secrets whispered through costume masks, each hour liaisons as numerous as the popping champagne corks. Everyone—including the Court—gave himself (and herself) up to *Fasching*. The most elegant event of the entire carnival was the final *Hofball*, the Emperor's court ball to which besides the highest aristocracy and the diplomatic corps each officer of the Imperial and Royal Army was invited.

Alfred Redl dressed more carefully than ever. Each piece of his dress uniform, the material pressed to knife-edge crease, the gold a mass of reflective brilliance, lay carefully on the bed. He stood before a marble-topped table that held a white china washbasin, a matching pitcher full of hot water, a mirror and his toilet articles. Standing in his underwear, his face lathered, he scraped the light blond whiskers with a straight-edge razor. As he finished each portion of his oval face, he stopped, dipped the razor in the basin and smiled.

He was pleased with life. A month earlier he had sat impatiently in the small office redolent of carbolic while the white-smocked military surgeon riffled the papers a final time. "No," he finally said, "there is no sign whatsoever, nor do I believe it is lying dormant. If you will permit me a little joke, you have had syphilis exactly the way the textbooks tell us you should have it." The doctor examined one of the papers closely. "Nine months now since the last papule appeared and it was minor with almost no weeping. No further exanthema, certainly no nodular appearance. True, we cannot say definitely it is cured, yet all signs point to it. I want you to remain cautious: avoid heavy drinking, rich foods, get plenty of rest. If you notice any skin eruption, have it looked at immediately." The doctor handed Alfred a bottle of pills. "The gonorrhea is quiescent—no major gonococci evidence—but you still have traces. I want you to take these pills—they are mercury—until the morning discharge entirely ceases."

Alfred emptied the basin, filled it with fresh hot water and cleansed the lather from his smooth face. He dried himself vigorously, splashed his skin with eau de cologne, then trimmed several disorderly hairs from his blond mustache. After waxing it, he examined it critically; satisfied, he smiled and winked at himself in the mirror.

He dressed carefully in the new uniform which was not paid for. Thinking of his reception in Szakely's he smiled again. The manager himself had welcomed him, congratulated him, told him of his distinguished military clientele and more discreetly how he, *Direktor* Poppelmann, understood the numerous expenses of a young officer assigned to the General Staff and was prepared to offer long-term credit as a basis for a pleasant future relationship.

Alfred's servant appeared as he buttoned his dark blue blouse and adjusted the gold tassel of his sword. He looked at himself in the full-length mirror of the wardrobe, flicked a spot of dust from his patent-leather short boots, pulled a thread from the light blue trousers. Picking up the tall *Tschako,* he adjusted it to his head. "My cousin, the *Herr Doktor,* will arrive later," he told his servant. "Inform him I shall return at midnight. See that he is given what he requests. He will spend the night."

"Very good, *Herr Oberleutnant.*"

Alfred strolled down the carpeted stairs. Pausing, he half turned, took from his pocket a gold case and lighted a cigarette. Seeing a group of officers on the other side of the ballroom he leisurely threaded his way through the rich uniforms and the splendid gowns to a circle of elderly couples.

"Ah, Redl," General von Werner said, "there you are." They shook hands and the General took his arm. "You know my wife," the General said. Redl responded to her smile with a click of heels before he bowed to take her hand and brush his lips against it. *"Grüss Gott, küss die Hand, gnädige Frau General."*

"Pardon me, Johann," the General interrupted the next couple. "I wish to present *Herr Oberleutnant* Redl—Baron and Baroness Bachmann von Echthof." Again a click of heels, a half bow to kiss the woman's hand. To the Baron's response, "We have been hearing something about you, Redl," Alfred smiled quickly. "Thank you, Your Excellency."

General Werner guided him to the last couple: "I believe you know this lady and gentleman." Alfred smiled his pleasure before performing amenities. "Good to see you again, boy," Colonel Pranton said, vigorously pumping his arm. "Congratulations, I knew you would do it."

"If it had not been for the *Herr Oberst,*" Alfred said quietly to General Werner, "I would still be on company duty in Stryj."

"Nonsense, nonsense," the Colonel boomed.

General von Werner laughed. "As your Chief, then, I should thank Colonel Pranton. Fred, this young fellow has learned more about the Railroad Bureau in a few months than some of my officers have learned in years." He turned back to Redl. "But come along, you have earned a glass of champagne."

Alfred quickly melded into the party's persiflage, listened intently to each item of army gossip, danced with the ladies, laughed when others laughed, answered correctly what was asked of him.

"Understand you are leaving for Budapest shortly," Colonel Pranton said.

"That is correct, sir," Alfred said. "General Staff officer to the 61st Brigade."

"Land of Magyars and Jews," muttered Baron Bachmann in the nasal tone affected by Austrian aristocracy, "do me hard to say which was worse."

"Good place to learn, though," Colonel Pranton said. "If you can learn to understand Hungary, you can understand anything."

"*Herr Oberleutnant* Redl," *Frau General* Werner interrupted, "is that not the Baroness Auerberg dancing with General Beck?"

Alfred looked at the old whiskered face of the Chief of the General Staff and at the body bent as if under the weight of the numerous medals hanging from its chest. The General waltzed like a man picking his way through a field of hornets. How stupid he looks, Alfred thought. He stared at the old man's partner, did not recognize her. "I believe it is," he said. "I have only met her once—a most charming young lady."

Hardly had he spoken when the waltz ended and couples in animated conversation began to stroll from the floor. It was exactly eight thirty. A roll of drums and a flourish of trumpets announced the entrance of the First Supreme Court Chamberlain at the top of the stairs, an old, uniformed, bemedaled man who rapped his staff of office three times against the hardwood parquet. Pages scurried to line themselves with military precision along either side of the carpeted descent. Then the uniformed, bent figure of Francis Joseph, Emperor of Austria and King of Hungary, appeared. Simultaneously the Court Music Director, Eduard Strauss, lowered his baton to begin Chopin's Polonaise in A sharp major. Slowly, in lumbering casual step to the music, Francis Joseph led Archduchess Maria Josepha down the stairs. Behind them in courtly precedence came the members of the House of Habsburg, a total entourage requiring fifteen minutes to cross the ballroom floor and settle itself in a semienclosed sanctum that rose above the common floor of the room.

"Magnificent," General von Werner said when the Emperor was seated. "But there are gaps." He shook his head sadly. "The Crown Prince dead, the Empress in France, the Heir Presumptive in Egypt."

"Yes," intoned Baron Bachmann, "and Francis Ferdinand is soon to die, mark my words. Lungs, they tell me—from his mother."

A page approached the group to bow before Alfred Redl and extend a silver tray. Redl took the card, the page backed away. "Archduke Ferdinand Carl," Alfred read quietly. He handed the engraved card to General von Werner. "What does this mean, sir?"

"It means," the General said excitedly, "that His Imperial Highness will receive you. You have been presented to His Imperial Highness?"

"I . . . yes, sir, in War College," Alfred stammered.

"Good, good, but go, then. His Imperial Highness may present you to His Imperial Majesty. You must not keep him waiting."

The party watched Alfred approach the royal dais. Not without envy Colonel Pranton sighed to his wife, "I have always told you, my dear, that young Redl is something quite exceptional." And as Alfred, his arm gripped easily by the young Archduke, was led before the Emperor of Austria, as each eye of the room's aristocratic, military and civil rank followed his small, neat figure and furtively whispered to discover its name, the old colonel sighed again. "Quite exceptional," he repeated and drank slowly from his champagne glass.

Alfred smelled the tobacco before he noticed the open medical textbook on his desk. By it was an empty glass, a half-full bottle of wine, a crumb-strewn plate and a filled ash tray. He poured himself a glass of wine, raised it in mock toast to the still night, and murmured aloud, "How easy it is." He drank the wine quickly, went to his bedroom and undressed. As he stood naked in the dark room, the clock in Parliament Tower gently sounded the twelve strokes of midnight. Alfred walked quietly into the other bedroom and stood looking down at the bed. In the moonlight he saw the soft, sleeping face of Arthur Schnitzel.

Later, holding Arthur in his arms, he had stroked his hair and talked to him as would a husband a wife. He told him of the evening, repeated the compliments paid him, told him of his original meeting with Colonel Pranton, described his audience with the Emperor. His conversation knew no restraint, he the quiet one, and because the young medical student was tired he had dozed off.

79

Watching his lover sleep, Alfred stretched his own small body under the covers and rolled toward the warm flesh he loved. He had to go to his own room soon. He had to leave this bed and go to his room, take money from his wallet and place it on Arthur's bureau. In the morning Arthur would be gone. In a month he himself would begin a two-year tour of duty in Budapest. He frowned at the thought of leaving Vienna—would he ever return, he wondered.

6.

ALFRED'S return to Vienna began three years later with an official letter. As in the case of his original commission, the letter arrived on a May morning in Galicia. It was addressed to him and to twenty-one other officers who held certain linguistic qualifications and who were also eligible for permanent transfer to the General Staff. Of the addressees, two were to be recalled to the General Staff for assignment to Kazan, Russia, in order "to bring their knowledge of Russian to perfection."

The company commander of the 12th Field Company of Infantry Regiment Number 30 lighted a cigarette, complemented its taste with a sip of black coffee, and read the letter again. Then he arose, walked to the open window of his company office, placed one foot on the window sill and challenged the bright morning with a stare. He saw a large field being raised to dust by the drilling feet of his platoons, the uniforms of the soldiers already sweated through from their exertions to gain the perfection demanded by the man in the window. Beyond the field he saw a few trees, the leaves dust-covered, already beginning to droop in the day's heat. Beyond the trees stood a group of shabby houses that flanked a narrow dusty road whose few hundred yards led to the heart of Mikolajow, a garrison village of several hundred inhabitants lying twenty-seven miles south of Lemberg. Excepting a few weekends he had seen this picture with seasonal variations each morning for a year. Whether it was painted with sun, rain or snow he found it exceedingly monotonous. He knew what each moment was to bring, the menu for each meal, even the odor for each dish—the frying grease of *Schnitzel,* the steam of boiling mutton—he knew that he would drink a beer or two each evening with his officers and he knew that he would return to his quarters where his servant, Rudolf Reiner, would be waiting for him. And because he had quashed a serious criminal charge against Rudolf, he knew that he could trust him to co-operate on those nights that the tautness of his body demanded physical release.

Alfred had not dreamed that troop duty could prove so picayune. It was not fair, he told himself, that he should have to waste his brilliant energy commanding eighty-five men in a forgotten garrison outpost—he above all: a graduate of War College, privy to the top secrets of the Railroad Bureau, two years' experience as General Staff officer of the 61st Brigade in Budapest. He thought frequently of those last two years. Jammed with professional and social activity, they had rushed by. He had taught in the corps officer school, set up and run pioneer and infantry troop maneuvers, participated in the Hungarian millenary celebrations which had brought the Emperor and Empress to Budapest, and he had satisfied his seniors and made friends with his juniors. He had been promoted to Captain Second Class in the spring of 1897 as Number 88 in grade, and then transferred to troop duty with Infantry Regiment Number 30 in Lemberg. Though from this transfer he was no longer assigned to the General Staff, it still had not been too bad. Many of his old comrades had remained with the Second Corps in Lemberg, while his own background insured special consideration resulting, for example, in his service as General Staff officer in the 86th *Landwehr* Brigade during corps maneuvers. But then had come the dismal assignment to the 12th Field Company, the frightful village of Mikolajow whose dust made recall of chandeliers and ballrooms and crystal goblets and vintage wines and top-secret transport plans

81

almost ludicrous. So remote was Mikolajow, such an utterly feckless environment, that Alfred actually began paying back capital to the moneylenders.

When on these mornings Alfred stood to survey the drill-field canvas he was wont to substitute another for it. Sometimes it would be Vienna, sometimes Budapest, and in either case it was a canvas overtoned with the bright colors of himself as a General Staff officer prominent in the Inner Councils of the Imperial and Royal Army. The picture was invariably dissipated by the Adjutant's report that the company stood ready for inspection. On this particular morning the Vienna canvas appeared rather more real and by the time the Adjutant reported, Alfred had made up his mind. "You take the inspection this morning," he told his young officer. "I am leaving for Lemberg—official business."

Colonel Schlesinger, commanding Infantry Regiment Number 30, leaned back in his chair and tapped the letter with his finger, at the same time studying the blond, tan captain who sat across the desk from him. Finally he said, "I think it is a damn good idea."

Alfred hid his relief with a frown.

"Don't misunderstand me, Redl," Colonel Schlesinger laughed. "If I were selfish, I would advise you against it. But I learned a long time ago, as you did yourself, that personal interests must be sacrificed to the good of the service. Besides, if I do not lose you now, I soon will. It is hardly a question in my opinion of your going back to the General Staff. I am most certain you will be recalled—the question is when and to what duty."

"To what would Kazan lead?" Alfred asked.

"Without doubt to service in the Intelligence Bureau. That is why we started sending officers to Kazan. Back in 1890 it became distressingly clear that Russia, backed by France, had opened a major espionage effort against us, an effort that, as you know, is in operation today. We decided to prepare at least a few officers to help counter it and broached the idea of an annual exchange between General Staff officers." The Colonel chuckled. "When Wannowski, the Russian Minister of War, heard the proposal he exploded. 'What?' he asked our ambassador. 'You ask us to furnish you the weapons that will beat us?' Fortunately the Czar intervened and the agreement was made—in return the Russian General Staff sends officers to Linz to learn German. But we know and they know that the exchange is more than for merely cultural reasons, that the students generally join their respective intelligence services later."

"The Intelligence Bureau," Alfred mused and to himself he thought of the thrill and secrets and power the words spelled.

"A neglected bureau," Colonel Schlesinger said. "We can not seem to understand the importance of military intelligence. Confidentially speaking, heretofore the Bureau has often been no more than a dumping ground for mediocrity. I happen to know that General Beck is not pleased with it—that is why he just ordered Colonel von Giesl to take charge and put it on a sound producing basis."

"That is interesting, sir," Alfred said.

"Well, it should prove a challenge to any young officer assigned to it," the Colonel agreed, "and I personally believe it would be a good billet to start your career as a permanent General Staff officer." Opening a desk drawer, he looked through some papers and selected one. "As far as your career to date goes, you have conformed to all the requirements. Six months in a General Staff bureau, two years as General Staff officer in the field and now troop duty here. You will have been here two years by the time they send you to Kazan and you will have made another General Staff trip or two." The Colonel snaked a finger down the sheet of paper. "I have just signed your fitness report and I have fully qualified you: 'As Company Commander suitable in every way.' "

"Thank you, sir," Alfred said.

"As I say, the Intelligence Bureau needs officers of your caliber and I think you can make a good mark there." He stood up. "Of course, I can not tell you what to do—but if I were you, I would apply."

Back in Mikolajow, Alfred stopped by a tobacco kiosk where for a penny he bought a white sheet of paper, the "chancellery double" required for all official correspondence. In his office he folded it, inserted a ruled guide between the fold, then in his neat, precise handwriting carefully copied from the corrected draft:

Imperial and Royal   Captain Alfred Redl
Infantry Regiment Number 30
to
The Personnel Bureau of the
Imperial and Royal General Staff
in Vienna

Lemberg, May 8, 1898
Reference: Letter number 875 of April 19, 1898

This is to report that I apply for eventual assignment to Kazan, Russia, in the General Staff Corps for the purpose of gaining complete knowledge of the Russian language.

I am able to read and write Russian almost perfectly; Russian conversation is still not fluent to me. I will, however, undertake to learn it by May, 1899. I am completely fluent in reading, writing and speaking the Ruthenian and Polish languages; I speak French slightly.

I am single.

(signed) REDL
Captain

Half of the solicited officers replied that they did not want the Kazan duty. From the eleven who did, the Personnel Bureau in June, 1898, selected two captains. Their names were Dokomal and Dáni.

To Alfred the news was incredible. There could be but one explanation, he told himself in his fury. Dáni and Dokomal had graduated from the Academy. Dáni and Dokomal had friends in the Personnel Bureau whom he did not have. Dáni and Dokomal were selected for reasons other than fitness. Alfred's mind would not admit that the Imperial and Royal Army held two other officers with talents greater than his own. He did not know that the Personnel Bureau had been hard put to make the final decision, that his name had been on a par with the other two and that the deciding factor had been his weakness in French, the second language of Czarist Russia. And as he stood by the office window each morning of that summer and autumn to cool his fury that boiled in the world's injustice, he did not know that on the other side of the Empire small events combined to send Captain Dokomal to his desk where on a piece of "chancellery double" he wrote the Chief of the General Staff that he could not go to Kazan as planned "because personal reasons make my presence in Austria-Hungary necessary during the next year." As a result of this letter, Redl was notified in October that he would leave for Kazan the next spring. On January 15, 1899, the Chief of the General Staff ordered his military attaché in St. Petersburg, General von Klepsch, to complete arrangements for the arrival of Captains Redl and Dáni in May.

The moment Lieutenant Pawlow entered his chief's office he divined the suppressed tension of the air that seemed to bristle the black beard of Captain Batjuschin. A wave of the hand signaled him to a chair, a supercilious smile preluded his words. "I have a document before me that will interest you. But tell me, please, why do the Austrians send two officers each year to Kazan?"

"Ostensibly to learn Russian, sir. In fact to spy, sir. They are sent by the Intelligence Bureau in Vienna and they report to the control of the military attaché in St. Petersburg."

"Quite right—exactly why we send our officers to Linz. But tell me, please, what quality of officers are sent by the Austrians to Kazan?"

"The best, sir. Only General Staff officers."

"And what happens to them when they return to Austria?"

"Generally, sir, they are assigned to the Intelligence Bureau."

"And tell me, please, have we any Austro-Hungarian General Staff officers in our service?"

"Unfortunately, no."

"The Vienna Intelligence Bureau—have we penetrated that?"

"No, sir."

Captain Batjuschin lighted a long cigarette. "Petersburg informs me that the Austro-Hungarian military attaché has requested approval for the assignment of two officers in Kazan. Does the name Dáni, General Staff Captain Adalbert Dáni von Gyarmata, mean anything to you?"

Pawlow thought a moment. "No, sir."

Batjuschin leaned forward. "Then what about the name Redl—General Staff Captain Alfred Redl?"

Pawlow jumped.

"You see, my dear Pawlow, your chief has been proven rather more right than wrong."

"Yes, sir," Pawlow agreed. "I see that, sir, what now?"

"Now?" Batjuschin reflected. He walked to the vodka bottle, poured them each a drink. "Now we take first things first. We approve the assignments." He drank quickly. "Without, of course, informing Petersburg of our previous acquaintance with Captain Redl. You understand that quite clearly, *without* informing Petersburg of certain information we have so assiduously collected."

Pawlow met the hard look. "Of course, sir."

"Petersburg will then welcome the presence of the two officers with their usual clumsy methods—they will spend a great deal of money, learn nothing and somehow place the blame on us. We in the meantime shall go our own way. I think we want Number 85 for this job. When is she due from Paris?"

"Early in March," Pawlow said.

"Fine. She will deserve a holiday first."

On April 15, 1899, both Redl and Dáni were transferred to the General Staff, promoted to Captain First Class and ordered to Vienna. There each was given 300 gulden for purchase of civilian clothing and 600 gulden to pay for the round trip, expenditures which had to be reported in approximate figures. In addition to his salary of 200 gulden a month each officer while in Kazan would receive a monthly allowance of 250 rubles.*

"Remember now," Colonel Baron von Giesl, the new Chief of the Intelligence Bureau, told them at the close of a week-long briefing, "you will be in the enemy's camp. Each movement you make, each word you utter, will be noted by agents of the *Ochrana*. Write nothing whatsoever of a compromising nature in your private correspondence. Avoid any private or official activity that may lend itself to possible compromise.

* Over 300 gulden—a generous subsidy.

We have good reason to believe that your Russian opposites practice active espionage in Linz—the Russian mind will therefore conclude that you are sent to Kazan to practice espionage. You are, in fact, primarily there to perfect your fluency in the Russian language. As General Staff officers you are of course charged to note mentally and later report any information pertinent to the categories you have been briefed on. Travel whenever and wherever you can, see whatever you can, but report only in person to General Klepsch in St. Petersburg. Good luck."

While Alfred Redl was being briefed in Vienna, a minor clerk in the Quartermaster Depot at Lemberg laboriously copied into final form a letter dictated by his colonel. And while a slow train carried Alfred to Warsaw and Wilna, St. Petersburg and Moscow, Nishinovgorod and finally Kazan, while at each stop he basked in the hospitality of Russian officers who met the train to whisk the foreign officers off to dazzling reviews and surfeits of food and drink . . . this official letter traveled to regiment and division and corps and to the Personnel Bureau of the General Staff. And while Alfred was being met in Kazan by his brother officers who had stayed on for the purpose, while he was ensconced in a comfortable hotel, provided with a capable language instructor and oriented on the year ahead, this letter was following on his heels. It reached him a week or two later.

According to the letter, shortly after Captain Redl's transfer from Lemberg his officer's bedding had been checked into the depot for him by an acquaintance, one *Oberleutnant* Ludwig Fest. Noticing at once that the original and valuable horsehair of the mattress had been replaced with cheap pig bristles, the depot refused to accept it and was holding Captain Redl responsible for the sum of 17 gulden, 10 kreuzer. An endorsement by the Personnel Bureau of the General Staff advised Captain Redl that if the circumstances were correct he need not send the money, it would be deducted from his pay.

Clad in pajamas and silk robe, Alfred sat at his desk to study the letter. As he read the petty words the frown on his face was replaced with a look of disgust, the volutes of his nostrils

widening, the lips sneering as if to ask how the question of
this ridiculous sum could be raised in the same mail that
brought two invitations to dinner in titled houses. He let a
finger stroke the fine engraving of the invitations, then pushed
them aside in favor of the letter. It is no serious matter, he
thought—still, it is a mild accusation. He took a pen, dipped
its nib carefully in the ink well, sucked its round end for a
moment, then on a piece of "chancellery double" wrote in his
careful hand:

Imperial and Royal General Staff   Captain Alfred Redl
to
The Personnel Bureau of the Imperial and Royal General Staff
in Vienna

Kazan, May 18, 1899
Reference: Command letter Number 1078 of May 9, 1899

I can find no explanation for the official inquiry made in connection with my mattress. During the time I used the bedding
there would have been no opportunity for anyone to have effected a substitution. Without doubt I received the mattress in
its present condition, but of course I did not examine it at the
time nor did I notice anything wrong during my subsequent use
of it.

Although I feel myself in no way concerned with this discrepancy, I will consent to pay the replacement charge purely in order
to avoid a protracted and detailed correspondence.

Alfred sucked the round end of the pen, thought of his next
month's pay, realized that it was already spent, then wrote:

I request, however, that the stipulated sum of seventeen gulden,
ten kreuzer, be deducted not from my June pay, but from that
of July 1, 1899.

Signing the letter, he stood up and walked to the window. He
could not remember why he had needed the money so badly
at the time. "Goddamn it," he suddenly said. Then he put the
fear of himself aside and dressed for the day.

Since the time he had requested assignment to Kazan, Alfred
had been aware of the danger inherent in exposing his perversion to Russian eyes. He had convinced himself, however,

88

that the dimensions of his new surroundings would offer an alternate claim to those forces that raged so incessantly, that they would be absorbed in the challenge of his assignment. He soon discovered that he had miscalculated. The major challenge was the Russian language. But previous years of study had taught him its syntax, his fluency in Polish and Ruthenian eliminated the pronunciation problem and his quick, retentive mind, now given full rein, coped easily with the remaining task of new words and idioms and usage. By the end of the summer a considerable fluency had already reduced the charm of this challenge.

There remained Kazan society. Unlike the titled landowners of Lemberg, Budapest and Prague who were essentially provincial nationalists in uneasy peace with the House of Habsburg, the Russian landowning aristocracy formed a major support of the St. Petersburg Court. As such, they accepted the Army in a different light; they opened the doors of their town houses and country estates to its officers, many of whom were titled in their own right. In turn these officers, sympathetic to the dictates of the international code of professional soldiers, hastened to introduce their Austro-Hungarian guests into local society. Glad in the knowledge that two young bachelor faces—and General Staff faces at that—would augment the annual season, Kazan hostesses quickly plucked the engraved calling cards from silver salvers to add the foreign names to permanent guest lists. For the first time in his life, and the last, Alfred found himself accepted into a supreme social circle as if it were his birthright.

Circumstance having provided the entrée, there remained the necessity of consolidation. Alfred's quiet appearance and pleasant manner, his increasing fluency in the Russian tongue and his evident interest in each aspect of Russian culture, his willingness to explain what was asked of him and the obvious intelligence of his answers, insured him a steady stream of invitations to teas, dinners, balls, weekend shoots, to everything the landed gentry evolved for its own amusement. Too, and at first quite unwittingly, he provided notes for the background music that must accompany any activity of the leisure class: gossip.

Alfred met Countess Kobiakov at a dinner some two weeks after his arrival in Kazan. Although she was a strikingly beautiful creature, a small woman whose soft olive skin showed from the black velvet décolletage set off by a single strand of white pearls, something about the cut of her face, perhaps the long cheekline, reminded him of Maria Montessi. Accordingly he had escorted her to dinner with no marked enthusiasm. By the end of dinner, however, his slight foreboding had been absorbed into the charm of her aristocratic bearing—a cultured worldliness unostentatiously displayed by casual reference to a variety of subjects in as many languages, but always in response to her Austrian dinner partner who felt his ordinary conversational restraint melt in the force of her dark eyes which so often drew his own. Everything about her was young except those eyes and Alfred was not surprised to learn that they had been aged by great sorrow.

Countess Kobiakov, he was told, as a girl had fallen in love with an older man, a cavalry officer far below her social station but with a cavalier's charm that veiled the moral vacuity of a skunk. Thinking to face her wealthy father with a profitable *fait accompli,* he had persuaded her to an elopement that resulted in her disinheritance. As a liability, she subsequently formed a receptacle for the fury of her lover's frustration; her disillusion was complete before the two-year marriage ended by her husband being convicted of embezzlement and sent packing to Siberia for nine years. A sympathetic aunt and uncle in Kazan had invited her to live with them until a reconciliation with her parents could be effected.

If the experience had embittered her toward men, Katrina Kobiakov did not show it in the subsequent weeks when nearly each social event brought her together with Alfred Redl. Kazan society was quick to note and respect her open admiration for him, her quick, searching glances when she entered a room, her warm smile of greeting at his approach, her undivided attention as he spoke, her frequent flattery and fulsome praise of his words. Nor was her attitude unreciprocated. Although Katrina failed to arouse any physical desire in Alfred, he did respect her brain and he felt comfortable in her flattery. Sincerely liking her as a person, he valued her as a convenience because she provided the answer to society's demand that a bachelor be provided with a member of the opposite sex. Accordingly he performed the exterior rites of courtship with a punctiliousness that more than satisfied the wagging tongues of Kazan matrons.

What the matrons imagined was actually limited to their imaginations. They could not know that the charming countess' overtures to a more physical expression of friendship were at first ignored and when insistently repeated were diverted with a half-sighed answer: "No, my darling. Not until you are free. Do not ask me to do what my Church disallows. Wait, Katrina, please wait until the annulment. . . ."

Hidden from Kazan hostesses, this piety was duly reported to Warsaw where it caused the pinched face of Captain Batjuschin to screw itself into an amused question mark. It did not worry him. He held infinite faith in Agent Number 85. As the past proved, Katrina Kobiakov's charms were capable of surmounting the moral insulation of the most chaste monk. Meanwhile he was learning a great deal about this Captain Redl. The reason for his earlier debts was obvious: Captain Redl enjoyed a luxurious life which cost him more, far more, money than he earned. Batjuschin was pleased—it was as he had told Pawlow originally: the situation was developing, there was no reason Katrina could not follow Redl to Vienna. But Batjuschin did not learn one fact, the most important of all. He would have been very excited had he known the workings of his intended victim's mind that autumn.

As Alfred forged his way to mastery of the Russian language and confirmed his presence in society, to that degree his control of his own passion began to slip. He recognized the symptoms clearly enough: at first the lassitude, the sagging of life's each day to a feckless mass of twenty-four hours presenting themselves to be endured, a task that became the more onerous as loneliness was joined by aloneness. And with the feeling came the admission of physical man into his mind by every means the senses could provide: by the eyes as they searched high-cheeked Slavic faces to run furtively down the broad shoulders and straight backs to the classic mold of muscular buttocks and the tight mound of genital in the close-fitting

91

trousers, as they read the old letters from Chris and Arthur and gave to the mind the smooth faces and nights of naked love; by the nose as it caught the heady dark smell of the male in a crowded salon; by the ear as each note of the sonorous voices sang to this troubled man; by the touch as his fingers gripped a friendly hand to slide away with reluctance lessened none by being unnoticed, by the feel of hips and legs brushing in the crowd of a roulette table.

Alfred identified the symptoms, but he did not want to admit them. Yet at such times his mind held no more resistance to them than does the smooth flesh of the oyster to grains of sand, and like grains of sand they gained nurture from irritation of time, they ate the control and they grew and grew to a great dominating pearl of desire that could be plucked only by powerful, tearing hands of man.

And in the sphere of this growth Alfred could only struggle to hide his imprisonment under a shell of acting that at least covered the growth from the eyes of his world. But even while he acted, even while Katrina and Batjuschin and Dáni and the Russian officers and others in Kazan suspected nothing of this awful, terrible growth, it continued to consume care and caution and common sense. And as he awaited the full bloom, as he anticipated the inexorable plucking, as he trembled in delight of approaching danger, the one event that could stem this growth of evil arrived unbidden and unsought.

Alfred sat on the sheet-covered table, his bare legs dangling short of the floor, his eyes fixed on the rubber-sheathed hand of Doctor Nikolitch who prodded the small, brownish-red splotch on the inside of his right leg. "I do not understand it," Doctor Nikolitch said. "When did you stop taking the mercury pills?"

"Just over two years ago," Alfred said. "In Budapest. I thought . . . it was cured."

The doctor waved his lithe hands as if to conjure an answer from the air. His gloved finger touched the sore once more and he said, "Everything I know tells me this is a papule characteristic to the second stage of syphilis. Yet it emerges after five years of quiescence and three years after the normal end of the second stage. No! A papule it cannot be—it is a gumma."

"What is that?"

"A growth indicative of the third stage of syphilis. It can be very dangerous if not properly looked after."

"Can anything be done?" Alfred asked.

The doctor wrinkled his high forehead. "We must go on a fishing expedition, you and I. See the blood as a big river fed by thousands of little streams. This syphilis sends germs like many fishes into the river where they fight to the quiet side streams to bury in the sand and breed trouble for us. *Voilà.* The river kills some and to kill the rest we poison the water with mercury. Perhaps the mercury has missed one little stream." He threw his hands into the air, clapped them as he caught the image of his words. "*Voilà.* We send more mercury to find this little stream. An expedition, *mon capitaine*—you will be my guest."

To the frown on his patient's face the doctor replied, "A week or two, no more. You must come here because the mercury fishes better when the water is calm. To Kazan you are ill with our common malady: Kazan fever. There will be no questions."

There were no questions. Alfred spent two weeks in Doctor Nikolitch's sanitarium, his ointment-covered leg hidden from the guests who called with flowers and liqueur bonbons to sympathize and wish the fever-ridden patient a speedy recovery. And on an afternoon when Katrina Kobiakov sat by him to read aloud Tolstoy's *War and Peace,* far off in Warsaw Captain Batjuschin read the finely written words of Doctor Nikolitch's report, his reading interrupted by herculean shouts of laughter. Wiping away tears of mirth he turned to the astounded Pawlow. "I knew it was not religion," he fairly shrieked. "Syphilis, my dear Pawlow, syphilis. Why did you not think of that? That is why our lovely Katrina has been repulsed. We are dealing with a gentleman, Pawlow—a cavalier."

Autumn slowly turned the vast sky of blueness to a more somber gray and took away some daylight and painted the rolling landscape a final burst of color before admitting the snow clouds that would blanket the surrounding plains against the long winter months. Autumn emptied the country estates in favor of the city town houses, livened Kazan with confined frivolity of nightly dinners and balls, musicales and theatre. A busy social life, this, and followed by long drinking and gambling bouts, gifts to Katrina and presents to hostesses, an expensive one. Not long after Alfred was released from Dr. Nikolitch's care, he was forced to his desk, to the writing of two long and difficult letters.

Imperial and Royal General Staff   Captain Alfred Redl
to
His Excellency
Feldzeugmeister. Friedrich Freiherr von Beck
Grand Cross of the Order of St. Stephan,
etc., etc., etc. [sic]
Life Member of the Upper House of the Austrian Parliament
Honorary Commander of the Imperial and Royal
Infantry Regiment Number 47
Imperial and Royal Chief of the General Staff
in Vienna

Trusting in the kindness and gracious understanding of Your Excellency, I beg leave, both in my name and in that of Captain Adalbert Dáni von Gyarmata, to most respectfully request Your Excellency to grant us a special monetary allowance equivalent to that received by our predecessors in this billet.

The reasons which determined us to submit this request, if described in detail to Your Excellency, would tax the patience of Your Excellency too greatly. I have reported these to the Chief of the Personnel Bureau, Colonel Viktor Dankl, along with the request to bring them at his discretion to the attention of Your Excellency.

I limit myself, accordingly, in most respectfully reporting to Your Excellency that our local group of acquaintances expands from year to year and that through this, naturally, our obligations also mount. In striving to fulfill them to the same degree as our predecessors, and thus to maintain the excellent and honorable position already achieved in local society, we must soon meet significant material demands which we can scarcely afford in the long run with the means currently at our disposal. In view of this, we deem it necessary to request respectfully that Your Excellency grant this allowance, even while we very unwillingly permit ourselves to tax the goodwill of Your Excellency just for this. May Your Excellency most graciously understand this respectful request to be compatible with our incessant effort of maintaining and furthering the extraordinarily favorable attitude toward Austro-Hungarian officers and particularly toward Austro-Hungarian General Staff officers that has been established here.

Permit us the respectful assurance on this occasion that we are working continuously toward the final goal of our assignment and hope to achieve it in its perfection as soon as possible.

May it please Your Excellency to receive graciously the expression of our deepest respect, most reverential esteem and highest regard from the signed,

> To Your Excellency
> Obedient
> > (signed) ALFRED REDL
> > > Captain

Kazan, October 22, 1899

He next composed a letter to the Chief of the Personnel Bureau in which, after repeating most of what he had written Beck, he plunged to the meat of the matter:

. . . we have attempted to maintain ourselves on the allowance previously furnished us. Economies that formerly were possible allowed us to accomplish this to some extent, but with the advent of winter such varied increased demands and social obligations approach us that in the long run we will scarcely be able to meet them with the means available to us. . . . Although the monthly allowance of two hundred and fifty rubles is not trifling under normal conditions and is sufficient for current living expenses, it does not suffice by far in meeting the approaching material demands of an extraordinarily social nature that are incumbent upon us in our present, unusual position. . . . The Austro-Hungarian General Staff officers occupy a particularly excellent and respectable position here in the highest society; they are very welcome in all salons and are very favorably regarded guests. One is overwhelmed with favors of every sort from all sides which naturally must be returned. The most fitting way to do this, albeit expensive, is to participate in or appear at charitable fetes of which there are an infinite number here, and we are absolutely obliged to attend fifteen or twenty of them. Here it counts as a matter of honor for each social leader to arrange annually at least one of these fetes and since we are acquainted with most of these persons, frequently enjoy their hospitality, and as a rule are personally invited by them to appear at the bazaar, it is thus, so to say, impossible for us to stay away. Consider also that on such occasions one is forced to buy something from each lady he knows (around forty of them) and in addition, since most ladies compete as much as possible for charitable purposes, one is invited or challenged to expensive purchases. Consequently, despite every economy and exercise of great moderation, these affairs are very expensive, and as yet one has been unable to escape from one of them with an expenditure of less than sixty to seventy rubles. All of these fetes take place in winter; we have already participated in a few and have accepted several more whereby I take the liberty to note that the number of fetes, in comparison with former years (as noted by our predecessors), has significantly increased. Further, it is rumored that this year, in order to alleviate the grim aftereffects of the last famine as well as to improve further the charitable institutions established in former years, the bazaars will be very numerous. To cut down our participation in them seems objectionable for a variety of reasons and would only cause gossip that could perhaps damage the excellent reputation of the Austro-Hungarian officers here.

While not suggesting that we be granted a still higher special allowance, may I further report that both Captain von Dáni and I were forced to spend considerably more (about three times as much) for our civilian clothing than was provided for by the allowance we received, since this was just enough to purchase the indispensable amount of the quality of clothes that are necessary here. For the procurement of other items we had to use money provided for other purposes (travel allowance, etc.) without, however, having bought with it the winter equipment now becoming necessary (furs, etc.).

Also the Most Worthy Colonel is requested to note and keep in mind that we have both been ill in September and, indeed, Captain von Dáni from a throat ailment that required an operation; I from the local (Kazaner) malaria; for a long period we were both under medical treatment which also meant significant, unexpected expenditures . . .

. . . Finally I report that we are presently healthy and are industriously continuing the study of the Russian language under the tutelage of a well-trained and experienced teacher. . . .

96

The appeal was not without result. On November 2 the Chief of the General Staff sent each officer 500 rubles to soften the tone of his accompanying letter: ". . . you were provided originally with extra funds . . . we are making this exception . . . it will be absolutely impossible to send you an additional emergency grant during this tour of duty."

In early spring of 1900 Alfred requested a twenty-day leave "to visit Turkey, Vienna, Lemberg and Cracow." The Chief of the General Staff recommended approval to the War Ministry because "this officer has had no leave in the preceding years." In May the War Ministry granted formal permission plus the necessary passport.

Alfred said his good-byes reluctantly, yet he was not sorry to leave Kazan. The turn of the century marked a turn in his career, for now he would enjoy his place in the General Staff sun that fifteen years of work had earned him. When in April he learned of his new assignment—General Staff officer to the 30th Infantry Division in Lemberg—he guessed correctly that this was only an interim post. For even as he entered his new duties, the Chief of the Intelligence Bureau was at work. The Russian desk in the Bureau was open; here was an able officer who commanded the language and whose Qualification List stated:

> . . . personal knowledge of Russia: the route Warsaw (and immediate surroundings), Wilna, St. Petersburg (and immediate surroundings), Moscow, Nishinovgorod, Kazan (and immediate surroundings), upper regions of the Volga, Kama and Vjatka rivers; northern parts of the coastal regions of the Black and Caspian Seas; the area Tiflis-Baku, parts of western Siberia, and the route Odessa-Kiew-Podwolocryska.

On October 1, 1900, Captain Alfred Redl was transferred to the Intelligence Bureau of the General Staff in Vienna. He was thirty-six years old.

Part II

THE PLAY

1.

HE LIVED in the Eighth District of Vienna, a good district for a General Staff captain or for a young doctor or attorney. The private homes there were many—large square buildings with long, gray noncommittal façades that hid prosperous rococo and baroque interiors kept splendid by staffs of servants. But Vienna was expanding and now in 1900 windows in a few of these houses held small cards announcing that gentlemen guests would be welcome and some hotels and shops had moved in to further pollute the suburban air. Alfred lived in one of the hotels, a small one at Number 50, Floriani Street. He rented an apartment of comfortably furnished top-floor rooms that were breezy and light in warm weather but in cold weather benefited from the heat that rose beneath them. He had taken them because they were on the top floor.

Each morning early he awakened, washed and shaved from a pitcher of hot scented water brought by his servant, drew on a silk robe and went to breakfast where he studied the morning paper. With the quarter-hour chime of the mantel clock, he rose, returned to his bedroom, dressed in the carefully laid-out uniform, issued brief but clear instructions to his servant, buckled on his sword belt, adjusted his garrison hat without his fingers touching the patent leather visor, picked up suede gloves, inspected himself finally in a long hall mirror and left the apartment. He normally walked to work, sometimes alone, sometimes with other officers; a twenty-five-minute walk past a large skating rink, town houses, small shops, a park, then past the Gothic-Renaissance Rathaus to Ringstrasse and across it and past the white stone Burg Theater to the second court-yard of Emperor Francis Joseph's town palace, the Hofburg. At eight twenty-five he returned a sentry's salute, marched across a wide courtyard to the Ministry of War building, re-turned another sentry's salute, climbed four flights to the In-telligence Bureau of the General Staff, was identified by a final sentry and walked to his office. By eight thirty he was seated behind a plain desk in a small, sparsely furnished room where he sipped a cup of coffee, smoked a cigarette and frowned at the papers before him.

Redl had been assigned two jobs in the Intelligence Bureau. The first was Chief of the Russian Section, an office which formed part of the positive-intelligence mission of the Bureau. Simply stated, this mission was to keep the Chief of the General Staff oriented on foreign armies of particular concern to Austria-Hungary. To supply the necessary reports, the Chief of the Bureau, Colonel Baron von Giesl, had assigned nine officers to six desks: Russia, the Balkans, Italy, Germany, France and England-America-Japan. Each desk based its reports on material culled from military journals and foreign newspapers—about eighty such a day were studied in the Bureau—and from reports forwarded by Austro-Hungarian military attachés in Paris, Berlin, Rome, Bucharest, St. Petersburg, Belgrade and Constantinople. This intelligence formed the basis for General Beck's strategic calculations which in turn provided the foundation for his annual budget request, his tactical dispositions of standing army units, his strategic and tactical considerations as tested by General Staff trips and unit maneuvers and, finally, his mobilization and deployment plans designed for war against Russia, the Balkans or Italy.

Captain Redl's second job was Chief of the Operations Section. As he quickly recognized, the Operations Section could control the Intelligence Bureau. Responsible for all covert work in the Bureau, it received the bulk of confidential funds. It recruited, trained and dispatched agents, either directly from Vienna or through field intelligence posts located in Army commands around the Empire. To Alfred's desk came specific requests for information from other Bureau sections; from his desk emanated instructions that sent agents out to find the answers; on his desk arrived agent reports that could be forwarded back to the sections. The Operations Section was also responsible for counterintelligence. It received all reports of military espionage, reports which came from its own informants, from diverse Army personnel or from State Police and Gendarmerie commands with whom it worked in close liaison. It investigated whom and what it wished; it recommended the arrest of suspects to either military or civil justice departments; it furnished military expert evidence necessary for conviction of a spy in a court of law.

At least the Operations Section was supposed to do all of these things. That it was not functioning properly was clear both from the meager record of the past twenty years and its effort at the time Captain Redl took control. He superseded an officer senior to himself in rank but not a member of the General Staff Corps. This person, Major Wissowski, pedantically instructed his new Chief in the use of codes, invisible inks, hollowed-out walking sticks and false-top brushes. When he had run through his bag of tricks he had smiled patronizingly and said, "Well, that is all there is to it."

Alfred had not returned the smile. Although he knew little about actual intelligence procedures, he recognized instantly the lack of any system at work in the various sections. He now understood why the Intelligence Bureau had come to be regarded as a burial ground for incompetency in the Imperial and Royal Army. Resolving to change matters, he began immediately to prepare himself for the task. He pored over Bureau reports and records, studied what treatises were available on the subject of espionage, picked the brains of the few qualified officers in the Bureau and consulted often with experts in the State Police. He studied volumes of domestic and international law, police-gendarmerie-customs regulations, post and telegraph organization and operations and passport-registration procedures. He visited the Bureau's field posts in Lemberg, Cracow and Przemyśl from where operations against Russia were supervised, in Graz and Innsbruck where Italy was the target, and in Temesvár, Agram, Sarajevo and Zara which faced the Balkans. Here he interviewed and interrogated agents, discussed current problems with his officers, met and worked with local police and gendarmerie officials. At the end of six months he had learned a great deal and he had formed certain conclusions. He decided to present them to the Chief of the Bureau.

Alfred leaned slightly forward in his chair and fixed his eyes on the older man opposite him. "I do not believe, sir," he said carefully, "that we are getting the results that we should get in this Bureau."

Colonel von Giesl puffed on his cigar. More than anyone else he was aware of a deficiency in his Bureau and he was annoyed by his own inability to locate it. He had liked Redl during their brief association at the time of the Kazan briefing, and the subsequent reports submitted by Redl had impressed him as much as they had the veteran military attaché, General von Klepsch, in St. Petersburg. Von Giesl had gone to some trouble to have Redl assigned to the Bureau. On this particular morning he suddenly felt that his effort was to be repaid. He pressed a button and an orderly at once entered. "I am not to be disturbed," he said. And to Redl: "Won't you continue, Captain? I am most interested in the subject that you have broached."

"In my opinion, sir," Alfred said, "our major mission is being neglected. From the sources that are theoretically available to us, we should be able to form an accurate estimate of a country's peacetime strength—its disposition of corps and armies, type and condition of armament, amount of matériel, effective reserve strength and the like—and from this we should be able to estimate a country's state of military readiness. From the reports of our sections that I have read and from the requests that I have been receiving in the Operations Section, I can only conclude that this is not being done. Most of the sections seem content to forward only the unchanged military attaché reports—in other words, no collation with other material, mere message center functioning. We are making no organized effort to determine the potential enemy's will to wage war. We are not thinking about key questions: when and where will a given country go to war, how rapidly can it mobilize and deploy? Please do not misunderstand me, sir. I am not maliciously criticizing our officers. I would feel honored to serve with any one of them in the field. But not everyone, in my opinion, is adaptable to the peculiar demands of military intelligence."

"I agree," Von Giesl said. "Most of them are assigned to the Bureau without any particular aptitude. You know the situation as well as I do."

104

"Not nearly as well, sir," Alfred said. "But one reason for some of the disinterest and lethargy, I believe, is the low degree of efficiency with which the Operations Section has been operating. I have found numerous requests filed with no action taken. For years my section has been almost totally dependent for positive-intelligence on our military attachés and on Agent Number 184." Colonel von Giesl's chuckle interrupted Alfred. Agent Number 184 was the German Intelligence Service which at times worked closely with the Bureau.

"The intelligence that we have gained on our own and at high cost," Alfred continued, "has been so low-level as to be useless. Penetration operations, particularly against Russia, have been ludicrous. The Russians probably know every agent we have operating there right now. Look what they did in 1889 when we picked up their agent, Wenzel Marek, who stole the Przemyśl fortress plans from us. In one day we lost Group Kiev-Zytomir-Woloczysk: twenty-eight informants lost because everyone knew everyone else and one person talked! Then the next day they picked up Group Warsaw and one man identified Agent Number 126, our best man in Russia! Nor is the record any better in Counterintelligence. We have arrested four spies in the last twenty years, the most recent of whom, Karl Saria, ran a paper mill."

"I beg your pardon," Colonel von Giesl said.

"Sorry, sir," Alfred said. "That is a term I translated from a French source. It means a fraudulent spy, one who writes reports based largely on his own imagination."

"A very good term, too," Von Giesl said, making a note to use it in his next conference with the Chief of the General Staff.

"Our present counterintelligence effort is no more than routine: setting up security procedures, warning officers not to discuss secrets in public, once in a while investigating a suspicious report. In so far as meeting the real challenge—that of protecting the internal security of the Imperial and Royal Army—we fail, and fail badly. We know very well and have known since the Bartmann case in 1889 that the Russian military attaché here in Vienna is running a penetration effort against us. And what are we doing? We have the State Police watch the Russian Embassy eight hours a day! *Mein lieber Gott!*"

"The Foreign Office permits us to go no further," Von Giesl said. He removed his *pince-nez* and rubbed his eyes. "We even have enemies in our own Officer Corps. Ever since the Bureau was established a century ago it has had to fight its own Army. Numerous officers today, my own friends among them, intelligent, patriotic officers, actually believe that espionage is incompatible to the officer code of honor. They say openly that the funds we receive would be better spent equipping a new cavalry regiment or buying the infantry new canteens."

Alfred nodded his head. "Certainly the Foreign Office hates us, sir. By challenging their monopoly in espionage, we threaten their control of the Empire." He laughed sourly. "At the same time the Empire is being surrounded by nations who plan its dissolution through military conquest if their present attempts to cause internal revolution fail. Russia is spending tremendous sums against us in Bohemia and Galicia, indirectly in the Balkans. France is backing Russia in addition to her own impressive effort against Germany. Our ally, Italy, is doing all she can to stir up the Tyrolean Irredentists against us. We are surrounded by enemies and our heterogeneous Empire is such as to offer them fertile ground for their propaganda and espionage."

"A depressing picture," Von Giesl said.

"It is, sir. Particularly when, in the final analysis, we are our own worst enemy."

Colonel von Giesl looked up sharply. "What do you mean, Captain?"

"Forgive me, sir, if I speak out of turn. I mean that we are as much in the wrong as those of our comrades who criticize our existence. We are trying to fight a scoundrel's war with gentlemen's weapons. Our approach is unrealistic. While our bodies are cloaked in General Staff tunics, our minds are smothered by General Staff conventions. As a result we are not producing good Intelligence and because we are not, we are being neglected. May I remind you, sir, that ninety-eight years after this Bureau was established it is operating on 120,000 kronen a year which is less than it received in 1805!* We must have more funds. We must make ourselves deserving of more funds." Alfred took a document from his briefcase and handed it to Colonel von Giesl. "I have taken the liberty, sir, of completing a staff study on some of the problems we are faced with. I hope the Colonel will see fit to consider it."

"I will certainly do that, Captain Redl," the elderly man said. "And thank you for coming to see me about this."

The next morning Captain Redl was called to Colonel von Giesl's office.

"I am very impressed with this study, Redl," he told him. "I gather that the impetus you desire should emanate from a reorganization of the Operations Section."

"That is my opinion, sir."

"You seem to have a number of ideas for that reorganization." Von Giesl riffled the pages of the report. "Complete records section, handwriting specimens, new modes of recruitment, training of agents and so on. Quite obviously, you have given this some very worth-while thought." He squared the pages of the report and rested his hands on top of them. "Redl, do you believe that you are able to reorganize the Operations Section along the lines you have indicated?"

"I would like to try, sir," Alfred said.

"You are aware that I could never condone some of the—uh—devices you have mentioned such as—uh—blackmail."

"I am quite aware, sir. It is my opinion that should an officer employ such devices and they are exposed, he must be prepared to assume the entire responsibility himself."

"It would probably mean a ruined career," the Colonel said.

"It would, sir," Alfred agreed.

"I am relieving you from the Russian Section today, Redl. Henceforth you will function solely as Chief of the Operations Section. You are at liberty to reorganize this section in accordance with your written proposals. Those of your suggestions that must be passed to higher authority for approval will be drawn up by you for my signature."

"Thank you, sir," Alfred said.

* The gold krone or crown currency replaced the silver gulden in 1900. One crown equaled approximately twenty-three cents in American money.

"One more thing, Redl. Go a bit slowly at first."

"I shall have to, sir," Alfred said with a slight smile. "There is too much about this business I do not know."

"You seem to be learning very rapidly, Captain," the Colonel said dryly.

Word soon passed around the General Staff that significant changes were taking place in the Intelligence Bureau and that Captain Alfred Redl was responsible for them. Not that the changes could be readily identified: under a security bill that Redl wrote and Von Giesl signed, each section became sealed off from the others by means of private offices. Office doors had to be kept closed, an officer calling on another had to knock. Each visitor had to be cleared through the Operations Section, his name, purpose and length of visit carefully recorded. A new classification system was introduced with each classified document numbered and recorded in a central file. Wire waste-baskets were installed by each desk: at the close of working hours the wastepaper was collected and burned under the supervision of a duty officer. The latter remained in the Bureau to inspect offices, search desks and test safes. A separate entrance to the Operations Section opened to an anteroom where visitors waited while being processed. Two other offices completed this section: in one sat Major Wissowski with his bag of tricks; in the other, Captain Redl with his thoughts.

After reorganizing the internal administration of his own section by introducing what Major Wissowski privately referred to "as a lot of scientific balderdash," Alfred concentrated on the problem of informants. Beginning fifty years before, the Bureau had divided informants into three groups: *Vertrauensleute,* who were unpaid, patriotic agents; *Konfidenten,* who were paid nationals of a foreign nation; and *Kundschafter,* who were paid or unpaid spies sent out by the Operations Section on specific missions. Most of these agents, when abroad, received instructions and funds through the appropriate Austro-Hungarian military attaché or, where there was no embassy, through Austro-Hungarian consulates. Alfred objected to this system. To begin with, too many people were being employed in relation to the administrative resources of the Bureau. It disposed of neither sufficient funds nor staff personnel to maintain the files necessary for cross-checking of reported intelligence; the Operations Section did not know, much less practice, the elementary technique perfected by Fouché's lieutenants, Réal and Desmarest, of spying upon one's own spies. The Bureau was thus at the mercy of any clever enemy counter-campaign which could feed its agents either knowingly or unknowingly false information or "smoke" designed to mislead Austria-Hungary. This, in Alfred's opinion a deficiency of centralized control, was partially remedied by placing agent supervision back in the Operations Section of the Bureau. From an arduous cross-check of past reports coupled with close surveillance by police officers, Alfred determined which agents were unreliable and which hopelessly compromised, and these he summarily fired. The survivors along with new recruits were carefully examined by him. If they were known to anyone else in the Bureau, it was by number only—their real identities and the amounts of money paid them were kept in a single, metal box in Redl's personal safe.

By the spring of 1901 Alfred had implemented these basic changes which in turn had spawned new ideas that he had not yet effected. He was working fifteen hours a day, often spent Sundays and holidays in the office. To the informed observer he resembled a quiet Messiah spreading a new word. In view of his evident ardor and zeal, he would not have been suspected of owning a private life. Yet during these months he did own a private life, one that was compartmented even more tightly than his office in the Operations Section.

2.

UPON his return to Vienna in the autumn of 1900, Alfred had been disappointed to learn that Arthur Schnitzel was in Germany completing his medical studies. When a month later he read in the paper that his young friend was opening a surgery in Vienna, he swallowed his displeasure in still not having heard from him personally and sent him a polite invitation to call. He had thought it would be a wonderful reunion, that Arthur would smile and put his arm around him and that everything would be the same.

No boy came through the door but a man, a bearded man wearing *pince-nez* and a black suit with swallow-tailed coat and a high winged celluloid collar with a silver stickpin showing through the cravat that flowed from an embroidered waistcoat. With a brisk movement he placed a black bag on the floor and turned to Alfred. "Good to see you again, Redl," he said, shaking hands firmly and briefly.

"I . . . Arthur . . . what . . . how are you?" Alfred at last managed.

"Just fine, thank you. You look well yourself. Apparently Russia agreed with you."

"But you, Arthur . . . so old."

Schnitzel chuckled. "I am in practice now. Our fine middle-class gentry won't look at you if they think you are under forty."

"I . . . had no idea. You . . . I had no letters from you."

"No, you did not."

Alfred's face hardened. "But you . . . received the money?"

"Yes, thank you."

"And you . . ." He hesitated, then smiled. "But I am being rude. Come sit here on the sofa and I shall pour some wine."

Arthur sat in a chair to take the proffered glass.

"To our future," Alfred said, raising his glass.

Arthur stared at him. "What do you mean, Redl?"

"Why . . . to our friendship . . . like old times."

Arthur put his glass down. "That is all over," he said.

"You took my money," Alfred answered quickly. "My gifts."

"I needed the money to get married," Arthur said.

Alfred sank back in the sofa as if someone had struck him. "Married?"

"Yes, married. A child on the way. I advise you, purely professionally, to adopt the same course."

"Never mind my course," Alfred said. "Do you intend to repay me?"

"I don't know what for," Arthur said. "But if you like, I can send the Chief of the General Staff a certain sum each month. With an explanation, of course."

Alfred controlled himself. "That would not be particularly healthy for your new practice, *Herr Doktor*."

"I would not sign my name," Arthur said. "Your General Beck is not stupid—would he believe that one was sending money for a practical joke?"

Alfred sprang from the sofa. "Get out of here!"

"If you wish," Arthur said casually. He drank the wine and stood up. At the door he picked up his bag and said, "Pleasant seeing you again."

When the outer door closed, Alfred sat trembling from rage. "The whore," he said aloud. "The ungrateful little whore."

His servant entered. "You rang, sir?"

"Yes, bring me a brandy. A large brandy."

Alfred's silent rage had not diminished when a few weeks later he received a note from Countess Katrina Kobiakov announcing that she had arrived in Vienna en route to Paris. She wanted very much to see him and wondered if he could come to tea at Sacher's on the following afternoon.

Leaving the War Ministry for the short walk to the hotel, Alfred found himself anticipating the meeting. He had liked Katrina in Kazan and she would bring news of several Russian friends he had made there. He wondered if she had gotten her annulment and if so who was paying for her journey. He had never determined exactly where her family stood but as near as he could tell they were quite wealthy. The thought had occurred to him several times that a marriage of convenience would not be a poor idea. And the night before in bed, another thought had struck him: the possibility of using Katrina in intelligence work.

"This way, sir," a porter addressed him. The porter led him to the Red Lounge and turned him over to the head waiter who showed him to a table. "The Countess Kobiakov has extended her apologies, sir," he said stiffly, "but she will be delayed. She requests that the gentleman wait."

Alfred smiled—this was the Russian way. He had been fifteen minutes late in Viennese fashion and now he was to wait another fifteen minutes before Katrina swept into the room, her furs still gathered about her, her tiny hands enclosed in a muff on which melting snowflakes had begun to glisten. Her cheeks were red and her eyes sparkled as she made a perfunctory apology while the head waiter removed her wraps. "You, Captain Redl," she said in Russian, "You never in your life told me how beautiful this city is. Why, this is paradise, this Vienna." She laughed lightly. "After all these years I have found paradise."

"Tell me, now," Alfred said when tea had been brought, "what brings you here and how long are you to stay and how are you—all about you and Kazan."

"How naughty you are to be so inquisitive," she said but some of her buoyancy dropped away. "My marriage was annulled, Alfred. It was not a pleasant time for me, but I am together with my family once more. We agreed that an extended journey would be convenient." She looked at him for a moment and added quietly, "I came to Vienna because I wanted to see you again."

"I am glad you did," Alfred said.

A string quartet broke the silence and when the two resumed conversation it was to discuss mutual friends and experiences. Before tea had ended, Katrina agreed to have dinner with him that evening. At dinner she told him her plans were indefinite, that she would stay on in Vienna for some time.

The porter who opened the wide door of the Austro-Hungarian Bank greeted him with, "Good day, *Herr Hauptmann* Redl." He flicked his brush expertly against the snowflakes on the dark green overcoat and smiled obsequiously. "Beggin' your pardon, sir, your former servant, Reiner, *Herr Hauptmann,* sir."

Of course. But Reiner with hair grown long and wearing this absurd uniform. Still the coarse voice speaking provincial German was the same and Alfred frowned because he had not recognized it. Coldly he said, "Yes, Reiner, how long have you been here?"

"A number of months now, *Herr Hauptmann.* Not much of

a place for me it isn't but what with the wife at work we are getting along, thank you for inquiring."

"You are married?" Alfred wondered why he asked.

"Two years now, sir." Reiner was still brushing him and Alfred noticed that he had been gently pushed into a corner of the bank's large anteroom. "We have a right comfortable place in St. Veit, sir," Reiner said in a low voice. "I know the Missus would want the *Herr Hauptmann* for a visit." Before Alfred could object to the familiarity, Reiner continued rapidly, "Many's the young officer what comes our way today. My heart's still with the Army, you can see plain, and what I says to the Missus, if these young bachelor gentlemen wants to get off by themselves for a little with no one the wiser the least we can do is keep a few rooms for 'em, of course they always pay us a little token and that helps us while we serve 'em. Absolutely private it all is, sir, and the Missus takes care of any food and drink. A nice group of young bachelors, very handsome boys they are, and as I say the Missus would want the *Herr Hauptmann* to visit and see for himself."

Alfred pulled himself from the reach of the brush. "I can assure you, Reiner, that I am not interested in your social establishment. If I were, it would be in my capacity as Counterintelligence officer." He stared a moment and said, "As Chief of Army Counterintelligence, Reiner, I work very closely with the State Police. Do you understand?"

"Of course, sir," Reiner said quickly. "Beggin' the *Herr Hauptmann's* pardon . . ."

But Alfred had wheeled from him to enter the bank. At a counter he took a withdrawal slip, stared at it, thought of the gift he had ordered for Katrina's birthday and entered a large figure. The thought of Katrina calmed him.

On the way from the bank he glanced briefly at Reiner. "The impudence of the fellow," he muttered to the crowd.

Something made the night different for him. Perhaps his encounter with Reiner, or Katrina's smile and warm kiss brought by the gold bracelet, or the crackling fire in her comfortable drawing room—perhaps all of these together that caused him to watch Katrina's grace with an inquisitive interest in his eyes, to enjoy her face lovely from the candlelight at dinner, to make him think: *Why not, why not?*

"You are so quiet tonight," Katrina said when again they sat before the fire with coffee and brandy. She patted the sofa where she lay half reclining. "Come, Fredl, come sit here with me."

He finished his brandy, placed the snifter on a low coffee table next to a small samovar and sat down by her. He felt the liquor warm his body, watched flames play on Katrina's ankles, felt his cheeks burn from the fire. *Why not?*

"It is wonderful being here with you, Alfred," she said. "After these last wretched months. I was very alone. Here it is comfortable and warm."

Alfred turned slowly to her face. "You have never looked so"—and then he kissed her open lips. She brought his head to the soft whiteness of her breast and pressed it against her and ran her fingers slowly back and forth through his short hair and tickled the hollow of his neck. They kissed again and this time she lowered his head to a cushion and stood up. "I won't be long," she said.

Soon they lay together on a white goatskin rug warm from the fire now sunk to coals. Alfred felt himself sweating as his hands played down the smooth, small back and over the round thighs, but then he thought of Reiner's private rooms and the smell of male and that made him ready. He was pleased when it seemed to work, even when she sighed, and he did not mind the pressure of her legs and her arms holding him. Then suddenly her nails raked down his back, she screamed, "Darling, darling," and the shriek of that God-awful voice of woman ripped through his genitals to make it happen before it had really begun.

"I am sorry," he said. "I . . . it has been a long time, you see."

"Of course, my darling," she said. She was holding him and she kissed his ear lightly. "Do not say words—we have many nights for each other. Many, many nights."

"I had thought . . . I had wished . . ."

"Ssshhh, my lambkin. Just rest."

Alfred felt suddenly cold and the small arms crushed him

114

like iron bands. Almost rudely he loosened himself, stood up, dressed quickly in the clothes lying strewn on the couch. "It is late," he said. "I must go."

"You will come tomorrow?" Katrina asked.

"Yes," Alfred said and hurriedly left the house.

He did not feel well when they entered the Prater grounds the next evening. He had to admit that it was his own fault. A week earlier he had asked Katrina what she would like to do on her birthday. She had taken a copy of the *Neue Freie Presse* from the table and read: "Barnum and Bailey Circus . . . two menageries . . . three elephant herds . . . two camel herds . . . four hundred horses. The world's largest circus brought to you from America in four long trains of sixty-six Pullman cars. One thousand wonders of the world." To Alfred's surprised look she responded with a laugh and said, "Please, Alfred, such a splendid circus. I have never been to a circus."

After tea at Demel's they had bundled in furs to be driven in an open fiacre down the Ringstrasse gay with falling snow and Christmas decoration and tinkling bells and across the Ferdinands-Brücke and finally to the meadow by the Prater Haupt-Allee where they walked through the bustle of the crowded air filled with the strange American voices barking German from the stalls of the Midway. "It is very exciting," Katrina said and squeezed his arm.

I was very excited that night. The champagne cleared from my head as I walked towards my father's grave in the crisp, autumn air of the dark, quiet night. I passed a beggar, I gave him a coin; I watched a couple hurry, I had no place to go; I heard carnival music, I turned to it; I found lights and tents, large signs and a crowd. The posters showed acrobats and lion tamers and jugglers surrounding an immense white stallion which held a lithe brunette name of Maria Montessi. I was at a circus. I bought a ticket.

"Here we are," Alfred said. He bought two programs, tipped the usher, helped Katrina to her seat.

I went to my box, I sat down. I had never smelled the sawdust air of a circus and as I looked at nets and rigging and heard

*music and young laughter I felt as heady as from the earlier
champagne. I bought a package of hot chestnuts. I leaned back
to watch the acts.*

"Do have a hot chestnut, Katrina."

Katrina looked at his outthrust hand. "Is it a joke you are
making, Alfred?"

Alfred stared at his hand. "I must buy some," he said.

"Are you feeling well, Alfred? Earlier, when you called
me Maria . . ."

"I am fine—a headache, that is all."

*The music is loud for one thing, so is the damn crowd. At
least it was quiet when the acrobats were performing. Why must
everyone laugh so hard over two clowns and some trained
bears?*

"Do you like the bears?" he asked.

Katrina did not hear him. She was watching a group of
clowns who had roared into the ring banging and smashing
fire equipment in a ridiculous attempt to rescue the occupants
of a tiny house blazing in one corner. As the clowns swung
ladders in each other's faces and squirted hoses anywhere but
on the fire, a line of midgets tumbled from the building to
add to the confusion.

"Do you like the bears?" Alfred repeated.

"Oh, yes. Are they coming on next?"

*Of course not. A special act is coming next. See, the tent is
darkening, drums are rolling, there is the spotlight, the tall
ringmaster. I know what he is going to announce: "Ladies and
gentlemen, the sensation of five continents, the greatest acrobatic equestrienne in the history of the world: Maria Montessi."
There! Hear the trumpet! there she comes on a brute of a white
stallion charging from a side entrance to canter easily around
the ring, a small woman in satin tights standing on the broad,
powerful back gracefully waving to the applause, twice, three
times around the ring. She is the most beautiful creature I
have ever seen. But she will fall, she will fall.*

Katrina sat upright. "Alfred, what is the matter? Where
are you going?"

116

He pushed by her. "I am ill," he said. "Stay here."

Katrina followed him with her eyes until he disappeared through a nearby exit. A trumpet sounded through the still air of the tent. Lights came slowly on to reveal a large metal cage in the center of the main ring. It held twelve tigers. A single man stood among them.

The index finger of Major Batjuschin's hand probed deep in his black beard for an irritant whisker. On his desk was a vodka bottle and beside it a half-filled glass. Immediately before him lay an opened correspondence folder which now and again his fist struck. His small eyes had reddened from the vodka; when they glared at the folder they looked unusually piggish.

Sitting across from him was a man also holding a glass of vodka which he had not touched. The most striking characteristic of this man was his anonymity. Nothing about him— not his skin, his face, his build, his clothing—suggested any impression contrary to that of the opaqueness at once offered by his eyes. Fluent in a dozen languages, this man rarely spoke. When he did, his native tongue carried the same nondescript accent that characterized his total being. He was an undercover agent. His name was Pratt. He was one of the finest intelligence agents in the world.

For some minutes the most noticeable sound in the room had been Major Batjuschin's sharp breaths, the aftermath of a furious outburst. Pratt, discerning that his employer was again under control, broke the silence.

"You imply, then, that they have doubled her?"

"No," Major Batjuschin snapped. "I admit it is possible because in this business anything is possible. I do not really think it is that bad, not yet. But she has failed. That is bad." He picked up the correspondence folder and slammed it to the desk. "Oh, yes, he buys her expensive gifts, he entertains her. She learns something: he is in the Intelligence Bureau, he evidently has been given the Counterintelligence Section, he travels a great deal. He is popular in the General Staff: he was elected a member of the Cavalry Fund last January, Baron von Giesl is friendly with him, he is often seen with young officers.

Bah! This is not the old Katrina. Where is she who snaps her fingers and the man falls cringing in his passion for her? There is none of that here"—he tapped the folder—"here in this mess of words." Major Batjuschin snatched at his glass, gulped its content, coughed and leaned back in his chair. "This Redl may become a menace. He has already inconvenienced my operations in Galicia; new border patrols, more careful scrutiny of documents, increased security in military installations. He is probably behind the arrest of Alexander von Carina. He may arrest more of my agents. I do not like it. This man could embarrass me. I will not—"

He was interrupted by a knock on the door. "What is it?" he called gruffly.

Lieutenant Pawlow walked to him with a large envelope. "I think the Major will find everything in order."

When Pawlow left the room, Batjuschin opened the envelope. As he spoke, he passed separate items across the desk to Pratt. "Here are your identity papers. Here is money—you can draw more from Colonel de Roop in our Vienna Embassy if you need it. But only in an emergency—I would prefer he does not learn you are in Vienna. Here is what we know about Redl. Here are photographs of him. The first thing I want you to do is to learn if Katrina is crossing me. If she is she will be dead in a week. Then get to Redl. I don't know what is going on but my nose tells me something is peculiar." Major Batjuschin stood up. "I want Redl. I am willing to pay for him. I would prefer him alive." His tiny red eyes flicked over the formless face. "If necessary, I will take him dead."

Pratt rose, folded the papers and put them in his pocket. In his flat voice, he said, "I shall get him for you—one way or the other."

3.

THE documents today are yellow and on some of them the black ink of the words written carefully in Gothic longhand has faded and a few pages are torn and probably some are missing. Yet, despite World War I and civil war and World War II and occupation, two bundles of official papers containing six hundred and seventy-two single pages have survived to describe the arrest, investigation, trial and imprisonment of a spy named Alexander von Carina.

As was the way in the old Empire, the State Police arrested Carina. An informant, probably the porter of the building where Carina rented an apartment, told the police that Carina carried on an active correspondence with someone in France from whom he received large sums of money. After a short surveillance, a squad of detectives entered the apartment at Number 3, Beethoven Street, arrested Carina and searched his rooms. Several incriminating documents were discovered and from Carina, himself, a statement was taken:

> Alexander von Carina was born in Drohobncz in 1854. After graduating from the Wiener Neustadt Military Academy in 1875, he was posted to a cavalry regiment in which he served until his assignment to the Third Section of the War Ministry in Vienna in 1890. For the next five years, Captain Carina concerned himself with the office of Horse Remount and Supply Trains. At the time of his assignment to Vienna, he became infatuated with Countess Mazzucheli, the attractive widow of a *Landwehr* cavalry officer who had killed himself because his wife had squandered his inheritance, a fortune of two to three hundred thousand gulden. The lovely countess proved very expensive: before long Carina was in severe financial difficulties. Despite repeated warnings he plunged deeper into debt until in 1895 a legal inquiry was brought against him for debt and fraud. Although insufficient evidence for a trial was produced, the inquiry, having stained his honor, caused him to be ordered before a military court of honor. He now suffered a nervous breakdown and tried to commit suicide. After his recuperation and before the court could meet, he requested and received retirement with a small pension.
>
> Once out of the Army, Carina married the countess which increased his poverty. When in 1896 he read a French advertisement in a Munich newspaper that sought an intelligent man for literary purposes, he replied. This led to a meeting in Vienna with a man who called himself Müller. A few weeks later Carina was summoned to Paris. At Number 17, Rue de Rivoli, he met another man, an alleged publisher named Heinrich Walter.

Employing Carina as a translator, Walter gave him enough money to return to Vienna to open a small office. In time Walter directed him to concentrate on translating articles of a military nature. Walter next ordered him to write studies on the impending Greek-Turkish war, the 1896 Prussian maneuvers in Bautzen, and the effect of Balkan neutrality in case of war between the Triple Alliance (Italy-Germany-Austria-Hungary) and the Dual Alliance (Russia-France). He was paid three hundred francs apiece for the first two articles and five hundred for the last which also received Walter's praise.

Carina now submitted a series of articles on the military forces of European powers, the influence of new railroad construction on the conduct of war, and the artillery of the Imperial and Royal Army. Although his articles contained only information that he translated from newspapers, he began to suspect that Walter was using him as a spy. Accordingly he severed connection with Walter in the spring of 1898. For his work of three years he had received four thousand francs and four thousand gulden.

On June 10, 1901, the State Police sent his statement and the incriminating documents to the Ministry of Justice in Vienna, which instituted legal proceedings against Carina under Paragraph 67 (Espionage) of the State Legal Code. Because Carina had been an army officer and was suspected of military espionage, Investigating Attorney Hanusch asked the War Ministry to undertake part of the pre-trial investigation. This request was forwarded to the Intelligence Bureau of the General Staff. Colonel von Giesl assigned Redl to the case.

Redl's initial task was threefold. He first had to trace Carina's career in the Imperial and Royal Army in order to confirm Carina's own statements and establish his character. He found this information in personnel records. In a confidential report of July 25, Redl confirmed the accuracy of Carina's testimony and noted in addition that Carina was described "as a man of resolute character, highly gifted, intelligent, clever and efficient."

Redl next had to determine whether Carina's personal associations could have resulted in his learning secret information. Redl reported that General Johann Huber von Pengl, Carina's Section Chief, stated "that during his service in the

Third Section of the War Ministry, Carina cultivated little comradely society and to my knowledge stood in intimate personal relationship with no one from whom he would have been able to learn other than nonclassified military affairs . . . the close examination of documents and classified field manuals available to Carina at the time of his catastrophe [the suicide attempt] did not offer the slightest suspicion that Carina had in any way exploited them." Redl then interviewed Von Pengl's Deputy, Colonel August Ceipek, who knew "nothing of Carina's way of life nor can he say if Carina stood in personal relationship with any officers from whom he would have been able to gain knowledge of classified military matters." A week later, however, Redl wrote that "of the officers who served simultaneously with Alexander von Carina . . . only the retired Captain Joseph Eisler is able to report that Carina stood in close personal relationship during his service [in the Third Section] with General Staff Captain Brückner and his successor . . . General Staff Captain Schirnhofer, and through this was in the position to learn highly classified military matters or, when unobserved, to examine documents relating to such matters. Regarding these officers, Schirnhofer is dead, Brückner blind and living in an insane asylum. . . ." In a still-later document, Redl concluded that Carina "as an officer in general, and as supply officer, regimental adjutant and particularly as policy officer in the War Ministry . . . had repeated opportunity to learn of military affairs which were considered secret to foreign countries."

Redl's third and most difficult task was to furnish a professional opinion: Could the total evidence against Carina support the State's accusation that he had performed military espionage? The bulk of memorandums, reports and letters submitted by the Intelligence Bureau to the Ministry of Justice during the next four months deal with this subject. They plainly demonstrate first how much Redl had learned about intelligence procedures in less than a year in the Bureau; secondly, how thorough his investigations were and the number of secret doors that he had to open to carry them out.

Redl first identified the French contacts known to Carina as Müller and Walter. In a secret progress report dated July 9, he wrote: "Monsieur Müller, Number 34, Avenue Duquesne, Paris. This is the cover address of Captain Henri Mareschal who served in the Second Bureau of the General Staff [French Intelligence Bureau] from 1898-1900 and who is known to have engaged in espionage activities more than once. In the register of 1896-97, he is listed with the General Staff of the Seventh Army Corps (Besançon), currently with the 17th Light Infantry Battalion." Further, "recent letters from the Bureau of Renseignements [to Von Carina] were signed, 'Lescure, Number 231, Boulevard St. Germain.' Lescure is the porter of the War Ministry." On July 17 Redl reported that Henri Mareschal "was born in 1867, is about five feet, seven or eight inches tall, very thin, dark brown hair, brown eyes, dark-colored skin, long lean face with sharply protruding nose; he speaks and writes German well; walks with quite long steps. In 1899 he wore a thin, bristly, black-brown mustache. Clothing: long frock coat, soft black felt hat." In a later report Redl noted that "in order to diminish the value of his work [to the enemy], Carina ostentatiously stressed in his statement that he had worked only for France. He did this because France is not essentially interested in our local military conditions. Contrarily, the Intelligence Bureau is convinced that Carina's activity through Paris was of value to a power more interested in our military conditions [Russia], which is to be concluded from the questions Walter gave to Carina and which must have been clear to Carina himself. Such espionage tactics are familiar to the Intelligence Bureau from earlier cases."

Having found Carina guilty by association, Redl strengthened his case by internal evidence gleaned from the documents found in Carina's apartment. On August 3, 1901, he ended a progress report to the Ministry of Justice with the statement: "In reference to the examination of the maps which showed the location of fortresses and were found with Carina at the time of his arrest, I can now say that entries in individual instances, particularly in the case of Cracow, do agree partly with actual fact and apply mainly to emplacements of older fortifications."

After spending the rest of August visiting the forts in question and in completing other loose ends of his investigation, Alfred wrote a final opinion which stated in part:

The notes on the fortresses of Cracow, Halicz and Zalesczyki [found in Carina's possession] prove that Carina was spying on these fortresses. His statement—the entries were merely the result of study—is simply untrue since in each case—particularly that of Cracow—the entries do not offer this impression but rather that of resulting from a hasty reconnaissance made without maps either by Carina or an accomplice. The entries on the other two maps are of value to a foreign nation in that they call attention to points of local importance. . . .

His written opinion, a very long and technical document submitted for Colonel von Giesl's signature on September 1, concluded:

> In that Walter and Müller are doubtlessly foreign intelligence agents with whom Carina stood in prolonged contact, he was without any doubt active in foreign espionage service. From his several years' employment as well as the significant payments which he received from abroad, it can certainly be concluded that Carina must have engaged in the betrayal of military secrets. It is also certain that he stood in connection with informed persons for the purpose of espionage.
>
> This, taken with his mental ability and significant military career, causes Carina to emerge as a dangerous spy who through his activities has doubtlessly injured the military interests of the State.

When a day later Von Giesl summoned Redl to his office, the written opinion lay on his desk. "I find this a splendid piece of work," he said. "I have just talked to the Investigating Attorney. There is little doubt that Carina will be brought to trial on the basis of your opinion. He wants a military expert witness for the trial and has asked specifically for you. I have agreed and shall so recommend to the Ministry of War. Hanusch said that his own investigation will not be completed for about four months, however, which allows me to entertain another matter. How busy are you going to be next week? Is there anything so urgent that you could not delay it?"

"No, sir, there is not," Alfred said.

"Fine. I have been asked by General Beck to recommend a briefing officer for the artillery demonstration at Veszprém on the seventh." He looked at a desk calendar. "You could take the train down on the fourth. It should mean a pleasant change for you, but I will not order you to go."

Recognizing the honor, Alfred did not hesitate. "I would like that very much, sir. It will freshen me up on artillery matters besides letting me breathe some fresh air."

The older officer smiled kindly. "I am glad you will be there, Redl. Our Emperor will attend the demonstration."

When Emperor Francis Joseph boarded the special train that was to carry him and his entourage to the artillery demonstration at Veszprém, he was a seventy-one-year-old man who had ruled an impressive portion of Europe for fifty-three years. His appearance was satisfactory enough for an emperor. Side whiskers overflowing into a gigantic walrus mustache covered his face which was topped by a bald pate and fronted by a forceful nose, the large eyes faded but still staring alertly from above magnificent pouches, the full lower lip of the Habsburgs, the neck straight in its uniform collar, a head at once benign and commanding, simple in its dignity and altogether and always exuding that essence of benevolent paternalism for which it stood. A resolute face, it could be called, wearing no suggestion of the artistic facetiousness of the baroque and rococo Habsburgs but rather embodying the solid Biedermeier lines familiar to its youth and seeming to lend it a serious recognition of its task to perform duty with honor.

Francis Joseph held duty very seriously. As he had done for so many years, he still arose at four A.M., took a cold sponge bath which his doctors had forbidden because of his asthma, pulled on a robe cut from an old army greatcoat and turned to the papers on the plain desk in his spartanically furnished bedroom—his choice from fifteen hundred magnificent rooms in Schönbrunn Palace. After working for two hours, he dressed in one of the army uniforms which he always wore, slipped out a back door of the palace, walked briskly across a formal garden and through a private exit that led into Frau Kathrina Schratt's garden. He breakfasted daily with this famous actress, a woman whom he had acquired many years before, a woman variously described by historians as friend, confidante, mistress and mother confessor—a woman said to have been the most powerful person in the realm, including, perhaps, its ruler.

After breakfast he returned to the palace, to the small desk where he read papers and received ministers, stopping only for his standard luncheon of boiled beef brought to his desk on a tray. He varied the routine occasionally by a ceremonial drive to Vienna, to his town palace, the Hofburg, where he turned to more papers, to ministers and visiting dignitaries. For relaxation in the Hofburg he stood by a window to watch the changing of the guard.

What were the papers, what did the ministers say? The answer is everything—every detail connected with the government, foreign affairs and armed forces of an empire numbering fifty million people. No single point escaped his notice and he could question as easily in the Polish, Czech, Italian and Hungarian languages as he could in German. He demanded instant action from his few close advisers—he once told a minister, "I know you are a late sleeper and I mean to be considerate; you need not come to me with your daily report until six o'clock [A.M.]." He suffered rather than enjoyed the presence of his ministers; he put his faith instead in the manipulation of papers by which he mistakenly believed he could move the mountain of empire. No one could have worked harder in pursuit of a false notion, no one could have known more trees of detail in the forest that was finally to be destroyed.

Perhaps half the papers that flowed in a day to his small desk concerned military matters: the result of a survey that he had ordered to determine the correct spacing of buttons on the Imperial and Royal Army blouse; a list of senior officers recommended for transfer and a short but thorough biography of each; a longer list of officers recommended for awards or decorations and the proposed citations; an intelligence report on the mountain artillery regiment recently activated in the Russian Army of Czar Nicholas; a new book on tactics by that Austrian officer, Conrad von Hötzendorf, who was winning fame in international military circles; a recommendation for a unit maneuver in Galicia; a report on the test of smokeless powder. He followed all such matters closely; he exercised the right of both

PART II

major and minor decisions. Each autumn he took to the field for the *Kaisermanöver*—the Emperor's Maneuver—in which he participated as a commander in chief with his own staff and his own ideas, and on the entire field no hussar lieutenant ran his horse with greater dash and dexterity than this seventy-one-year-old Emperor. He held no desire to fight a war with his Army, but he could use its existence at the international table of diplomacy, and he could enjoy, even love, its simple splendor. He missed no opportunity to display his feeling: on the fiftieth anniversary of his reign he struck a Special Jubilee Medal for each officer and enlisted man. In 1901 he struck a special "remembrance medal" which he presented to four hundred and fifty of his sailors who had fought in China that year. He gladly accepted honors accorded him by foreign regiments: he was colonel in chief of at least ten such units and the uniforms hanging in his wardrobe were a matter of great pride which he acknowledged by sending ornate oil portraits of himself in parade uniform to officers' messes in Italy, Russia, France, England.*
He personally rewarded duty at home: in the 1896 maneuvers one Colonel Baron Hagen led his cavalry regiment to the attack at full gallop only to have his horse fall dead and throw him; though severely hurt, he at once ordered another mount and continued the attack. So impressed was the Emperor at the sublime nobility of the act that he presented the colonel with a beautiful horse and a cash award of one thousand gulden! He kept a sharp lookout for similar outstanding service which he rewarded with medals, decorations, even titles.

But such largesse—and he distributed it in civilian circles as well—counts for little when given with the head rather than the heart. Francis Joseph gave for purpose more than for pleasure. He was not a warm man. His emotional reflection is caught in his Court: austere, cold, uncomfortable, a supreme bore for those called into its attendance. Etiquette was stiff and precise in the tradition of the Spanish Habsburgs. Dinner guests, for example, had to arrive fifteen minutes earlier than invited because the Emperor normally appeared early. At the table he was immediately served and immediately began to eat. No one

* One English regiment, the North Irish Horse, still displays his portrait and his gift of a silver cavalry trumpet in its mess.

126

could speak unless spoken to by the Emperor. Since his appetite interested him far more than his guests, he spoke little, ate rapidly and ravenously and pushed his empty plate away, the signal for the course to be cleared. "We are always astonished," wrote Baroness Redwitz, "at the speed with which the younger and hungrier gentlemen, who are served last, manage to swallow such large helpings. Indeed, these meals make a very unpleasant impression." * It is no wonder that when young nobles or officers were summoned to Schönbrunn for dinner, they stopped by Sacher's Hotel first for a plate of *Beinfleisch* and a bottle of Gumpoldskirchner.

Post-dinner conversation was no more lively. In the drawing room where he stood by the fireplace to smoke a cigarette, the Emperor would now and again confront a guest with a question. Etiquette demanded that the answer be the shortest possible, preferably a positive or a negative. At these sessions, to which Francis Joseph attached the incongruously cozy word, *Feuersitzen*—fireside chats—there was no general speaking out, telling of jokes or hearty laughter. When once in a while this did happen, the subject received a regal stare and his *faux pas* was never forgotten.

Nearly a half century before, Francis Joseph had allowed himself an emotional fling when against his mother's wishes he rejected the bride chosen for him, the Wittelsbach Princess Helene of Bavaria, and married instead her sixteen-year-old sister, Princess Elisabeth. As if ashamed of this burst of passion, he seemed bent on destroying its result as soon as he could. He succeeded. One of the most withering remarks ever recorded by a wife when speaking of her husband was the young Elisabeth's lament, "What can you expect from Francis Joseph? He is nothing but a sergeant!" Her constant rebellion against the cold formality of her marriage culminated in her leaving the Court for a life of aimless vagabondage that was cut short one morning on a Geneva quay when a madman plunged a file into the unhappy breast.

The Emperor was able to offer his children no more love than he offered Elisabeth. One day a daughter, Archduchess Valerie, was reminded that she should be more affectionate to

* Tschuppik, Karl, *The Empress Elizabeth of Austria.*

127

this man who was after all her father. "But I always think of him as His Majesty," she replied. He tried to force his son and heir, Crown Prince Rudolf, into the Habsburg mold of a military education and succeeded only in losing any affection which the young romantic might have felt for him. Rudolf's liberal political views aroused the wrathful scorn of the Emperor, who called his son a "babbler" of "romantic nonsense." Rudolf himself wrote: "There was a time when the Empress took an interest in politics and talked to the Emperor about serious matters; and in doing so she expressed views that were diametrically opposed to his. These times are past: there is no longer a place for liberal opinions . . . three or four years ago the Emperor, up to a certain point, was liberally inclined, and had become reconciled with the nineteenth century. Now he is like he was in poor Grandmamma's time: clerical, harsh, and suspicious. . . ." *
He was particularly harsh later when it came to the matter of Rudolf's young mistress, Baroness Maria Vetsera. Called on the carpet, Rudolf admitted the relationship, promised to end it. He did. In a hunting lodge at Mayerling he killed both Maria and himself.

His suicide brought forward his cousin, Archduke Francis Ferdinand, as Heir Presumptive, but Francis Ferdinand fared little better. After an early audience with his uncle, the Archduke was said to complain: "I will never officially learn if I am Heir Apparent or not. It is exactly as if I were guilty for the stupidity of Mayerling. So coolly have I not earlier been treated. My appearance awakens unpleasant memories, it would seem." The Emperor's lack of enthusiasm toward his nephew is not difficult to understand. Nothing about Francis Ferdinand portended future prosperity for the Dual Monarchy. He had never gotten along with people, he had neither talent nor will for languages, his military career was constantly interrupted by attacks of tuberculosis which forced him on long recuperative trips, his political notions seemed to embrace little more than sympathy for the Greater German movement, he idolized the sword-rattling Kaiser Wilhelm whom he increasingly tried to emulate. When he finally did recover from his disease, his uncle recognized him to the extent of allowing him a certain voice

* Tschuppik, Karl, *Ibid.*

in military matters but, much to Francis Ferdinand's annoyance, almost no voice in political affairs. The relationship was further strained when he married Countess Sophie Chotek. An inviolable Habsburg rule was an *ebenbürtig* marriage—a member of the House had to marry one who was the direct blood issue of a ruling dynasty. In the Emperor's eyes, Sophie was a commoner, and the old man only permitted the marriage after the principals agreed that none of their issue could ever claim the Habsburg throne. The Court's subsequent rude treatment of his wife deepened Francis Ferdinand's anger; by 1901 he was a blustering, embittered, sarcastic man whose personal credo was summed up by his statement to Prince von Hohenlohe: "Most men are scoundrels." There is little doubt that his uncle was included in this category.

That would have been wrong, for Emperor Francis Joseph was not a scoundrel. But neither was he the Divine Emperor that he thought himself. In fact he was a man who forever practiced an emotional parsimony that made the least display of human feeling an overdraft on his heart, that forbade him to entertain those spiritual values necessary for an understanding either of his own family or of the peoples of his Empire. Like Milton's Lucifer, he possessed many fine qualities, but he lacked those two that are essential to human greatness: compassion and understanding. A father figure he was so long as the children were wax dummies bending to this living embodiment of Old Testament philosophy, a prohibitive negativism best expressed in the unwritten Eleventh Commandment: "Thou Shalt Not Live." A life spent within the dark shadow of deep duty, a tomb that could admit of no light from simple humanism. A life as sterile as a worn-out womb, but being sterile and thus not subject to the thrust and friction of creation, a life that ran its pinpoint schedule to lend itself that quaint quiet grace which superficial poets have forever bestowed on old stones.

"Commencing at six A.M. tomorrow morning," the officer told the group, "a combined infantry, cavalry, artillery force will commence a two-day attack against a simulated enemy. The primary purpose of this two-day maneuver is to demonstrate recent developments in the artillery arm of the Imperial and

Royal Army, particularly as concerns the 15 cm. howitzer and the 21 cm. mortar. The secondary purpose is to test the field co-ordination of infantry and artillery in the attack. The forces involved are from the Fourth and Thirteenth Army Corps: Infantry Regiments 48, 71, 72; Artillery Division Regiments 3, 14; Hussar Cavalry Regiment 11; independent pioneer and transport units. I shall now discuss each problem separately. . . ."

Emperor Francis Joseph leaned back in his chair. His special train had arrived in the village of Zircz that afternoon where it had been met by Archduke Friedrick, General Baron Beck and General Artillery Inspector Count von Kropatschek. As was customary, local officials had greeted the Emperor with effusive and tiring speeches to which he had listened politely, replied briefly and sealed his sincerity with a gift of three thousand crowns to the poor of Zircz. He had then been driven to Army Headquarters at Veszprém for the briefing. He looked again at the briefing officer and felt his original impression confirmed. Here was a General Staff officer who meant business. A short man, but erect of carriage and his uniform fitting perfectly, an assured manner, his German correct if slightly stilted, his entire manner serious. "What is his name?" the Emperor asked an aide. "Redl, Your Majesty, Captain of the General Staff. Intelligence Bureau, temporarily assigned as briefing officer for this demonstration."

"Although every attempt will be made at realism," Captain Redl continued, "priority has been given to safety measures. This is necessary because of the new recoilless mechanism which is being tested. I need not emphasize the importance of this innovation." He paused, passed his glance swiftly around the room. "Until recently our artillery service has fallen considerably short of the standards achieved by Germany and especially France. We are probably behind Russia as well. . . ."

The Emperor smiled wryly in memory of his artillery genius, General Uchatius, who had developed the 8 cm. and 9 cm. cannons in 1875. A few years later Uchatius had invented a new 28 cm. cannon that would have revolutionized the artillery corps. Unfortunately the special alloy which he developed to line the bore could not stand up to the large projectile. The failure threw the General into despair: one morning he was found in the Vienna Arsenal slumped against one of his cannons, his throat cut by his own hand.

"Last year," Captain Redl continued, "the introduction of our 10.5 and 15 cm. howitzers helped to reduce the disparity. To increase our effectiveness further, our artillery experts have now placed the recoil apparatus on the gun carriage proper in order to eliminate the need of resighting after each shell is fired. For observation purposes, a cable balloon has been developed. This will be released out of range of enemy counterbattery fire. The observer in the balloon carriage will be in constant telephonic communication with the battery. By thus increasing the accuracy of our artillery fire, we hope to be able to speed up the attack proper. . . ."

"A good briefing, Beck," the Emperor told his Chief of the General Staff later. "What is that officer's name?"

"Redl, sir. Alfred Redl."

4.

AS instructed by the writer of the anonymous letter, Alfred Redl left the fiacre in Mödling, walked two blocks along the main road leading up the valley, turned off on a smaller road that soon dwindled to a path winding to the Vienna hills. He was dressed in civilian clothes. Against the cold air he wore a heavy overcoat with fur collar, and to counter the frostslip of the steep slope he carried a heavy walking stick. Halfway up the path at a junction he stopped, removed a glove, pulled a piece of paper from his pocket. It was the letter he had received the previous evening—on the back of it was a crude map. He oriented himself, chose the path to the right and began climbing. He was breathing heavily. He was frightened.

The trees thinned out along the new path and he could hear the gentle whine of wind through their barren trunks. He stopped at the next junction, referred quickly to the map, chose one of four paths before him and began a fresh ascent. He thought: *This person is no amateur; he is up there watching me, watching to see if I am followed.* The trees were very thin now and he could see a hundred yards in any direction through their winter nakedness. Bending into the wind he walked until a hundred yards farther he reached a small plateau, a height that commanded the local terrain. In the center of the plateau was an iron cross. A man stood beside it.

Alfred walked across the flat until he faced the man. The man wore a black overcoat with its collar turned up and a hat pulled low over his face. Only the redness of cold distinguished the few flaccid features that showed, but they were enough to jar Redl's memory to recognition. "*Herr Diploma Ingenieur* Kaufmann," he accused.

"Yes, that name is sufficient," Pratt said. He looked swiftly down the slopes. "No one is following you, Captain Redl?"

"No one is following me, but if I should not return within—"

"You will return, my dear Captain. I mean no harm."

"What do you want, Kaufmann?"

The man pointed northeast to the Kahlenberg, then to the spire of St. Stephan's Cathedral rising like a needle from the inner city of Vienna. He indicated the expanse by slicing a flat hand through the air, then he cupped this hand and held it to Redl. "I want to give you all that, Redl. Everything you can see and much more besides."

"What do you want, Kaufmann?"

"An arrangement, Redl. You have debts, I believe?"

"Of course," Alfred snapped. "A few—nothing exceptional."

The man pulled a paper from his coat and handed it to Redl. "Surely the General Staff would consider your debts exceptional. If you were to devote your salary for the next three years to their payment, you would still owe considerable money. And my list is far from being complete, I am sure."

Alfred shrugged. "I have means," he said. "An inheritance is due . . ."

"You have nothing, Redl. Your father died all but a pauper. Your brothers: a minor civil servant, an army officer; your sisters teaching school in Galicia; your mother dying in a sanitarium, a free one at that."

Without changing expression Alfred said, "General Beck would understand. He expects his officers to live well."

"That may be so," Pratt said. He handed Alfred a second sheath of papers. "Perhaps the Chief of the General Staff would understand the major reason for your debts?"

Alfred's mouth contracted as he glanced through the pages. "You are very thorough, Herr Kaufmann," he said.

"I am paid to be thorough, Captain Redl. Shall we talk business?"

"Apparently we must," Alfred said. "How much are you asking for these papers?"

"Only your future co-operation—I am prepared to pay for that in cash as well."

"Could cash not otherwise dispose of this tedious matter?"

"It could," the man said easily, "if you had enough money."

"How much would that be?"

Pratt laughed a short, hard sound. "More than you have ever seen, Redl. More than you ever will see. Let me tell you something. You are new in this business of espionage but I am not. Oh, you are clever, you have already worried some important persons. Still, you are new, you lack experience, particularly in dealing with professionals. There are not many of us. I am one."

"Who are you, Kaufmann?"

"I do not know myself, Redl. Sometimes I think I am everyone, sometimes no one. To your hotel clerk, I am Kaufmann, an engineer from Potsdam who, not liking street noises, preferred rooms on the third floor which happens to be directly under your apartment. To one of your friends, never mind who, I am Schmidt, a detective from the State Police. To the innkeeper in St. Veit I am a harmless Munich *Bürger* who just happens to sit with his wine where he can observe who enters and leaves that interesting little villa run by your friend, Herr Rudolf Reiner. To some in Paris I am Guillard, an Alsatian winegrower; to those in Belgrade I am a Prague publisher with Slav sympathies; in Warsaw, I am Pratt, an Estonian. That last is the most accurate, but the name is wrong. I was raised in an orphanage—my real name was lost."

"You have a price?"

"Yes, I have a price. Every man has a price. But I have contracted already for this job. A good professional, Redl, will never double . . . and live to enjoy it."

"I am sorry to hear that," Alfred said. He had removed his glove. With his free hand he scratched an eye, then began lowering the hand casually toward his overcoat pocket. Pratt's rapid words halted the movement. "I am holding a pistol aimed at your stomach, Redl. Now give me your weapon, butt first." He took the revolver. "You can't buy me and you can't kill me, so perhaps you are ready to listen to me." He pulled an envelope from an inside pocket. "Here are ten thousand crowns which I shall pay you for the plans of three fortresses: Cracow, Halicz and Zalesczyki—the plans that Alexander Carina had been told to secure. Do not try a bluff—your reports will be compared with information already in our files."

"In whose files?"

"Russian Army Intelligence," Pratt said. "My employer is Major Batjuschin, Chief of Espionage Center West, Headquarters, Warsaw. You will find Batjuschin a generous man. He wants information, he will pay for it. He is also a dangerous man to cross."

"If I refuse your Major Batjuschin?"

"I will mail a report directly to General Beck."

"He would not believe it," Alfred said.

"But he would be forced to investigate. An investigation would prove that you have male lovers."

"Do you think they would admit it, ruin their own careers?"

"A few would, to save themselves. Your servant, Joseph, has no career to ruin. An ignorant, eighteen-year-old peasant. To keep from going to jail during the Carina investigation, he accommodated himself to your pleasure. To keep from going to jail during the Redl investigation, he would accommodate himself to another's pleasure. He would talk—that peculiar habit of yours, Redl, the one Joseph does not like, transvestitism I believe it is called."

Alfred flinched. "Did Joseph tell—"

"No, Redl, I have never spoken to Joseph. When you return to your apartment, look behind the stove in your bedroom.

134

Look on the floor under the porcelain connection to the chimney. There you will find my ear—a piece of pipe that leads to my own sitting room. I have recorded your interesting conversations, Redl, both with Joseph and others."

Redl's tongue wet his lips. "I could go to the Chief myself," he said. "I could tell him everything. To avoid a scandal I would be allowed to resign without trial. I would remain a free man."

Pratt removed a flask from his pocket. He drank from it and handed it to Redl. "A free man, Redl? A free man has never lived on this earth. Even birth carries its basic obligations. We must eat, sleep, be sheltered—all so that we may grow to harbor other more complicated desires within our minds, desires which in turn enchain us in pursuance of their fulfillment. Not being a free man, Redl, you cannot remain a free man. If your Chief were especially kind, if instead of a choice between a pistol or a trial he gave you your liberty, you could go on as you have been until now seeking comfort, fame, success. But where would you find it? If you were to remain in the Empire, you would find nothing because you would be a social pariah. Where would you go, where *could* you go? England, America, South America? You do not know the languages. You are thirty-seven years old, you are trained only for the military. What would you do?"

Alfred stared at the trees that lined the slopes like so many thousand soldiers standing stupidly at attention. "I do not know," he said. "I do not know what I would do."

"Don't you understand the dirty trick society has played on you, Redl? What do you owe it, what do I owe it, this nebulous mass of hypocrisy that would dance us like puppets on the strings of its precious will? Duty, honor, loyalty, flag, country— bah! Concepts as empty as the consciences of those who created them, words used by the few to exploit the many, words to gain and hold and wield the power denied to us by poor birth. Do you think I care if you are homosexual? Do you think I care if you dress Joseph like a woman and make love to him? Do you think I stand here to trap you like some forlorn animal? Society has trapped you, Alfred Redl. I am offering you escape."

Alfred turned from the man. He looked at the gray sky, the

135

trees massed like regiments waiting for a final order on a formal battlefield. "I must think," he said. "I must have time to think."

"There is no time," Pratt said. "There is only this way out. Take it, Redl. Take the money, the power I am offering you. It is your only hope, Redl."

Alfred turned slowly until he was facing Pratt. "Give me the envelope," he said. "I shall get you the plans."

Pratt handed him the envelope along with a small piece of paper. "Meet me at this address, the day after tomorrow. Four P.M. sharp. I will take the night train to Warsaw."

Alfred glanced at the address. "But this . . . is impossible," he gasped.

Pratt looked blankly at him. "Katrina, too, must live," he said.

Katrina handed him a glass of brandy and sat down beside him. "Pratt should arrive any minute," she said.

"In Kazan," Alfred mused. "But, of course . . . you were working for them then."

"Yes," Katrina said, "I was."

"The story I was told—your marriage, the unhappiness, that is all false?"

"Not all of it. I was married once." Katrina fitted a cigarette to a long holder and lighted it. "I murdered my husband," she added calmly. "Oh, don't look so shocked. He was filling me with the poison of himself. It was killing or being killed. I refused to die."

"Batjuschin. Where did he come in?"

"My husband worked for him. When I was arrested he intervened. He was very good to me. We made an arrangement."

Alfred smiled tightly. "You must have wondered about me in Kazan."

"I did," Katrina said, "until Batjuschin showed me the doctor's report."

"You knew about that? And you were not afraid, here in Vienna?"

"For being so worldly, Alfred, you are very naïve. To me this is a job—only a job."

"But weren't you surprised to find me still—uh—reluctant here in Vienna?"

"I was, rather. But I thought you were simply unwell. The obvious escaped me. I am not in Batjuschin's favor for it, either."

"This Batjuschin," Alfred said. "What kind of a person is he?"

"He is clever, a genius in some ways. Like all men, also stupid in some ways. He has been good to me, but that proves nothing. I do not know him well—no one does—but I have heard . . ." A bell interrupted her and she arose. "That must be Pratt," she said.

"Did you bring the plans?" Pratt greeted Alfred.

Alfred indicated a manila envelope lying on the coffee table. Pratt looked at Katrina. "You will leave us," he ordered. He opened the envelope, read quickly through the pages, examined the drawings and nodded his head. "Is this all?"

"For now, yes. I will have more after my trip next week."

"Good. And the report on the Veszprém demonstration—as soon as possible." Pratt handed him a small envelope. "There are your cutouts and letter drops with alternates and instructions. As you will see, we shall use courier whenever possible. Memorize all instructions and burn them." As Pratt spoke he removed Redl's reports from the envelope and placed them on the table. With a small tool he punched an invisible peg from his walking stick, folded back the heavy handle, rolled the pages and inserted them in the hollow interior. He snapped the handle back to its proper position, inserted the peg and tapped the stick on the parquet floor. "That is all for now," he told Alfred. "We must leave soon for the station. It is time for you to go."

On his way from the house Alfred saw several packed bags in the large vestibule. He heard Pratt's voice calling to Katrina to hurry with her packing. He looked at the bags, shrugged and closed the door behind him. He would never see Katrina again.

Alfred sat in his office in the Bureau, his brow furrowed in concentration. Any notion that he may have held about the

simplicity of contracting with the devil had soon been dispelled
by the demands levied on him by Batjuschin. And then the
courier last night—Batjuschin wants this, Batjuschin wants
that, Batjuschin is very interested in your mobilization plans.
Mobilization plans! The most carefully guarded secret in the
General Staff. Did Batjuschin think that he had this kind of
information at his finger tips? He of all people should know
that time was needed, that haste could only mean exposure.

Idly fingering his mustache, Alfred tried to forget the unpleasant interview of the previous evening. His eye fell on the
Carina file that he had just been discussing with Colonel von
Giesl. "I do hope we get a conviction," the old man had said,
"I would like to teach that fellow in Warsaw a lesson—you
know, the one you say is behind this case." "Major Batjuschin,
sir?" "Yes, that fellow, Batjuschin—whoever the devil he is."

Alfred suddenly sat upright. That last remark of Von Giesl's!
Of course! ". . . Batjuschin, whoever the devil he is." Who
is Batjuschin? And Katrina, what had she been saying when
Pratt came in: ". . . I do not know him well—no one does—
but I have heard . . ." What had Katrina heard? Alfred's error
suddenly leaped at him: he had allowed the shock of his exposure to jar him from a logical course, to mislead him into regarding Batjuschin as some kind of inhuman behemoth, omnip-
otent in this world. And all the time Batjuschin was nothing
but another man, albeit a clever and cunning one, who had
concentrated on Redl while Redl had ignored him. Batjuschin
was a human being, he must be vulnerable to something. His
hands trembling in excitement, Alfred drafted the message that
would send his agents in search of the information he so des-
perately needed. He read over his words, made a few corrections
and pressed a button. "Have this coded and sent off immediately," he told his corporal.

It was snowing when he arrived at the estate in the woods
outside Kowno. An armed sentry scrutinized the driver of the
sleigh, grunted, then pushed open the wide wooden gate.

"Ah, so it is good," Major Batjuschin said when Captain
Redl was ushered into his office. "Come, my dear Captain, sit
here before the fire where the Russian cold will vanish in the

warmth of my pleasure at seeing you. Vodka? Good. We drink vodka, then tea comes. Tell me now about your trip."

While Alfred sketched his recent movements, he studied the small figure pacing back and forth before the fire. Without the fierce black beard, he concluded, Batjuschin would look like a worried farmer.

"So, now," Batjuschin said when Alfred had finished. "I am deeply honored you come so far to see me. Too, I am impressed by your excellent Russian. I see you are a clever man, Captain Redl. I am not surprised—I have followed your career for many years." He refilled their glasses and sat opposite his guest. A note of impatience appeared in his next question: "Tell me, you have brought something for me?"

"I have," Alfred said.

The little eyes narrowed. "What you suggested in your letter? Some papers from your General Staff, perhaps?"

"No, I have brought no documents, Major."

Batjuschin frowned. "Then what is it, what brings you this uncomfortable way at great risk to yourself?"

Alfred smiled. "A greater risk to myself by remaining in Vienna. I have come to see if we could reach an understanding, Major."

"We have an understanding, Redl. You do as I say and we shall—"

"That is a Russian understanding, Batjuschin. If I continue to do as you say, I will be playing your brand of roulette with all chambers loaded."

"If you do not, you will be exposed!"

Alfred bit out his next words: "Then where will you get the important information which you must have?"

"What are you talking about?"

"About a powerful clique in your General Staff in St. Petersburg which would like to see you relieved and sent to Siberia. I have learned that certain of your associates are asking embarrassing questions, for example what happened to fifty thousand rubles that you claim to have paid the Bohemian-Russian Cultural Society in Prague."

"I paid it," Batjuschin growled.

"Perhaps your Chief believes that," Alfred said, "but I do

not. I penetrated that organization six months ago. I know everything about it, including your payment of only ten thousand rubles."

Colonel Batjuschin stared at his guest. "You are a clever man, Redl. You would not be so stupid as to try to blackmail me?"

"I am in no position to blackmail you. I am trying to save both of us, if you will let me. The situation is obvious: unless you offer your superiors a startling espionage coup you will be finished. I suppose that is the reason you are putting so much pressure on me right now. Is that correct?"

"If it is?"

"Then you would do well to hear me out. I cannot deliver our mobilization plans to you. My Chief has never mentioned them to me, much less discussed them with me. He will in time, of that I am quite certain. In the interim I can provide information that would prove a sop to your General Staff."

Interest flickered across Batjuschin's pinched face. "And what is that?"

"The name of one of my informants. He is a senior officer in the Imperial Russian General Staff!"

"Who is he?"

Alfred laughed. "It is not quite so easy, my dear Major. Our present situation calls for what I have been taught is a Russian characteristic: patience."

"Go on, go on," Batjuschin said.

"You have ordered me to deliver the plans of the fortress at Przemyśl. To avoid raising suspicion, I must have a reason for personal investigation of this fortress just as the Carina case allowed access to the other fortresses. You could provide that reason."

"I am beginning to understand," Batjuschin said.

Alfred smiled. "You undoubtedly have agents at work in the Przemyśl area."

"An exchange of spies," Batjuschin said.

"Precisely. Our reputations profit as a result. No one likes a spy. The man who catches spies is a hero. Decorations, promotions. He will be trusted. Doors, secret doors, will be opened to him. He will learn plans, General Staff plans, Batjuschin.

And there is other profit. The funds you normally expend to catch spies will be yours to retain."

Batjuschin licked his lips. "Yours as well."

"Oh, yes, mine as well." Alfred leaned forward in his chair. "My plan will profit us both. But it is a long-range plan. If we hurry, we are ruined."

"That General Staff officer you mention. What is his name?"

Alfred removed a small book and a pencil from his pocket. "You will learn that on the day your spy in Przemyśl confesses to me."

"You are careful, Captain Redl."

"We have a word in German: *Rückversicherung*. It means 'back insurance.' Do we understand each other, Major?"

Major Batjuschin slapped his palms against his legs. "All right. We understand each other. In Przemyśl you will find a master locksmith named Zaleski, Joseph, born 1872, former Austrian subject, now a Russian national. He began working for me six years ago after he contacted our border watch and delivered a marked map of the Przemyśl installations to my officer in Kiev, General Staff Captain Tolmaczew. His accomplice is his stepfather, Schuster, Peter, born 1861, Austrian subject. They have reported on roads, railroads, canals, regimental depots, supply centers. . . ."

Soon after tea, Alfred left the estate in the woods. He returned to Lemberg that night.

At ten A.M. on January 7, 1902, Alexander von Carina stood before the President of the *Landesgericht* Court in Vienna, *Oberlandesgerichtsrat* von Distler. Carina was forty-seven years old, a tall, slim man whose closely clipped gray hair and mustache coupled with his careful dress and straight posture to bespeak a military background as his educated accent, the fine bones of his face and his long, sensitive fingers bespoke an aristocratic heritage. At a table behind the accused man sat his attorney, Doctor Viktor Rosenfeld. At the prosecution table sat Prosecuting Attorney von Kleeborn, two assistant attorneys and the military expert witness, Captain of the General Staff Alfred Redl. A jury of twelve males sat on the left of the President and two other judges. Press representatives had been temporarily admitted; when the evidence became classified, they would be asked to leave.

The President of the Court cleared his throat and said to the accused: "Will you state yourself guilty or not guilty?"

Carina replied sonorously: "Before I can answer the question I would like to make a statement. I am accused of a series of crimes which could only have been committed by a person holding entrée to the most secret Bureaus of the War Ministry, a person who must have had at least ten officials in his pay. Since I have not entered the War Ministry after 1895, since I went only to Military Headquarters in Vienna in connection with my pension, and since I have never dealt with a military specialist, I could not therefore have committed the crimes of which I am accused."

"Will you," the President repeated, "state yourself guilty or not guilty?"

"Not guilty."

In his capacity of military expert witness, Alfred Redl played a star role in this two-day trial. The prosecution rested on Redl's written opinion which was early read into the record and unsuccessfully attacked by the defense. Redl himself was frequently called to the witness stand to explain technical details such as the meaning of military symbols found on the maps in Carina's possession or the espionage techniques used by Carina's employers. On the second day of the trial, Redl was placed on the stand to render an oral opinion to the Court, a lengthy and technical performance that began: "In my opinion the prosecution has shown that the accused has doubtlessly practiced espionage. The questions answered by Carina [to the French] refer to classified subjects, and thus to information not available to the general public. In order to answer these, Carina had to practice espionage."

As in his written opinion, the most striking characteristic of Redl's oral opinion is the expert detail with which he treats the military subjects involved. After exhaustive analysis of Carina's espionage in armaments, of his exact employment in

The Play

the Third Section of the War Ministry, of the secrets in this section which would have been available to him and of his work in spying out various fortresses, Redl returned to the subject of his employers: "The manner and way in which Carina was recruited by Walter fully corresponds to the ordinary methods employed in such cases, methods which the Intelligence Bureau has been able to substantiate from many other similar cases. The dispatch [of money] from Albbrück characteristically illustrates the kind of relationship that must have existed between Walter and the accused. It is a kind of deception employed by the foreign Intelligence Bureau not to send payment for delivered work directly, but rather from Switzerland or a foreign village. The unusually high payments received by the accused are striking and certainly justify the supposition that the work delivered by Carina was of great importance. This is further confirmed in that the accused received a loan from his foreign contacts—a most unusual procedure, but understandable in that the accused, who had already delivered important information and could be expected to deliver more, would by the money be chained all the more securely to the foreign power! I must completely reject the statement of the accused that he had duped Walter with his work . . . a foreign General Staff . . . will allow itself to be deceived perhaps once or twice, but it is absurd to suppose that if the accused delivered only information of general knowledge [the General Staff] would have remained in contact with him for years, and would have given him a definite income, even cash in advance."

After delivering his oral opinion, Captain Redl was asked several questions for the purpose of clarification by the President of the Court. Both prosecution and defense were apparently satisfied. The President then allowed the accused to make a final statement. The decision of the Court was announced in the afternoon: Alexander von Carina was found guilty of espionage as charged. He was sentenced to four and one-half years of hard labor with a hard bed and dark cell on the first of February each year, and with loss of title and final expulsion from Austria.

An account of the trial in the evening edition of the *Neue*

143

Freie Presse stated that "the sentence, in so far as the verdict of guilty, depended to a considerable degree on the opinion of General Staff Captain Redl. . . ."

About a month after the Carina trial, Emperor Francis Joseph sent Archduke Francis Ferdinand to the court of Czar Nicholas the Second in order to repay the Czar's earlier visit to Austria-Hungary. Upon completion of his visit in St. Petersburg a week later, the Archduke asked the Austro-Hungarian military attaché, Major Erwin Müller, to accompany him as far as Warsaw. The Archduke had been impressed by the Czar and especially by the courtesy shown him in the Czar's court— a courtesy that he was not used to in his uncle's court. On the train he talked to Müller at length about the future of Austro-Hungarian diplomacy, the possibility of reviving the League of Three Emperors (Germany, Russia, Austria-Hungary), the importance of cementing friendship between Russia and Austria-Hungary. As a first step in the *rapprochement,* he suggested that Austro-Hungarian Intelligence operations against Russia be cut to the minimum.

Although Müller paid lip service to the Archduke's idea, he was not in the least impressed when he left the train in Warsaw. To save the journey from being a total waste of time, he contacted one of the best spies he had in Russia: Lieutenant Colonel Grimm of the Imperial General Staff. The contact, he thought, was providential. Grimm was in a position to borrow a folder of high-level plans from his office in Warsaw—could Müller return them in two days?

Müller at once took the plans to Vienna where he reported to the Chief of the Operations Section in the Intelligence Bureau, Captain Alfred Redl. After hearing him out, Redl leaned back in his chair. "That is good, *Herr Major,*" he said. "The Russian may soon learn to respect us." He tapped some papers on his desk. "The confessions of Zaleski and Schuster," he said. "They arrived from Przemyśl only this afternoon." Redl took the envelope that Major Müller had laid on his desk. "I will have these ready for you in the morning, *Herr Major*. Go now and rest—you look tired."

Major Müller was surprised when the next morning he was

ushered into Baron von Giesl's office. "Ah, Müller," Von Giesl tersely greeted him. "We could be in serious trouble."

"Sir?"

"The plans, Müller, are false. Cleverly so, but none the less false."

"I . . . the plans . . ."

"The Russian is also clever, *Herr Major,*" Captain Redl interrupted. "Either Colonel Grimm is a fraud or the plans were planted as a check on him. They are false—there is no doubt."

"You are certain, gentlemen?"

"Of course we are certain," Von Giesl said petulantly. "This could easily prove to be an international incident. *Mein lieber Gott,* just when the budget is coming up for discussion. The Foreign Office would . . ." The baron passed his hand over his face. "How were you to return these plans to Grimm?"

"By letter drop, sir, in Warsaw."

Colonel von Giesl nudged the thick envelope. "Well, we had better try it, anyway, don't you think so, Redl?"

Alfred nodded. "Our only chance. I can send them with Number 186—he is very clever. I believe, sir, that the *Herr Major* should return directly . . ."

"To St. Petersburg," Von Giesl said. "Just as soon as possible."

"I have Number 186 waiting in my office," Redl said. "You will need only a few minutes to brief him, *Herr Major.*"

The trial of Joseph Zaleski and Peter Schuster was held in a Przemyśl civil court on May 20, 1902. The defendants were found guilty of espionage under Paragraph 67 of the State Code. Zaleski was sentenced to four and one-half and Schuster to three and one-half years of hard labor.

Less than a month later, the trial of Lieutenant Colonel Grimm was held in a secret military court in Warsaw. On June 14 the forty-two-year-old Russian officer was found guilty of selling strategic information of great value to a foreign power. He was sentenced to loss of all rights and to twelve years of forced labor.

On the same day, Major of the General Staff Erwin Müller was relieved as Imperial and Royal military attaché in St.

Petersburg. Upon his return to Vienna, he was posted to a
cavalry division for duty.

5.

TO the old Emperor the involvement of Major Müller in the
Grimm case was disgraceful. My military attachés will not en-
gage in such dishonorable affairs, he stormed. His advisers
argued: It is a matter of tradition; for fifty years we have posted
military attachés abroad, for fifty years they have spied. Our
only successes, the securing of the Italian mobilization plans
and the Russian War Order of Battle in the 1890's, have been
their work. But the Emperor had made up his mind. With
the exception of Colonel Hordliczka in Belgrade, military attachés henceforth were to refrain from covert espionage. It was
a matter of honor.

"I agree with him," Alfred said when Baron von Giesl had
informed him of the ukase, "but for rather different reasons."

"Oh? What are they?"

"If an attaché's role is obviously overt, he will be invited to
most inspections, demonstrations and maneuvers where, as a
trained observer, he will learn as much if not more than an
average spy. If he is above suspicion, he will be accepted in the
highest society where he may overhear important information
or, for the price of a magnum of champagne, be told such information. But let him be suspected of running covert operations
and doors will be closed to him, just the way we have all but
ostracized the Russian attaché here in Vienna. Too, he will be
under surveillance. Once his contacts are discovered, they can
either be arrested or 'doubled' by bribery or blackmail."

"But who is to take over his role?"

"My answer would be resident agents," Alfred said, "a system
that Napoleon used with great success. It is much safer. Under
the resident agent system, when Grimm originally contacted
Müller, he would have been courteous to Grimm but taken only

146

his name and address and sent it to our resident agent in St. Petersburg or Warsaw. The resident agent would have arranged initial contact and reported directly to us. We could then have decided whether to run the case or not. Whatever our decision, Müller would have been left out of it." Alfred paused. "And Grimm was undoubtedly caught through his contact with Müller."

"But the expense, Redl. How can we afford to maintain resident agents all over Europe?"

"I actually believe that we would save money, sir. Our military attachés have not always spent their confidential funds wisely, nor have they always consulted us prior to spending. It is not necessarily their fault. When one serves a long time in one post—"

"I have always said," Von Giesl interrupted, "that they serve entirely too long. Klepsch, for example—he went to St. Petersburg as a captain; twenty-five years later he came back to Vienna a general and retired."

"Exactly, sir, though I would like to say that General Klepsch was exceedingly kind to Captain Dáni and me when we were in Kazan."

"Oh, Klepsch is all right. I object to the system."

"Precisely, sir, the individual attaché is allowed too much latitude which can result in duplication. The resident agent would eliminate part of this danger as would more effective control of the individual attaché. I see no reason why attachés cannot be ordered to report on a systematic basis." Alfred removed some papers from his briefcase and handed them to Von Giesl. "I have consulted with the other sections, sir, and have drawn up what could be called a target list for an army division. You will note that numerous elements of unit performance are listed, not unlike our own annual officers' report. This is merely one example—I would prepare such listings for equipment, topography, even for personalities. This should insure that we learn small indications which are often overlooked and it should eliminate hit-and-miss work according to the whim of an attaché. More important, it would offer us a simple tabulation of our knowledge; at a glance we could tell in what areas we should increase or decrease our efforts. With such a system, we would learn everything that an attaché learns by legitimate methods. What is not fully reported and is still of further interest to us can be concentrated on by covert means, either by an agent especially dispatched by us or by our resident agents."

"One thing, Redl. That would give me a splendid argument for an increased budget, would it not?"

"Indeed it would, sir. And if we are going to safeguard the security of our Army, we are going to need more funds."

Baron von Giesl smiled. "Every time an increase in our appropriation is mentioned to the Emperor, he asks why we can't use patriots to spy."

Alfred chuckled. "Patriots too often cover their minds with a flag of prejudice to report what they hope to be the facts but never are. They are about as objective as a woman spy who falls in love with her victim. In the end, sir, if you take ordinary men and pay them well, you have the best spies."

"You allow money that much power?"

"Yes, sir, in this business."

The older officer sighed. "Perhaps you are correct. Anyway, draw up a plan along the lines we have discussed. It is probably our best answer."

"Fine, sir. I shall have it for you early tomorrow."

Back in his office Alfred lighted a cigarette and stared into the air. Then he took a pencil and began writing himself into full control of the Intelligence Bureau.

Arrests . . . investigations . . . trials.

In January, 1903, an Austrian civil court convicted Anton Alois Burghardt and three accomplices of attempting to secure the mobilization plans of the Tenth Army Corps in Przemyśl. In February, Theophil Fedyk and his accomplices were convicted of delivering information on Galician fortresses and key terrain features. In March, a soldier named Futschik was sentenced for having supplied secret information to Burghardt. At the end of March, Doctor Bronislaus Ossolinski was arrested in Lemberg. After interrogation by Redl, Ossolinski confessed to stealing railway mobilization plans in Galicia. He was tried in August and was convicted.

A close study of these trials by an acute observer should have
raised certain questions. Why would the Intelligence Bureau
suddenly trap twelve spies when in the previous five years only
two had been caught? Why would an espionage war break out
with Russia when that country was intent on pacifying her
European neighbors so as to free her hand for the approaching
war against Japan? In view of the Empire's other enemies at
home and abroad, why were all the defendants working for
Russia in Galicia? Why would such low-level agents be assigned
penetration missions that called for the most skillful work?
Burghardt was an ignorant fool who had earlier been convicted
of fraud; Fedyk was an enlisted man who had deserted the
Army; Ossolinski had lost his civil service job because of suspected embezzlement. And if these persons were so seriously
implicated, why were their punishments mild? Fedyk was sentenced to three years (two under maximum), Burghardt to only
fifteen months, Ossolinski to a year, the others to a few months
each.

But these questions were not raised. Instead, the trials served
the purpose which had been planned by their perpetrators. They
first of all enabled Redl to furnish Batjuschin a continuous flow
of secret information. Alfred's testimony in the Ossolinski trial,
the complete record of which is extant, proves his access to
highly secret railroad mobilization plans. Similarly, his investigations in the other cases made him privy to secrets of the
Galician fortress complex, over which he was already in part
instructed, and to the war mobilization plans of the Tenth
Army Corps. Far more important in the long run, however,
was the effect of the trials on Redl's professional standing. Even
before the Ossolinski prosecution, Redl's reputation as a
couterintelligence expert was made. For in the summer of 1903,
when Redl was due for transfer to troop duty, the new Chief of
the Intelligence Bureau, Colonel of the General Staff Eugen
Hordliczka, recommended that he be retained in the Bureau.
This was an almost unheard-of action in the case of a junior
General Staff officer, yet General Beck himself approved the
recommendation. Alfred Redl was to serve another two years in
the Intelligence Bureau.

Seemingly nothing could stop Redl now. Reigning as an un-

disputed expert of espionage, he was consulted daily by Hordliczka and frequently by the State Police and officials of the
Ministry of Justice. He lectured to officers of the General Staff
and to police detectives. He began preparation of his first trea-
tise, "Methods for the Recruitment and Supervision of Informants." He traveled the length and breadth of the Empire
visiting his field intelligence posts, questioning, advising, cau-
tioning, exhorting.

Concurrently his private life expanded. In the autumn of
1903 he traded his apartment for a more expensive one on the
top floor of a neighboring building. Junior officers, particularly
bachelors, soon learned to know the pleasure of informal champagne parties at Number 48, Floriani Street. He gave dinner
parties in leading Viennese restaurants; head waiters in exclusive night spots began to recognize the small, immaculate figure
of the *Herr Hauptmann* for whom good tables were held because he always tipped generously. He was seen increasingly in
leading salons whose hostesses welcomed his quiet, smiling
presence that now and again was broken by a cryptic remark.

In a fitness report for that year, Colonel Eugen Hordliczka
summed up the flow that life seemed to hold for Alfred Redl.
Redl's character, as judged by this urbane and worldly superior
officer, was "strong, honorable, open . . . with even, quiet temperament." His mental ability: "highly gifted with very quick,
grasping conception." As for his value, "in his present service
capacity he has proven a highly intelligent and very skillful
counterintelligence officer, and has brilliantly demonstrated
these qualities in several espionage cases." He was judged "very
zealous and indefatigably active from devotion to and interest
in the service, with excellent success. Works assiduously on
furtherance of his military education." On duty he was "very
respectful to superiors and conscientiously frank. Very friendly
and tactful to contemporaries. Very demanding of subordinates,
proper, strict, but kind and thoughtful." Off duty he was "very
co-operative and modest with senior officers; very companion-
able with excellent manners and frequents only elegant society.
Very popular, correct comrade with excellent influence on
younger officers." His record was equally impressive in the
field: "As company commander suitable in every way. Accord-

ing to reports of General Staff trips and maneuvers: judged tactical situations pertinently, managed easily, clear and precise, works very quickly and accurately, eminently suitable; completely suitable for General Staff Chief of an infantry division." He was "generally qualified for promotion" but "still had to take the General Staff examination for major." Colonel Hordliczka's judgment was echoed by the Deputy Chief of the General Staff, General Oskar Potiorek, who endorsed this fitness report: "Eminently suitable in the Intelligence Bureau. Generally qualified for promotion."

Still, there is always a mad spider of fate to spin a web of doom and if the strands so far strung across Alfred Redl's life seemed frail in the strength of his success, they nonetheless existed while the patient spider lived content, slowly to twist, slowly to spin, neatly and cautiously, a camouflaged trap for a man.

Alfred thought little about it when Rudolf Reiner interceded for a fellow servant in the Austro-Hungarian Bank. The man's name was Johann Hromodka, a man of limited ability whose wife eked out his tiny wage by running a vegetable stall on the wrong side of Vienna. Johann had heard Rudolf bragging about his close relationship with the famous Captain Redl and one day he asked Rudolf if he thought the captain would help get his boy, young Stefan, into the Army. The boy could have gone into trade, into the *Handelsakademie* with free tuition, but between prayers in the Peterskirche he had seen the beautifully uniformed officers of the Imperial and Royal Army and that is now what he wanted to be. The father was delighted when a few days later Rudolf told him to send young Stefan around to Number 48, Floriani Street.

The servant, Joseph, admitted the fourteen-year-old boy whose apprehension was plain when he entered the presence of the officer who to him was already a hero.

"Ah, there, young Hromodka," Alfred greeted him easily. *My dear God, he is the most beautiful boy I have ever seen.*

Stefan bowed the way he had been taught in school, then gripped the friendly hand that stretched toward him. "Come over here now and sit down," Alfred invited. He placed his hand on the boy's shoulder to guide him to a chair. "There.

Now I shall pour us a glass of wine and we can have a little talk.
You take wine, do you?"

"Ye—yes, sir."

Alfred walked to a sideboard. *I used to blush like that. He is
a lovely boy. I want him to like me.*

"Ah, damn," Alfred said. He had spilled a glass of wine on
the sideboard. When he righted the glass he noticed that his
hand was trembling. "There," he said and handed a glass to the
boy. "I understand that you would like to enter the Army,
Stefan."

"Ye—yes, sir."

"Well, that should not be too difficult. I joined the Army
when I was your age. Tell me something about yourself."

*He speaks well once he gets started. Intelligent enough, a
trifle small physically but he is still growing. He will make an
incredibly handsome officer. Seems a pity he should have to
work up the way I did. Why should he suffer for his low station?
I am going to help this boy.*

"If you go in the Army, Stefan—you would start in Cadet
School here in Vienna—would you be willing to study very
hard?"

"Oh, yes, sir."

"That is very important, Stefan, because if you do not do
well in Cadet School I could not help you go on to the Wiener
Neustadt Academy. If you wish to be an officer, that is the only
way to do it correctly."

"I . . . I think I understand, sir. Will you help me, sir?"

"Only if you promise to work as hard as you can."

"I promise, sir. I really cross my heart and hope to die if I
don't."

"I believe you. Now tomorrow afternoon you report to the
Ministry of War *am Hof*." He removed a calling card from a
silver pocketcase and scribbled a few words on it. "Give this
card to the porter and he will show you to Major Reinmann's
office. The Major will help you fill out the application forms
and arrange for your physical examination." Alfred put his
arm around the boy's shoulders. "I shall wish you the best of
luck right now."

Two days after this meeting Alfred faced the embarrassed

father in the bank. *"Na, ja,"* the man said, wiping his hands along his trousers, "after all you have did for him, the more's a pity he should of went and fell down on that physic exam. Too frail, the doc said, go home to grow a year, he said. Near busted the young'un's heart, it did. Cryin' round to home, sayin' wisht he was dead."

Alfred frowned. "That is the first I have heard of it," he mused. "What time do you finish work, Hromodka?"

"Five o'clock, sir."

"All right," Alfred said. "You stop by the Café Kaisergarten. Ask for my table. I shall do something about this."

In the War Ministry Alfred called briefly on Major Reinmann, then went to the office of the medical examiner, Doctor Gerö, whom he knew slightly.

"Oh, I *could* have passed him, *Herr Hauptmann,*" the doctor said. "I thought he would be better off with another year at home—he is about fourteen pounds underweight, you know."

"I know he is," Alfred said. "But I doubt if he will pick it up at home as well as he would in Cadet School. His parents are not well off." Alfred smiled. "That side of the family has not done so well."

"I didn't know you were related," Doctor Gerö said.

"I thought Major Reinmann would have mentioned it. Yes, young Stefan is my nephew. Nephew once removed, technically. You know how complicated our Galician families are."

The doctor laughed. "Being Hungarian myself, I have a good idea, *Herr Hauptmann.* Well, if you want him in I am more than willing to pass him." He looked at an appointment book. "Send him around the day after tomorrow about ten."

"That is fine, *Herr Doktor.* I appreciate it very much."

"It is nothing at all, *Herr Hauptmann.*"

Alfred repeated himself on the telephone a few mornings later when Major Reinmann informed him that Stefan Hromodka would enter Cadet School the following autumn. He hung up, sat for a moment to think of his new young friend with the lovely brown eyes. The click of a messenger's heels claimed his attention. Standing stiffly at attention before his desk, the soldier said, "Compliments of Colonel Hordliczka, sir. Colonel Hordlickza and Captain Redl are to report immediately to the Chief of the General Staff." And with the words, the comfortable and serene feeling of Alfred Redl disappeared.

You must remain calm at all costs. You can deny everything, give your word, gain time—stop that kind of thinking! It is probably some routine matter. No, the Chief of the General Staff would not consult you on a routine matter. If he knows, he will tell you bluntly. Nonsense, stop it! He could not know. You must keep calm.

Alfred walked on the left side and slightly to the rear of Colonel Hordliczka whose firm, swift stride fitted the sober set of his face. "I wonder what the Chief wants," he said.

Damn, if you were not told on the telephone, then it must be serious. Could Batjuschin have double-crossed me? Calm down. For the love of God, calm down or you will give yourself away.

"General Beck will see you at once, gentlemen," the Adjutant said. "This way, please."
General Beck looked up at the two officers.

He is upset—the tic in his left cheek, his left hand is trembling. My God, he is old.

"Ah, Hordliczka."
"Good morning, sir. You remember Captain Redl, sir?"
"Ummm. Sit down, gentlemen."

He is not very polite. He does know, somehow he has learned. No, he asked me to sit down. You fool, get hold of yourself. Give him a chance to say something.

"I have just received a report of the most damning substance," General Beck announced.

Oh, God. Here it comes. If he accuses me directly I must smile at the absurdity

"The Minister of Foreign Affairs sent it directly to me. It is Top Secret—Personal."

of the charge. The Foreign Office. Damn the Foreign Office. Is Beck looking strangely at me? Look back at him. Relax, damn it. They are smoking—light a cigarette.

"Our Ambassador in St. Petersburg was informed last night by an important Russian diplomat who is sympathetic to Austria-Hungary that Russian Intelligence is aware of our northern war plans."

"No," Colonel Hordliczka gasped.

His hand steady, Alfred lighted a cigarette and leaned forward slightly in his chair.

Oh, God, he has learned. But the source. The source could save me, at least give me time. I can dispute the source, that will give me time to

"Unfortunately, the source could not furnish precise details. He did say, *inter alia,* that knowledge of our military readiness is what lies behind the conciliatory attitude shown to us by Russia in the last year. That would explain the rumors that we have signed a secret treaty with Russia promising to remain neutral while she is fighting Japan."

think. Wait a minute. Could not furnish precise details. Go on Beck, damn you, out with it.

"He said that the information was furnished by Espionage Central West in Warsaw—a certain Colonel Batjuschin. Batjuschin's techniques, he said, were of course not known to him. But he has reason to believe that Batjuschin's principal source is an officer in the Austro-Hungarian Army!"

"*Mein lieber Gott,*" Hordliczka whispered.

General Beck stared at each of the officers. "A member of the Officer Corps, gentlemen!"

What—he does not know. Steady. I am not clear yet. Perhaps he is testing me for a reaction. If he knows more

"Have we any idea who this officer is?" Colonel Hordliczka asked.

The General's irritation was evident. "Certainly not. If we knew that, you would scarcely be here now."

he would build up to it. So—he does not know more. Thank God Hordliczka asked. Start thinking now. Beck is going to want to know what to do next. He is obviously shocked which is to my advantage.

"Do you believe that we have a traitor?" Beck snapped.

"Well, sir, there is always a possibility," Hordliczka said.

"What do you think, Redl?"

Exhale slowly, let him wait a moment. Now analyze it for him.

"Sir, I think that we should examine the darkest side of the picture first. There is little doubt that Lieutenant Colonel Batjuschin has been trying to determine our precise military situation in the northern area, particularly in Galicia. His intensive effort is partially reflected by the number of his agents we have exposed in that area within the past year. Batjuschin has probably gained some valid information. As we know from our own loss of agents, Galicia is the Achilles Heel of our internal security. The Poles, Ruthenians, Jews—"

"Yes, yes," Beck interrupted. "I know all about that."

No you do not, General. Nor does anyone who has not lived there.

"Of course, sir. I am just pointing up the enormity, if not impossibility, of the counterintelligence task we have in that region. Unfortunately, the mood of civil dissatisfaction has been known to rub off on a few of our officers prior to this time. At the very worst, sir, one of these officers could have been turned."

"Why are you so certain the traitor would be serving in Galicia?"

Be careful, he is not as stupid as he looks. Try to disarm him.

"Because the General spoke of 'our northern war plans' only. Cognizance of those would be limited to officers serving in Galicia—in fact, to those serving in a corps or division headquarters." Alfred paused, then added dryly, "Unless of course, we have a traitor in the Operations Section of the General Staff Corps."

Hordliczka smiled. "Thank God we know that is impossible."

Exactly, Colonel. See, even Beck smiled at the preposterous notion. Now I can handle him. He wants to be reassured.

"As I said, sir, that is the worst side. Without further investigation, I would hesitate to doubt the Foreign Office report.

But I will say that the majority of such sensational reports received by us in the Bureau turn out to be invalid.

He is listening to me now. He loathes the Foreign Office. I am on the correct tack.

"While not wishing to enter spheres beyond my legitimate purview," Alfred continued, "I think the possibility of—uh—exaggeration on the part of the Foreign Office could be entertained. In my opinion, several of its officials would be only too pleased if the General Staff, particularly the Intelligence Bureau, were to be embarrassed."

He is obviously impressed with that. Now emphasize the point.

"If Batjuschin is so *completely* informed about our war plans, I find it strange that he is dispatching still more agents to uncover them, particularly when his country is struggling in a war with Japan. As you know, sir, we arrested two of his spies, Lawrow and Dyrcz, just last week. Apparently they were after our transport plans. We are currently investigating several other leads."

"That is a good point, Redl," Colonel Hordliczka said. "If the Foreign Office report *is* true, this would indicate that Batjuschin's knowledge is not complete."

"Exactly, sir. There is another point to consider, too. Although our Ambassador, Baron von Aehrenthal, is an experienced diplomat, I do not believe his experience extends to the intelligence sphere. The Russians may have a reason for telling him this information—perhaps it is the old trick designed to confuse us, perhaps something more involved. There is a possibility that the informant could be an *agent provocateur*." Alfred paused and added casually, "It would be interesting to know his identity."

"You could have something there, Redl," General Beck said. He scanned a paper on his desk. "No name is given in the report. He is identified only as a former Russian Ambassador to the Court of St. James."

Which is quite enough to know.

"Well, that is no help," Alfred said.

"Aehrenthal wholeheartedly vouches for him," Beck said.

"He may be correct in his trust, sir," Alfred said. "Whether he is or not, one thing is certain: this report must be thoroughly investigated."

I shall rub Batjuschin's nose in this report. If this is his idea of keeping me in my place, he will learn what it is to—forget that now, pay attention to what Beck is saying.

"And immediately," Hordliczka said.

"What do you propose, Colonel?" Beck asked.

"The usual procedure, sir. Query all channels immediately. This will mean a trip north for Redl, here."

The sooner, the better, Colonel.

General Beck placed both hands on his desk. "Gentlemen, I appreciate the way in which you have already grasped this alarming situation. If there is a traitor in our Corps, I want him exposed! I am charging you with the task. I will back you to the limit. You will notify me of any developments at once— day or night. That is all."

Colonel Hordliczka walked more slowly on the way back to the Bureau. "Do you really think there is anything to it, Redl?"

"There may be, sir. Like the old proverb: in every barrel of apples you will find a rotten one or two."

"I hope you are wrong," the Colonel said.

6.

HIS beady eyes half shadowed by heavy lids, a crooked finger propping the dispassionate face—a bland, uninterrupting countenance into which the storm words tumbled with no more effect than grasses thrown to air. Quiet followed the outburst and was followed in turn by the silky candor of Lieutenant Colonel Batjuschin who did not move his position to speak: "So it is that you distrust me, Captain Redl." He sounded genuinely offended. "A great deal you distrust me to think that I myself would risk Siberia in order to play jokes on you. And to what would you explain this . . . I can only say, phenomenon? Have I not honored our bargain during the past years? I had thought our work was prospering. I had looked forward to more years of our mutual welfare. But now? I am deeply grieved, Captain, that you should think . . ."

"What else can I think?" Redl demanded.

Countenance suddenly lost kindness, the answering voice darkened: "In your semihysterical state, probably nothing. You are being very stupid, Captain Redl. I do not enjoy working with stupid persons. I will tell you several ways in which this information could have reached improper ears! We Russians are a bombastic people. We drink vodka and play the balalaika and argue and duel and boast and sometimes say too much. Perhaps my officer, Pawlow, piqued by some dashing cavalry officer into defending intelligence work, allowed himself a foolish indiscretion. Perhaps my Chief, General Mikoshin, had an argument with the *Ochrana* and like the child he is, told the little he knows. Oh, he knows something, Redl—I cannot furnish detailed mobilization and deployment instructions of Imperial and Royal Army units without explaining something. Perhaps it is no more than the informant's imagination, Redl—think for a moment of the Russian imagination. Have you, yourself, a non-Russian, never embroidered a piece of information to lend it a more dramatic effect? This informant —could he not logically have invented this bit which has so concerned you? He could have, my dear Captain, *n'est-ce pas?*"

"He could have," Alfred said curtly.

"Ah, you still doubt me, I see. Very well, I shall seek your pacification with another possibility." Colonel Batjuschin rose and walked to a large safe behind him. When he returned to his desk he held a thick folder, its flap sealed with a circle of red wax. "Your Officer Corps is large, Redl. Salaries are small. Do you suppose that debts are a possession exclusive to you? Ah, I see that at last I have impressed you." He tapped the folder. "Yes, Redl, that is the probable source of your empty fury. 'Dossier H.'! An Austro-Hungarian lieutenant colonel whose career for his country and for mine is most unfortunately concluded."

"Hekailo," Redl gasped.

"Yes, that is correct. Lieutenant Colonel Sigmund Hekailo, Judge Advocate of the 43d *Landwehr* Division, Lemberg. A greedy man."

"But . . . Hekailo . . . he . . ."

"Absconded is the word you want. I see that you recall the case. Your people began probing into certain financial discrepancies of the good colonel. He was suspected, I believe, of manipulating receipts for his own profit."

"That and more," Alfred said. "After he disappeared we learned that he had cashed the negotiable assets of his ward and that he had spent a cavalry captain's marriage bond."

"As I said, he was greedy. He was also working for me. The investigation probably would have determined this, so we thought it expedient to get rid of him."

Alfred's tongue ran quickly over his upper lip. "Permanently?"

Batjuschin laughed. "What an ungrateful employer you must think me. I spent a great deal of money and time arranging Hekailo's escape. I even secured him one of our passports for his trip to South America."

Alfred's hand toyed with his mustache. "Hekailo," he mused.

"Very probably he is the officer. A number of persons learned his identity in the process of arranging his escape. Identical dossiers to this are on file in Warsaw and St. Petersburg. I had thought the case to be closed, you see."

"The proof of his treachery," Alfred said. "You have proof?"

"Ample proof is sitting on this desk. Before I forget, with whom did you say your Ambassador spoke in St. Petersburg?"

Alfred had not said. "I do not know his name. Only that he is a diplomat who is sympathetic to Austria-Hungary. At one time he was your Ambassador to the Court of St. James."

"Ah, my dear friend the Baron," Batjuschin said quickly. "A revolutionary. I have known about him for some time. It is regrettable that he has such powerful friends at Court. Regrettable, I suppose, that we have become corrupt. But that is another matter." Batjuschin's finger lifted the flap of the dossier to hurl particles of red wax over the smooth desk. "What we must now determine is the most efficacious manner of treating the present situation."

"He could be extradited."

"Or the case could be left to die. But why make that decision yourself? Why not let your superiors make it? Show them a few pieces of evidence, tell them the price, a high price. They want revenge, they will probably pay. If for some reason they should refuse, you have lost nothing. You have found the traitor, you have removed all doubt." Colonel Batjuschin removed a sheath of papers from the envelope. "I assume that we share whatever proceeds these papers may bring?"

"Yes, of course," Alfred said quickly.

"Very well, then. Sigmund Hekailo is living in Curityba, Brazil, under the cover name of Karl Weber. He is teaching in a Polish colony there. Here is a photograph of a recent letter that he wrote to a friend in Lemberg. Here is a photograph of one of his reports to me. Note the cover address—it is that of my housekeeper's grandmother in Warsaw . . ."

". . . and here is a photograph of one of his last reports on the Tenth Corps Mobilization Plan. That is Hekailo's own handwriting."

"Incredible," General Beck said.

"I believe it is accurate, sir," Alfred Redl said. "I compared the handwriting with records kept by him in the 43d *Landwehr* Division. They are the same. We arrested and interrogated his contact in Lemberg. He admitted that Karl Weber is Sigmund Hekailo. He himself proved to have nothing to do with Hekailo's activities—he is only looking after Hekailo's mother. We let him go."

"Have you more evidence?" Hordliczka asked.

"No, sir. Our source said that he is able to photograph an entire dossier that was kept on Hekailo but that he would not run the risk unless we would buy the information."

"Who is the source, Redl?" Beck asked.

161

"One of our most promising recruits, sir, Agent Number 431. He is a Russian General Staff officer badly in need of funds."

"How much is he asking?"

"29,000 crowns, sir."

"A significant sum," General Beck said, "but we can pay it if we have to. The question is, gentlemen, is it worth it? You say we can get Hekailo back?"

His question was directed to the fourth officer in the room, Major-Auditor Wilhelm Haberditz of the Judge Advocate Corps. "There is no legal obstruction, sir. Our current treaty with Brazil specifically provides reciprocal extradition of criminal fugitives, which is Hekailo's status. We would have to use fraud and embezzlement rather than espionage as grounds, however, which means that he could not be tried here for espionage. But our espionage penalties are so light that he stands to receive a much more severe sentence if he is convicted of fraud and embezzlement."

"Hekailo would also know that because he is a lawyer," Hordliczka said. "I should think as a result he would be willing to talk freely about his espionage activities." He turned to Redl. "I assume he had accomplices."

"I would say so, sir. He seems to have had access to certain information remote from his own office," Alfred said. "To tell you the truth, I am blaming myself in part for this entire matter. I should have realized the possibility of espionage when he was first investigated."

"Nonsense," Hordliczka said. "You can't work more than twenty-four hours a day, Captain."

"Still, I *should* have . . ."

"It is not too late, fortunately," General Beck said. "If he has accomplices, if there is some kind of spy ring up there, we must learn about it. I say, bring him back, gentlemen. He is a traitor. He shall at least pay for some of his abominable crimes!"

When Sigmund Hekailo alias Karl Weber was arrested in Curityba, Brazil, he displayed his Russian passport and placed himself under the protection of the Russian consul. But when

Town Square in Lemberg, circa 1875

(From: *Die österreich-ungarische Monarchie in Wort und Bild.* Vol: *Galizien*)

The Emperor Francis Joseph
(1892)

(From Taylor, A.J.P.,
The Habsburg Monarchy)

Captain Alfred Redl of the Imperial and Royal General Staff, c. 1902 (decoration is the 1898 Jubilee Medal)

Colonel Nikolai Stepanowitsch Batjuschin of the Russian Imperial General Staff, Chief of Espionage Center West, Warsaw

Simon Lawrow, a Russian spy caught by Redl

(Ronge, Max, *Spionage*)

Sketch found in the possession of an Italian spy, Pietro Contin, who was caught by Redl

Colonel Eugen Hordliczka of the Imperial and Royal General Staff, Chief of the Intelligence Bureau, 1903-1909, at the Emperor's maneuver of 1909 with Kaiser Wilhelm of Germany who is on the far left

(Ronge, Max, *Spionage*)

Schönbrunn Palace

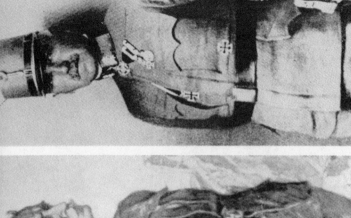

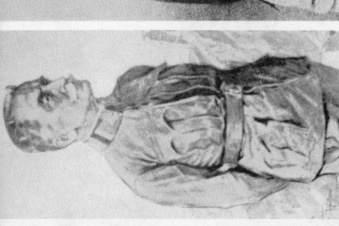

Précis of Redl's career and recommendation for appointment to General Staff Chief, Eighth Corps, submitted by Chief of the General Staff to the Emperor

General Franz Conrad von Hötzendorf, Chief of the Imperial and Royal General Staff, 1906-1911 and 1912-1918

General August Urbanski von Ostrymiecz of the Imperial and Royal General Staff as colonel was Chief of the Intelligence Bureau, 1909-1914

(Kriegsarchiv, Vienna)

(Urbanski, August von,
Conrad von Hötzendorf)

General Baron von Giesl and Colonel Alfred Redl, Prague, c. 1913

Alfred Redl's
first automobile

(Courtesy: Doktor Josef Reichelt.
Vienna)

Headquarters of German Army Intelligence (Section III-b of the
German Great General Staff), Berlin, where Major Walter Nicolai
found the first clue that led to Redl's exposure

One of the letters that helped to expose Redl

(Ronge, Max, *Spionage*)

Personal note written by Redl a few days before his death

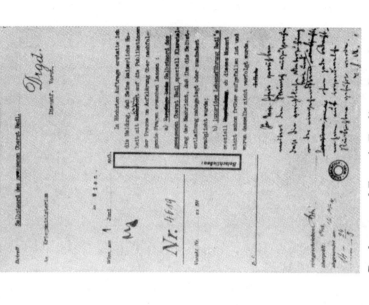

Draft copy of Francis Ferdinand's written demand to the Minister of War for the truth in the Redl investigation

(*Kriegsarchiv, Vienna*)

Excerpt from one of the many parliamentary inquiries levied against the Government in the Redl case

(*Kriegsarchiv, Vienna*)

Wiener Zentralfriedhof.

Eigenes Grab: *Redl Alfred*

Gruppe: *79* Reihe: *29* Grab-Nr.: *38*

Beerdigung *28/5* *1913*

Zentralfriedhof Nr. 51. 1912. G. W.

Burial certificate, Alfred Redl

Popular satirical cartoon published in Vienna
and Germany after the Redl affair

(Die Weltskriegsspionage)

Brazilian officials confronted him with his Austrian parade uniform, found in the bottom of his trunk, he confessed his true identity and was jailed. Brazilian officers, in allegiance to the international code of soldiering, placed a loaded revolver in his cell. This was spurned, as was the opportunity to leap into the sea that was offered to him by his escorting officer on the voyage from Paranagua to Rio. At the latter port, Hekailo was locked in a nearly airless hold of a coal collier which eventually landed him, more dead than alive, in Trieste from where he was brought to Vienna.

Hekailo had spurned suicide because, as Hordliczka suggested, he knew that he could not be extradited for suspected embezzlement, then tried for another crime. As a result he did speak freely about his espionage activities to the investigating commission composed of Captain Redl, Major-Auditor Haberditz and a recorder, First Lieutenant Hans Seeliger of the Judge Advocate Corps, who later told his brother:

. . . From the extensive interrogation of the defendant which often lasted far into the night, I had my first opportunity of getting to know Redl as a military expert. He repeatedly interfered in the course of the inquiry, pumped the defendant as to all details of his treachery, and thereby displayed a knowledge of places and facts which astounded me, and which often was nearly dumfounding. On one occasion I told my Chief: "Redl knows nearly as much as the defendant himself," a statement that elicited a laugh from Major Haberditz. . . . Now the over-zealous effort of Redl to make the defendant confess that he had sold the deployment plans to Russia was striking to me. Hekailo spiritedly denied this when with an easy laugh he said, "Captain, where in the world could I have obtained this deployment plan. Only someone in a General Staff Bureau in Vienna could have sold that to the Russians."

As I took those words in shorthand, I involuntarily looked up from my paper and looked questioningly at Redl. I clearly saw how from the words, "General Staff Bureau," a slight quiver passed over his face which momentarily held the faintest suggestion of paleness.

I thought possibly he would certainly interpret that unexpected statement of the accused as an unheard-of insult against his Corps and would now sharply protest it. Major Haberditz, who might have expected the same reaction, also looked at Redl. But he at once began to leaf through the folder lying before him and simply muttered something unintelligible.

After long pressure, Hekailo identified his accomplice: Major Wieckowski, Commandant of the Supply District in Stanislau, also a Pole. The next day, Major Haberditz, armed with the most extensive authority, and accompanied by Redl and me, left for there [Galicia].

The Commission of Three arrested Major Wieckowski in his Stanislau office. Neither interrogation of the officer nor a search of his office produced evidence to contradict his fervent assertion of innocence. As a last resort, Redl suggested a search of his private quarters, an imposing house that by itself formed a questionable contrast to the owner's known financial resources.

After a three-hour examination of the large, beautifully furnished rooms had disclosed nothing of interest, Major Haberditz wiped his perspiring forehead. "Wieckowski appears to have covered his tracks very effectively," he said gruffly.

"It rather looks that way," Alfred said. He opened the door of the last room, a bedroom on the third floor. "Probably nothing . . ."

"Oh, please, gentlemen," a nurse intoned in poor German, "please will the *Herrschaften* not frighten little Sylvana more." The old Polish woman held a fat protective arm around the thin shoulders of a little girl who looked to be about six years old. As her large eyes stared at the three officers, they filled with tears and her lower lip quivered. "What have they done to my daddy, Nana?" she demanded in Polish.

Before her nurse could answer, Alfred Redl dropped easily to one knee in front of her. "My little lambkin," he said in Polish, "we have done nothing to your daddy. He has not come home for a few days because he is in the service of our beloved Emperor. He knew you would be sad so he asked us, his friends, to come see you. You must not cry now."

"Did you come to play with me?" the little girl asked.

An idea suddenly occurred to Alfred. "We certainly did," he said. "While my two friends stay here for a minute and talk to Nana, you and I will go down in Daddy's library and play a game. Would you like that?"

"Oh, yes, I would."

Alfred stood up and took the little girl's hand. In German he said to Major Haberditz, "I have a hunch, sir. Would you and Seeliger search this last room and find out what the nurse knows? Sylvana and I will be in the library."

"What in the—"

Alfred looked steadily at the major. "No time to explain, sir."

A few minutes later Haberditz and Seeliger entered the library. They stopped in amazement. On the floor, his immaculate appearance vanished, was Alfred Redl. Sylvana sat astride his back, laughing with childish glee each time he pretended to buck her off. Finally in near hysteria she fell to the floor. "Oh, Uncle Alfred, that was wonderful. Do it again, do it again."

"Redl," Major Haberditz said, "we didn't come here to play. . . ."

"There is a purpose in my game, sir," Alfred answered in German. Turning to Sylvana he said in Polish, "We can do that again later when I catch my breath. But now we shall play another game." From his pocket he pulled a small coin which he held up for Sylvana's examination. "Would you like to have this coin?" he asked.

"Yes, Uncle Alfred."

"All right. You go out in the hall for a minute and when I call you, you come in and hunt for it. If you find it, you may keep it.

"You aren't peeking?" Alfred called after the girl.

"No."

Alfred returned the coin to his pocket. "Come in now."

He sat on the floor to watch the little girl hunt through a bookcase, dig behind a vase and open a cigar humidor in the corner. "Where is it, Uncle Alfred? Please tell me."

"That would spoil the game. But I will help you. You are very cold now so I shall give you a hint. The coin is hidden where your daddy usually sits in this room."

"Oh, over here," the little girl said, running to an armchair.

"No, where your daddy sits when he is working."

Sylvana ran to the desk and looked in an inkwell on its surface.

"Now you are very warm," Alfred said encouragingly. "But I would not hide it in the inkwell, that would be too easy." With no change in his tone or expression he said, "Maybe I would hide it where your daddy hides his papers."

"Oh, I know," Sylvana shouted, her ecstasy apparent. "Here." She slithered beneath the desk to indicate its left corner. "That is where it is, Uncle Alfred. But my daddy told me I must never play there."

Alfred stood up, walked to the corner of the desk. Bending down he ran his fingers across the seemingly smooth interior panel. He stopped when his finger struck a small, concealed button. "All right," he said with a laugh. "You win this time." He gave the coin to Sylvana. Ignoring her fervent gratitude, Alfred instead looked coldly at the nurse. "Be off with the child," he ordered.

While Haberditz and Seeliger looked curiously on, Alfred pushed the button. The inner panel of the desk pivoted outward to reveal a secret compartment. Alfred reached for the portfolios of papers. "I suspect these are the proofs we want," he said dryly. He leafed through them quickly. "Yes, these are what we want."

He did not notice the look exchanged between Major Haberditz and Lieutenant Seeliger, a look of surprise . . . and of disgust.

If Haberditz and Seeliger were disgusted at the means employed by Redl, Colonel Batjuschin was infuriated at the end they achieved. He had not imagined that Wieckowski could be so stupid as to *keep* proofs of his guilt, much less that the investigating commission—for whose existence he was indirectly responsible—would find the proofs. When this did happen, he foresaw the disintegration of an intelligence network that had taken him considerable effort and an enormous amount of money to build. It was now his turn to feel cheated in the partnership, his turn to storm and finally to threaten Redl with exposure unless he steered the investigation away from the guilty and on to the innocent.

Had an officer less intelligent than Major Haberditz been in charge of the investigation, Alfred might have succeeded in carrying out Batjuschin's orders. His first attempt was made a few weeks after the Wieckowski arrest when the commission, which had gathered "two hundred and fifty pounds of evidence" throughout Galician provinces, arrived in Lemberg. From the papers found in Wieckowski's study, it was evident that someone in the Lemberg garrison had supplied secret information to Wieckowski. Suspicion at once fell on an officer named Captain Acht who, as Personal Adjutant to the Commandant, was also custodian of classified documents. To Haberditz's surprise, Redl seemed unimpressed by the evidence against Acht. Instead, he argued that a young cavalry captain in Corps Headquarters was more than likely the guilty man. Although this officer, whose record was perfect, was seriously ill from a bout of summer typhus, Redl pressed his interrogation so brutally that Haberditz himself had to intervene on the defendant's behalf. Despite Redl's every attempt to implicate the young officer, he stuck to his story: Yes, he had checked out secret documents for his superior, the General Staff Chief of the Corps, but he had never kept these papers in his own possession for a minute. When the General Staff Chief confirmed this story, the young officer was cleared and suspicion focused stronger than ever on Acht. But Redl, on the grounds of insufficient evidence, still opposed Acht's arrest and protested strongly when Haberditz, convinced of his guilt, overruled him and ordered Acht arrested and sent to Vienna.

The ill temper that Redl had aroused in Haberditz was not soothed when the commission, having concluded its field investigations, returned to Vienna. In the words of Major Haberditz as reported by *Oberleutnant* Seeliger:

> A striking change now came over Redl. As eagerly as he had once worked for the conviction of Major Wieckowski, he suddenly began just as eagerly to argue his innocence. This went so far that finally I had to reproach him privately and indeed question our further collaboration on the case. A rather severe argument ensued with the result that I requested the Chief of the

Intelligence Bureau, Colonel Hordliczka, to relieve Redl as military expert. Colonel Hordliczka sympathized with my objections and promised that he would discuss the matter with Redl; he could not, however, agree to his relief since to do so would be to deprive Captain Redl of his share of the reward in convicting the criminals which would be unfair in view of his splendid work.

Colonel Hordliczka's subsequent talk with Redl apparently righted matters. Alfred reverted to his earlier co-operative attitude; once again an air of harmony prevailed in the commission. Not long after the *rapprochement,* Alfred even volunteered to obtain a missing piece of evidence: he ordered Agent Number 431—a Russian officer—to steal the mobilization orders that were allegedly in Major Wieckowski's handwriting.

One morning a few weeks later, Alfred entered Major Haberditz's office. "I have just been informed," he announced dully, "that Agent Number 431 was arrested while removing the material from the files. Other evidence of his work for us was discovered in his desk. He has committed suicide. He . . . was my best agent!"

"I am very sorry, Captain Redl," the major said.

Redl nodded wordlessly. He, too, was sorry. But that was the price Batjuschin had demanded in return for the loss of his two spies, Wieckowski and Acht.

7.

LONG after the end of Alfred Redl's life, a detective in Prague who had worked with him was discussing the case with a young intelligence officer. In conclusion, the detective said, "Had Colonel Redl himself told me that he was a spy in the pay of Russia, I would have laughed in his face." The day in 1904 that the young and inexperienced member of the investigating commission, *Oberleutnant* Seeliger, voiced his own suspicions of Redl's integrity to his Chief, Major Wilhelm Haberditz, the latter felt toward *Captain* Redl as the Prague detective later felt toward *Colonel* Redl. Although Haberditz was himself momentarily piqued by Redl's seeming procrastination, he laughed away Seeliger's doubts as youthful if not childish fancies worth forgetting rather than repeating. Lest Haberditz be judged a fool, consider that nowhere in the available record of the ensuing years is testimony found which places any shadow of doubt on Alfred Redl's loyalty. The majority of persons who knew and worked with him not only liked him but, in the case of junior officers, generally idolized him. Even the few persons who years after the event claimed a dislike of Redl as a man never by their own admission suspected him of the infamous activities that would cause him to rank as one of the most notorious traitors in history.

The temper of the time partially explains this seeming naïveté. Despite a subterranean political evil that beat through Empire with a tom-tom persistence, the citizens of Vienna more clearly heard the sweet violins that epitomized the conservative optimism that they had grown to love and that they were certain nothing could destroy. The note is plainly heard from a passage in Stefan Zweig's autobiography:

> Everything in our almost thousand-year-old Austrian monarchy seemed based on permanency, and the State itself was the chief guarantor of this stability. The rights which it granted to its citizen were duly confirmed by parliament, the freely elected representative of the people, and every duty was exactly prescribed. Our currency, the Austrian crown, circulated in bright gold pieces, an assurance of its immutability. Everyone knew how much he possessed or what he was entitled to, what was permitted and what forbidden. Everything had its norm, its definite measure and weight. He who had a fortune could accurately compute his annual interest. An official or an officer, for example, could confidently look up in the calendar the year when he would be advanced in rank, or when he would be pensioned. Each family had its fixed budget, and knew how much could be spent for rent and food, for holidays and entertainment; and what is more, invariably a small sum was carefully laid aside for sickness and the doctor's bills, for the unexpected. Whoever owned a house looked upon it as a secure domicile for his children and grandchildren; estates and businesses were handed down from generation to generation. When the babe was still in its cradle, its first mite was put in its little bank, or deposited in the savings bank, as a "reserve" for the future. In this vast empire

everything stood firmly and immovably in its appointed place, and at its head was the aged emperor; and were he to die, one knew (or believed) another would come to take his place, and nothing would change in the well-regulated order. . . .*

An integral factor of the well-regulated order was its social compartmentation. At the bottom of the scale were the peasantry and the working classes who—the bulk of the people—had little to say about their own destinies. At the top was the aristocracy—a few persons, relatively speaking, who fashioned destiny. Supporting the fashion were the members of the Church, the Bureaucracy and the Army, and condoning the fashion so long as it was to their profit were the landed gentry, the industrialists and the professional classes. The extent of the social gulf is suggested by the later reminiscence of a contemporary Vienna schoolboy, Paul Frischauer, the scion of a wealthy publishing family:

> My school was attended by two archdukes, both of them placed in my form. The two imperial princes were not allowed to speak to their fellow-pupils. They would appear each morning accompanied by an adjutant, who would sit at the back of the room, stiff and motionless, looking like a big toy-soldier. We noticed that he always followed the teacher's words with the closest attention, but thirst for knowledge was not the reason for his presence. It was his official duty to see that no harm came to his imperial charges from proximity with their less highly born fellow-urchins, and that the teachers did not fail in the respect they owed to members of the reigning imperial house. When either of the archdukes was asked a question, the teacher had to preface it by saying: "Will Your Imperial Highness deign to . . ." If His Imperial Highness, the thirteen-year-old Archduke, did not deign, the [Adjutant] would rise from the back of the room, click his heels like a drill-sergeant and explain that His Imperial Highness was that day disinclined. . . .**

To this general distinction must be added the internal division common to each social segment. Aristocracy, for example, was graded as of Habsburg blood, non-Habsburg but still royal blood, nonroyal blood but titled by royal favor as a wealthy

* *The World of Yesterday,* Viking Press, 1943.
** *The Imperial Crown,* Cassel and Co., 1939.

industrialist or a successful civil servant. As an ancillary and important support of Monarchy, the distinctive social body of the Imperial and Royal Officer Corps was also carefully sub-divided. Its most important members, no matter the rank, were titled, next came officers of the General Staff, and finally senior and junior officers.

To place Alfred Redl in this environment is first to recognize his comparatively rarefied position. If anyone outside Alfred's immediate social milieu thought about him at all, it was in flattering terms: the prevailing way of life should be preserved and Captain of the General Staff Redl, the officer whose name was constantly associated with the prosecution of enemy spies, seemed bent on preserving it. Inside the Army, he had little to do socially with senior officers: when he was conducting the Carina investigation in 1901 he had asked Carina's former superior, a colonel, about the defendant's private life and had been told, "I know nothing of his private life because my home is in a different section of Vienna." Had Alfred's senior officers been asked about his private life, they would have given similar answers. He was further protected by his membership in the General Staff Corps. In 1904 the General Staff numbered only four hundred officers (out of nearly twenty-eight thousand) who formed, in the Duke of Wellington's classic phrase, "a clique within a caste." As a General Staff officer, Alfred was automatically remote from the scrutiny of the bulk of the Officer Corps to whom he was a unique person whose word was not for doubting. When he told Doctor Gerö that Stefan Hromodka was his nephew, the good doctor believed it just as did scores of other officers in later years; when he told Colonel Hordliczka that in his opinion Wieckowski and Acht should not be tried, the colonel, though contradicting Redl's judgment, never once suspected his motives. As in the rest of society, there existed in the well-regulated order of the General Staff a feeling of security that bred contempt of curious sus-picion.

In mixed society, the protective channel of Alfred's life was further deepened by a rather stringent code of mores. Because society accepted a person far more at title than face value, the personal little inquisitions common to our modern day were almost totally absent. Instead conversation evolved about the theatre and the opera and fashion and racing and indulged the supposed witty persiflage familiar to Victorian novels. Subjects like business or profession were considered to be in poor taste and certain other subjects were taboo. Money was rarely discussed: a person was supposed to live within his means and if he lived ostentatiously then he must have sufficient means. Wealth was no novelty. Many people lived on a scale as grand as Count Szemere, for example, who maintained splendid apartments in the Sacher Hotel where he kept busy a retinue of agents and secretaries, one of whom was responsible only for reading European newspapers in a search for the best wine and tobacco cellars that were up for auction. When one aristocrat lost two million crowns in a night of baccarat at the Jockey Club, he prosecuted not because "of the money lost, but because the game was dishonest, and therefore it was a matter of honor." Compared to such standards, Alfred Redl's public expenditure aroused no interest, much less comment, and when the time came that it would have appeared striking, he furnished a plausible reason for it. Sex was another forbidden topic. This was a day when a pregnant lady did not appear in public and when ignorance in sexual matters was considered bliss. Venereal disease—feared by everyone—was simply not discussed, nor was homosexuality, despite a certain amount of publicity it had gained from the earlier Oscar Wilde trial. Certainly no one would have found Alfred Redl's bachelorhood at forty years of age surprising, and when he did emerge in company with his young nephew, that formed not the slightest cause for comment. A gentleman's private life was governed by a live-and-let-live philosophy designed by the practical Viennese to admit those personal pleasures not always associated with sterling character into their lives. Nearly everyone of importance had one or more skeletons in the closet, and it was a matter of honor that one did not go about opening closet doors. Moreover, a person would have been a fool to have pried into Redl's private life: as Chief of Counterintelligence he could have retaliated a thousandfold.

Although this genteel, honorable and rather artificial society provided a perfect stage for Alfred Redl, the success of his continued imposture ultimately depended on himself. It was no easy task: he was not insane, nor did he suffer a manifestation of insanity such as a schizophrenia that blacked out one aspect of his being in favor of the other. His evil was forever present in his thoughts. It provided the challenge that his surface existence had to meet, it formed the essence of the life game that he had to win in order to survive. To hide the horrible fact of his calculating being, to impress none of the truth and all of the fiction of his distorted existence on society, required a force of will so great as to almost defy human imagination.

See him, for instance, on the morning of July 27, 1904, when he appeared in civil court for the trial of Simon Lawrow and Bronislaus Dyrcz, the two Russian spies whom Batjuschin had betrayed to him the previous autumn. In pre-trial statements, Simon Lawrow had first claimed to be a Russian officer, then denied it, and now the Court is trying to settle this technical point. The military expert witness is called. He rises easily, walks smartly to the stand. There is not a crease in his splendid uniform, not a blemish on the brilliance of his saber, not a waxed hair of his mustache awry, and as he sits, his soft hands with their carefully manicured fingernails folded in his lap, a foot crossing the other, his countenance relaxed and slightly aloof, the judges, the jurors, the newspaper reporters, all are impressed even before the sonorous voice proceeds to demolish Lawrow's claim to a commission in the Czar's army. He halts a moment, his blue eyes flick to the judges, to one or two of the jury, to the defendant sitting beneath him and then he concludes:

". . . during my stay in Russia I had frequent opportunity to learn to know Russian officers serving in various categories, but I never encountered one, militarily speaking, so unknowledgeable, uneducated and so slightly conscious of his position as is Lawrow, for if their social education is limited, their military knowledge—at once obvious to any officer—is not to be denied, an appearance absolutely lacking in Lawrow's case. Lawrow is no officer, but he does possess the minimum knowledge necessary to be a noncommissioned officer. In any event, he is a military man."

The Court is satisfied—Lawrow's status has been expertly determined.

The President now orders the press to leave the courtroom because the charges that are about to be read involve classified military information. A ten-minute recess; the Court is reconvened. A new prosecuting attorney, Doctor Viktor Pollak, is present today. He is nervous, his tongue trips over the words that relate how Lawrow spied out secret supply and rail dumps intended for use in time of war. The defense replies, there is argument, several jurors frown their confusion over the legal jargon, Alfred Redl listens intently. What a contrast it is when he again takes the stand to offer factual, logical testimony couched in words that even a layman can understand:

> ". . . At the time of mobilization, each [Austro-Hungarian] village has to deliver a previously determined quantity of grain, fodder and the like to a previously determined area, and also to make available a certain amount of transportation. . . . The planning of all this is naturally done in peacetime, and each mayor knows how much will be demanded from his village in time of war. In turn, he informs each inhabitant who then holds in readiness a certain quantity of grain and a wagon with team. Despite the fact that such measures are treated as highly secret, here and there some information filters down to the populace. From such information a spy can at once conclude where a [storage] depot will be established, where a quantity of land transport will be assembled. With that, he knows approximately where an army will be concentrated. And the knowledge of the deployment area offers him a very solid basis for determining the intention of the army command. Railroad installations also play a valuable part in such conclusions. If in a small railroad station with light [peacetime] traffic [the spy] sees significant ramp installations and numerous auxiliary tracks, he knows that here large troop movements will occur, that here large amounts of supplies will be loaded or unloaded. . . ."

And then, to seal Lawrow's fate, the irony perhaps unconscious:

> "In answer to the question, if in my opinion Lawrow was really sent as a spy by a neighboring state, I can affirm this with full certainty. We know the instructions of the neighboring state and Lawrow has followed them to the letter. He knew exactly how to maintain contact with the officials of his land, he knew

that he had to transmit the results of his work immediately. He never received money by mail, but always through a middleman. In a word, he possessed a knowledge of these arrangements so exact as to be held only by a person actually employed in this work."

The defense questions a point or two of testimony, the President requests elaboration until all are satisfied. Court is adjourned until the next morning. Alfred, accompanied by Viktor Pollak, is stopped by reporters as he leaves the courtroom. Most of them know him and several greet him personally and respectfully. He is friendly to them, answers what questions he can. Then, pleading that he must rush to the Bureau, he makes his way through the crowd to the waiting fiacre.

The next day it is the turn of Bronislaus Dyrcz, a twenty-seven-year-old Pole charged with the more serious crime of spying out the fortresses of Cracow. After the necessary preliminaries, the military expert witness is again called. His voice is sharp with the threat of his opening testimony:

"I must stress that Cracow is the barrier against an invasion of Vienna [by Russia]. The fortresses lie so close to the border that they can be bombarded from foreign territory. Thus the enemy can begin siege preparations before the outbreak of war so that Cracow on the first day of hostilities would have to defend itself against an enemy attack. Indeed, the attack of Cracow is the act through which war could begin. . . . It is thus for the enemy particularly valuable to learn of the present state of the Cracow defenses. . . ."

His eyes turn from the jury to drill the face of the somber defendant:

"Concerning the confession of Bronislaus Dyrcz, the following is to me striking. His sketches reveal knowledge only possessed by the professional. The layman will perhaps be able to state that here and there lies a defensive work and would consider the larger one as the more important, but he would not be able to comprehend so systematically and accurately the Cracow defensive system with the three interdependent defensive lines and the tied-in supporting complexes. Further, Dyrcz was completely correct in his use of the technical terms with which he designated the works that had come to his attention. . . ."

For another thirty minutes the calm voice expatiates on what Bronislaus Dyrcz had betrayed to Russia. At the end it changes to a derisive tone:

> "When the defense argues that Dyrcz as a spy would have had the necessary funds at his disposal while we have heard that he had to support himself in dishonest ways [during his espionage], then I must reply that the foreign power in question [Russia] rewards such spies only after they have delivered something, and indeed pay for delivered information only after they have proved its importance and accuracy."

The prosecution summarizes, the defense replies, there is argument, Alfred Redl is called upon to explain a further point. Finally the jury retires. The President reads the verdict: Both are guilty. He sentences Simon Lawrow to twelve months and Bronislaus Dyrcz to eighteen months of hard labor. In the July 28th evening edition of the *Neue Freie Presse,* the Viennese public reads that "the verdict was based chiefly on the testimony of Military Expert Witness Redl."

The act was repeated the next month when an accomplice of Dyrcz named Sylvester Markiewicz was found guilty and sentenced to two years of hard labor. Then came the highly secret trials of Hekailo, Wieckowski and Acht, who were each found guilty and sentenced to twelve, ten and eight years of hard labor, respectively. In July, 1905, a spy in the pay of France named August Doré was tried and sentenced to eighteen months of hard labor. While Alfred was investigating his next case, that of Peter Contin, a spy for Italy, he received orders relieving him from duty in the Intelligence Bureau as of September 30, 1905.

The esteem in which he was held by his superiors at this time is made clear from the official record. Originally ordered to report to the 46th *Landwehr* Divison, he was soon notified that instead he would remain in Vienna as General Staff Chief of the 13th *Landwehr* Division, a change that would keep his expert knowledge of espionage immediately available to the Bureau and one that would allow him to serve as military expert witness in the Contin trial (which was held that December). Shortly before his transfer, Colonel Hordliczka recommended him for a decoration "on conclusion of his five years' service with the Bureau." This document was sent to the Minister of War via the office of the Chief of the General Staff where it was endorsed: "In agreement with the recommendation." Upon actually signing the endorsement, however, General Beck inserted the word "Completely" at the beginning of the sentence, and recommended Redl for a Military Service Cross, an extremely high decoration which on September 26 the Emperor authorized "in recognition of excellent service." Finally, and by far the most astonishing of the three honors, a few days later Redl, who had passed the staff promotion examination to major with the lowest possible grade, was not only promoted to major, but was listed as Number Two in grade, which meant that of the seventeen General Staff captains promoted from the one hundred who were eligible, Alfred Redl was considered to be next to the top in professional ability.

He probably was. Although his intelligence reputation grew from the prosecution of spies betrayed to him by Colonel Batjuschin, and although he acted in an environment favorable to his nefarious purposes, Redl obviously boasted a military genius independent from either Batjuschin or environment. Even in these early years he used his own methods to trap several spies, of whom August Doré was one and Peter Contin another. In his reorganization of the Intelligence Bureau—which was not yet complete—he had already introduced several new espionage techniques, at least two of which survive in western intelligence organizations today. His ideas were developed at length in four theses on Intelligence work that he wrote and left behind him in the Bureau. As proven by extant espionage cases, his pre-trial investigative work was performed thoroughly and scientifically and his actual opinions, both written and oral, are masterpieces of their kind.

Nor was his ability in the field any less widely respected. Although his troop duties from 1900 to 1905 were limited, the pertinent entries in his fitness reports are uniformly excellent. In the spring of 1905 he was paid the impressive compliment of being one of thirteen General Staff officers ordered to accompany the Chief of the General Staff on a secret field reconnaissance to Krain in Dalmatia. But it was during his tour as

General Staff Chief of the 13th *Landwehr* Division that he emerged as an excellent field officer. In his fitness report of 1905, his new commanding officer, General Sir Mansuet von Versbach, parroted the remarks of former fitness reports, but qualified these by writing: "The above remarks are based for the greatest part on data supplied by the Intelligence Bureau of the General Staff." This report bears a rather lukewarm endorsement by the Commanding General of the *Landwehr* Army, General Ferdinand Fiedler: "[Redl is] still not yet known well to me. According to the record, eligible for promotion." One year later, General von Versbach wrote: "As General Staff officer of the 13th *Landwehr* Division in the large maneuvers in Silesia, [Redl is] in every respect qualified, and proved himself an especially well-versed, extraordinarily able and very resourceful General Staff officer." In another section of the report he wrote that Redl is "a well-disciplined officer, very tactful, and with best manners." General Fiedler, in turn, endorsed this report: "[Redl is] an able and superior General Staff Chief. Very learned, tactful, trustworthy and accurate. . . ." Presumably it was these reports that caused the new Chief of the General Staff, Conrad von Hötzendorf, to include Major Redl as one of forty-eight General Staff officers chosen to make the important "large" General Staff trip in the spring of 1907, a staff and command exercise in which Redl commanded the simulated 11th Infantry Division.

Other honors fell to Alfred Redl during this tour of troop duty. Early in 1906, upon completion of twenty-five years of honorable active duty, he was awarded the Military Service Medal, Third Class, a yellow ribbon bordered with black holding a bronze cross overlaid with the Imperial Eagle. In the spring of 1906 he was chosen as one of several officers to host a Spanish military mission that had come to Vienna for technical instruction in the new *Schwarzlose* machine gun. For this service he was awarded the Royal Spanish Military Service Order, Second Class, a decoration normally reserved for the rank of general. In November, 1906, the death of Archduke Otto brought to Vienna a Russian Grand Duke and a deputation from the Russian Imperial *Lubonskischen Dragonen* Regiment of which Otto had been honorary colonel. Shortly before their arrival for the funeral, the General Adjutant to Emperor Francis Joseph wrote a "very urgent" letter to the Personnel Bureau of the General Staff requesting assignment of a staff officer and a captain "who speak Russian fluently and who are personally suitable" to act as hosts to these visitors. The Chief of the General Staff selected Major Alfred Redl (and Captain Ferdinand Kostellezky of the Intelligence Bureau) for the detail.

Alfred's personal life simultaneously expanded. Early in 1906 he moved again, this time to a much larger apartment located on the top floor of a modern building at Number 42, Floriani Street. He was often seen now in the company of Doctor Viktor Pollak, the learned prosecuting attorney in the Lawrow-Dyrcz trial. Their continued association in espionage trials had ripened to a personal friendship that was to last until Alfred's death. Other officers sometimes joined them as in an evening they sat over a bottle of wine in the Café Kaiserhof to discuss the latest espionage cases or argue their theories of criminal behavior. Another of Alfred's friends at this time was a young General Staff officer named Theodor Körner von Siegringen who was assigned to the Telegraph Bureau of the General Staff. A half century later, when he was President of the Republic of Austria and shortly before his own death, *Bundespräsident* Körner said: "Yes, I remember Alfred Redl very well. We often met for morning coffee in the café near the Telegraph Bureau. Like everyone else who knew him, I liked Alfred very much. He was always dignified—entirely the gentleman—but in a very friendly way. I think he liked me because I held a number of radical ideas for the reformation of the Army which we used to discuss. I personally enjoyed our association because he was a brilliant man to talk to. He knew a great deal about military and international affairs, but more than that, his knowledge of human behavior was startling."

Thus did the actor grip his audience, thus did the audience applaud. Theodor Körner and Viktor Pollak, Wilhelm Haberditz and Eugen Hordliczka, Ferdinand Beck and Conrad von Hötzendorf, officers of the Bureau and those of the *Landwehr,* judges and jurors, ladies and gentlemen of society—all saw and heard only a small, healthy, debonair officer, a brilliant person with a quick, sometimes sardonic sense of humor and impeccable manners, a gentleman who at forty years of age had already proved himself an outstanding field officer and a recognized genius in intelligence. But what of the Alfred Redl who escaped their notice? What of the confused child of an ignorant and impoverished Lemberg freight clerk, the unstable youth who blamed the smell of cabbage soup and the sound of circus music for himself, the sick man who had suffered damn mercury in the fetid air of sweat baths, the sterile being who derived his physical pleasure from forbidden traffic with male bodies, the criminal who sprayed betrayal of country and comrade across the secret pages that went to Warsaw, the grotesque, embittered, twisted egomaniac who could only measure mankind by the cup of his own pleasure?

This Alfred Redl was also present—a voracious appetite for sensation that could never be satiated. He made the applause articulate, he feasted on the recognition and respect and even awe embodied in the trinket kudos, and when these palled he sent his body slave to feast with panthers and walk the thin line of the razor's edge in pursuit of danger and thrill and passion with which to fill the empty void of being that is man who has forsaken mankind. This was the Redl who spent long hours writing a secret report and cursed the sum returned to him by Batjuschin as niggardly; this was the Redl who thrilled at the touch of a new lover and wept bitter tears when truth dissolved itself into a young man with a blackmailing demand for money. This was the Redl to whom there was no past, no future—only a present that had to be goaded into some kind of activity, only a constant, furious seeking of the nothing that was his to realize.

And in the spring of 1907, another one of the nothings was Stefan Hromodka. He had finished Cadet School the previous year. His Uncle Alfred had pulled the right strings and gotten him into the Wiener Neustadt Academy. He had done well the first year. Now it was time for a holiday. Alfred took him to the Dalmatian Coast. They rode down by train, visited the Marine Academy at Pola, traveled on down the coast to Fiume. Wherever they stopped, Alfred's military friends met them to roll out the red carpet for their pleasure. The weeks sped by in a galaxy of luxurious hotels, splendid meals, opulent balls, attractive and important persons vying in a display of hospitality to the distinguished General Staff officer and his handsome cadet nephew. To Stefan it was the kind of life inherent in the glittering uniforms that had claimed his attention as a boy in the Peterskirche. He fell in love with the new life; he worshiped the man who was responsible for giving it to him. On the night that they sailed from Fiume to Trieste, they ate a late dinner, then stood on deck smoking and talking. Stefan said he was sorry that their holiday soon must end—the Academy would certainly be boring in comparison. Alfred replied that there would be other holidays. He was glad, he said, overjoyed that Stefan had so thoroughly enjoyed himself, that he had made such an excellent impression on the officers whom he had met. Alfred was very proud of Stefan, he said. He felt a great love for Stefan—there was nothing in the world that he would not do for him. He outlined Stefan's future with words that promised importance and luxury, and standing there at the rail in the moonlight the boy clung to each of the words as though a prophet were speaking of an everlasting land of milk and honey. He did not mind the prophet's hand on his own. He did not object to being led below to the cabin. The caresses surprised him but they did not annoy him. He accepted what followed. Later, lying next to his sleeping lover, he stretched his spent young body and there in the darkness he smiled contentedly. Surely in all this world there was no easier way to get what he had always wanted.

8.

THE new Chief of the General Staff, fifty-four-year-old General Baron Franz Conrad von Hötzendorf, was a handsome, hard-charging professional soldier who held the notion, considered quaint in some quarters of the Empire, that the primary mission of the Imperial and Royal Army was to fight and win wars. The contrast to his predecessor, General Beck, was obvious. Where Beck, in ordering officers on a General Staff trip, wrote that "each participant . . . will make known immediately and directly to me how many servants (including grooms) and how many of his own horses he will bring along," Conrad neglected such niceties from the start. In his order for the 1907 General Staff trip, he stated that the artificial concept of previous General Staff trips was to be replaced by that of the "free maneuver," a radical departure from tradition and one designed to place the participants "under those conditions of advance as they correspond to the situation in actual battle. . . ." General Auffenberg, later Minister of War, wrote disgruntledly that "Archduke Albrecht and General Beck served what amounted to a court table on General Staff trips, but under Conrad this was thoroughly, perhaps all too thoroughly, changed." The new Chief's attitude was further emphasized by the subsequent 1907 Emperor's Maneuver, a fast-moving, aggressive action that left the troops exhausted and filthy. Immediately after this maneuver, Conrad recommended to the Emperor that Austria-Hungary invade her ally, Italy, in the first of several "preventive wars" that would save the Empire. Although his recommendation was bluntly refused, that did not alter his aggressive attitude in the slightest and he now set about expanding his Army as rapidly as he could.

Conrad later wrote in his *Memoirs* that "simultaneously with my appointment to Chief of the General Staff, I turned my attention to [the Intelligence] service. I recognized that the financial means heretofore provided did not begin to satisfy the organization of this important service in a large-scale manner. . . ." Although Conrad was frustrated in his attempt to gain additional funds with which to build up the Bureau, he did succeed in sending Colonel Hordliczka several new officers during 1907. As one of these officers, Major Alfred Redl was particularly well received. He arrived back in the Bureau on October 1. A day later he began his new duties, this time as Deputy to the Chief of the Bureau.

Had it not been for the new Foreign Minister of Austria-Hungary, General Conrad's militancy would undoubtedly have remained suppressed. Baron Alois Lexa von Aehrenthal had been appointed to this important post a few months before Conrad's own appointment. The Baron was as large in physical stature as Conrad was small. A heavy face with drooping jowls and a severe myopia tended to belie his ambitious and forceful nature. Because he was not very intelligent, he practiced a flagrant rather than clever diplomacy, a course of action designed more to increase his own prestige than to save the peace of Europe. Aehrenthal held no brief with Conrad's desire to invade Italy, but because he wished to settle the vexatious "Serbian question" he emerged as a natural if unwilling ally of Conrad in the matter of power politics. His most recent effort to gain a *rapprochement* with this tiny Balkan country had gained him only humiliation, and for some time now he had been waiting to square accounts in the manner befitting the foreign minister of a large and powerful empire. Early in 1908 he had sounded the prelude to his ambition by proclaiming that he would build a railroad through the Turkish province of Novibazar to the Macedonian port of Salonika. He had no intention of building such a railroad, but his announcement confirmed, he thought, what he wanted to know: that Austria's emergence into the Balkans would be permitted by the Great Powers. Aehrenthal thought he saw his chance in the summer of 1908 when the Revolt of the Young Turks succeeded in Constantinople.

In its flush of victory, the Turkish Reform party proclaimed a new constitution designed to help Turkey recapture pieces of its empire long since whittled away by the Great Powers. Since such a course would have insured Turkey's ruin in that any attempt to reclaim Egypt or Algeria would have meant war against the powerful British and French, the new Ottoman rulers should not have been taken seriously. But when their plans to hold elections in Bosnia were announced, Aehrenthal seemed to take them very seriously. The Balkan provinces of Bosnia and Herzegowina had become protectorates of Austria-Hungary by the 1878 Congress of Berlin, and a joint warning from Austria-Hungary and Russia to Turkey would have maintained that status. Instead, Aehrenthal decided to annex the two provinces. Not only would this action forestall the Turkish threat, it would forever negate Serbian aspirations to this territory. More, it would give Austria-Hungary a legal spring-board from which she could extend the "greater Austrian" idea southwards. If Serbia interpreted the action as a *casus belli,* so much the worse for her. For Aehrenthal knew that Conrad von Hötzendorf wished to fight a "preventive war" against Serbia as well as against Italy. If Serbia stood alone, Austria-Hungary would beat her and would partition her with Bulgaria. To insure her isolation, Aehrenthal turned to Russia.

More accurately, he turned to the Russian Foreign Minister, Baron Izvolsky, a fat little man whose ambitions and intelligence matched those of Aehrenthal. Izvolsky's impossible dream centered on the Turkish Straits—if he could win exclusive transit rights for his battle fleet, Russia would at last have her Mediterranean harbor: the entire Black Sea. Meeting at Buchlau in September, 1908, the two diplomats quickly reached agreement. In return for Russian neutrality upon the announcement of the annexation in three weeks' time, Austria-Hungary would withdraw from the Sanjak of Novibazar and would agree to Russia's freedom in the Straits. Izvolsky at once traveled to Paris where he persuaded France to agree in the Straits matter, but his reception in London was not nearly so prosperous— Lord Grey refused to countenance any such move. On October 5, 1908, while Izvolsky continued his futile discussions with the English, Aehrenthal announced to the world the formal annexation of Bosnia and Herzegowina. To his astonishment and consternation, he unleashed international mayhem. France, England, Italy, Turkey—each hurled furious protests at the Ballhausplatz; Serbia announced mobilization; Czar Nicholas, ignorant of Izvolsky's diplomacy, assured Serbian Prime Minister Pašić that Russia would not tolerate the annexation. Izvolsky, seeing himself double-crossed in the Straits matter, performed a swift *volte face,* denied that he had agreed to "the dirty Jew" Aehrenthal's action and, to appease the furious Serbs, demanded that the Great Powers meet to award Serbia territorial compensation against Austria-Hungary. Germany, alone, remained sympathetic to Austria-Hungary, and it was with Chancellor von Bülow's assurance of Germany's support in case of war that Aehrenthal persuaded his most reluctant

Emperor to authorize partial mobilization in answer to the Serbian "threat."

The dress rehearsal for World War I continued into 1909. An inflamed Serbian press continued to demand war, destruction of the Habsburgs, the freeing of enslaved Slavs, a revolt of the Slavic peoples in the Austro-Hungarian Empire. Serbia's vicious terror instrument, the *Slovenski Jug*, had been reorganized the previous November into the larger and more powerful *Narodna Odbrana*. Championed by Crown Prince Alexander and supported by the Serbian General Staff, this underground organization, the instrument of numerous brutal crimes in previous years, continued to spread panic and propaganda through Bosnia and Herzegowina while the Serbian Army continued its mobilization to war strength which Austria calculated to be nearly seven thousand officers and 285,000 troops. Simultaneously Serbian diplomats continued their pleas for help to St. Petersburg and Paris.

Austria-Hungary answered in kind. Although Aehrenthal was beginning to see that a war with Serbia would gain him nothing, he had not yet fully decided against it and so publicly blustered its cause with a propaganda effort that considerably topped that of Serbia's. Militarily he was fully supported by Conrad von Hötzendorf who was doing everything he could to persuade Francis Joseph to an invasion of Serbia. Believing that Russia was still too weak from her defeat by Japan and from the revolution of 1906 to intervene, Conrad was content to guard his north and east with local forces, provide a screening force against Italy and deploy his main force to the south. As tension mounted, his buildup of strength continued. On March 16, 1909, he mobilized his Fifteenth Corps, a force of eighty thousand troops, which completed its march into Bosnia on March 24. Five days later the Austrian General Cabinet decided that war with Serbia was necessary.

But calmer minds had already taken control of the situation. Germany's Foreign Minister, Kiderlen-Wächter, told Baron Izvolsky that Austria would ask all the signatories to the Treaty of Berlin to agree to the annexation provided she was previously assured of the correct answers. If Izvolsky would not agree to this, Germany would concur in Aehrenthal's publication of the secret notes of his meeting with Izvolsky at Buchlau, and would back Austria-Hungary in an invasion of Serbia. England submitted a similar proposal. Meanwhile Aehrenthal successfully completed negotiations to buy the two provinces from Turkey and thus legalized his deed. The Russian Foreign Minister was left with one move: he informed Serbia to resolve the crisis. On March 31, 1909, the Serbian ambassador in Vienna delivered a formal note to Ballhausplatz stating that Serbia agreed to the annexation. The crisis was over.

In theory, Austria-Hungary had won. In fact, she suffered a severe defeat. By his action, Aehrenthal had insured the lasting enmity of the Serbs, he had humiliated Russia who would never forget it, he had taken formal possession of two poverty-stricken provinces which would become natural fountainheads of dissatisfaction, and he had physically placed Austria-Hungary in the Balkans where she could not in time avoid colliding with Russia. Far from intimidating Serbia, Aehrenthal had strengthened her by giving her a popular cause: union of Slavic brotherhood. With Russia's backing, Serbia almost at once moved her propaganda headquarters *inside the Austro-Hungarian Empire* to Prague whose anti-Habsburg citizenry were so overtly sympathetic to her cause.

But Aehrenthal was not yet finished. Prior to the announcement of annexation, Baron Paul Rauch, the Viceroy of Bosnia, had imprisoned a large number of Serbian-Croats for seditious activities. Aehrenthal now foolishly agreed that these persons should be tried. The result was the infamous Agram treason trials which were so patently prejudiced against the defendants that Emperor Francis Joseph personally pardoned each of the thirty men found guilty. Another scandal followed. During the Annexation Crisis, Aehrenthal had received from his Minister in Belgrade some documents purporting to prove that the leaders of the Serbo-Croat Coalition Party in Croatia were guilty of treason. Aehrenthal passed these documents to the famous historian, Heinrich Friedjung, who used them as basis for a series of inflammatory articles to justify a war with Serbia. Although Aehrenthal had been warned that the documents were false, he concurred in their publication even though by then he had decided not to go to war against Serbia. After the

Annexation Crisis, the principals named in Friedjung's articles brought a libel suit against him and his paper. During the course of the trial, which was held in Vienna, Friedjung was forced to admit that the documents were false and the persons accused were innocent. The case was settled out of court, but taken with the Agram trials it constituted a moral black mark against Aehrenthal and Austria-Hungary in every European chancellery.

The total effect of the Annexation Crisis on its perpetrator was to change him from an impulsive to a cautious fool who now whined only for international friendship, an attitude that brought him into conflict with General Conrad von Hötzendorf. Maintaining that an aggressive policy was better than *no* policy, Conrad loudly insisted on the strengthening of his Army as the only practical means of saving the country. Thus, to Austria-Hungary, the true legacy of the Annexation Crisis was a division of policy that in either event was unrealistic. On the one hand, Aehrenthal wanting to play ostrich with no policy and yet having too much power to do so; on the other hand, Conrad von Hötzendorf wanting to play aggressor with a preventive war policy and having insufficient power to do so. Firm leadership could have resolved the conflict, but from where was it to come? At the beginning of the Annexation Crisis, Archduke Francis Ferdinand was on holiday in Switzerland and only returned when his Military Adjutant, Lieutenant Colonel von Brosch, reminded him that his place was in Austria. At Salzburg he was met by Brosch and Conrad von Hötzendorf, the latter at once pressing his desire to invade Serbia. Francis Ferdinand asked Conrad to orient his wife, Archduchess Sophie, to the situation. He did so. Sophie promptly retorted that there should be no military action. Conrad remarked that ladies ought not to interfere in military matters, a truism that infuriated Francis Ferdinand and effectively broke up the meeting.

Emperor Francis Joseph proved no more dynamic than his nephew. At the time of the Crisis he was eighty years old, a tired, disillusioned man who in his own mind had suffered the trials of Job without the reward of Job. Had the old Emperor held a firm grasp of the issues at stake in the Annexation

Crisis, he would never have permitted Aehrenthal to make the Crisis. He did not want war, he had prevented Conrad and for another five years would prevent Conrad from waging war. Yet he had known of Conrad's aggressive ideas when, at Francis Ferdinand's urging, he had appointed Conrad as Chief of the General Staff; he had subsequently supported and would continue to support Conrad's demands for higher military budgets. His contradictory behavior was not only the result of age and fatigue. It stemmed from an illness endemic to the Habsburgs: an addiction to military power as the *sine qua non* of rule. Though Francis Joseph's many and various defeats had caused him to question the drug, he forever returned to its use until finally he was a muddled victim in whose mind complexity had long since changed to confusion until that seemed the natural order of things. Never having produced victory with power, he was not going to do it now that the shadows of Armageddon began to emerge from the twilight of Empire. He was going to do nothing more than to sit quietly by juggling Aehrenthal's negative pacifism with Conrad's positive annihilism, a lonely man whose only enjoyment in life was the daily card game in the quiet garden of Kathrina Schratt, the understanding woman who dealt the hands of cards and pretended not to see when the Emperor cheated so that he might win.

The Annexation Crisis placed particularly severe demands on the Intelligence Bureau of the General Staff. Forewarned by General Conrad, the Bureau had prepared an intensified counterintelligence plan against Serbia and Montenegro which was implemented simultaneously with Aehrenthal's announcement of annexation. In co-operation with local police and customs officials, Army Intelligence officers sealed the border between Austria-Hungary and Serbia, instituted full surveillance of political unreliables, rounded up and deported suspicious Serbian and Montenegrin nationals, raided and disrupted subversive political organizations, implemented a post and telegraph censorship plan, and extended its wire intercept operations from Italy to Serbia. An additional counterintelligence effort became necessary when a sudden plague of Russian agents disguised as knife grinders and woodsmen swarmed into

Galicia, upper Hungary and Bukowina to reconnoiter possible invasion routes should Russia go to war in defense of Serbia. Of the score or so of these spies actually caught, most of them had marked maps in their possession. Then in November, various anti-Habsburg newspapers throughout the empire began to publish classified military information including in several instances actual details of operation plans. From November to the following March the Bureau had to order over two hundred such papers confiscated. Simultaneously the Bureau had to conduct a positive-intelligence effort to gain the information needed by the Chief of the General Staff. Early in the Crisis the Bureau made contact with a Russian colonel that resulted in the purchase of secret war plans for the immense sum of eighty thousand crowns. Mainly through intercept operations, it was able to offer Conrad a good estimate of Italian capabilities and it "scored an astonishing success in the Balkans with slight financial and personnel means." It was on the basis of the information provided by the Bureau that Conrad risked leaving his north and southwest weak in favor of concentrating his strength in Bosnia.

The splendid showing made by the Intelligence Bureau was due to a number of factors. Thanks mainly to Conrad's earlier interest, it had grown to about thirty officers by the beginning of the Crisis. Half of these officers served in Vienna, half in field intelligence posts. For the most part they were well-qualified men who had been painstakingly trained by Hordliczka and especially by Redl. Since November, 1907, counter-intelligence had been in the hands of a young General Staff captain named Max Ronge, a small, balding and very intelligent officer who was Redl's protégé and would later play a crucial role in Redl's death. Another officer who was to be intimately concerned with Redl's future was a General Staff lieutenant colonel named August Urbanski. When the Crisis forced Urbanski's recall from Macedonia where he held an international gendarmerie command, he was appointed to the Bureau in an advisory capacity and subsequently contributed to the high quality of the Balkan intelligence that was given to Conrad.

But towering over these officers and in fact every officer in the Bureau was Major Alfred Redl. During these tense months, Redl was in the main responsible for the excellent performance of the Bureau, and it is a final insult to the value of the Annexation Crisis that he emerged from it as the high priest of intelligence in the minds of Hordliczka, Conrad and the Minister of War, Baron von Schönaich. Conrad's attitude toward Redl was foreshadowed by a document dated November 7, 1908: a letter that Redl wrote to the Ministry of War asking for "a new, broken-in horse" to replace the one that had expired. This letter, in every sense a routine request exercising the legitimate right of an Army officer to a government-owned horse—a *Chargepferd*—was not only *read* by the Chief of the General Staff during the trying days of the Crisis, but actually elicited his personal and completely superfluous endorsement that ". . . the request of this officer, who is in every way honorable and respectable, is most warmly recommended."

Two months later Colonel Hordliczka submitted an annual fitness report on Redl. In his words, Redl "qualifies remarkably as Deputy to the Chief of the Intelligence Bureau. In dealing with civilian officials he shows great skill and extraordinary tact." He "is able to introduce officers to service and to control their accurate performance of duty. Is demanding but is kind and very considerate. Holds the trust of his subordinates." Besides being suitable for Chief of the Intelligence Bureau or for General Staff Chief of an army corps, Redl was fitted for "military service of any secret nature which demands personal contact with civilian officials." In summary, Redl was "an excellent staff officer who is also fully qualified for the most difficult service posts." General Conrad von Hötzendorf endorsed this report: "I completely agree—a particularly excellent General Staff officer."

Redl had impressed other important persons. On March 20, 1909—a few days before the Austrian Cabinet answered Serbia's threats with the *ultima ratio* of war—General Conrad wrote a "Top Secret—Personal" letter to the Minister of War, Baron Franz von Schönaich. Conrad began the letter with a discussion of General Staff Plan "B" [invasion of the Balkans] and explained how, in the event of war with Serbia, the Operations

Bureau of the General Staff would go into the field with himself in over-all command. He then wrote:

> Relative to the Intelligence Bureau [in case of war], *the desire of Your Excellency that Major Redl would receive the post of Chief of the Bureau has been fully complied with.* Lieutenant Colonel von Urbanski, who was proposed for this post, is now, with my agreement, designated to command the War Attaché system. . . .*

Great as was the influence of Von Schönaich, Conrad would never have agreed to appoint Redl to this responsible position over the head of the senior and competent Urbanski unless he were convinced of his special fitness for the task.

The sudden termination of the Annexation Crisis prevented Redl from becoming Chief of the Intelligence Bureau, but it did not prevent Conrad from giving him other rewards. On May 1, 1909, he was one of twelve out of sixty-four officers selected for promotion to lieutenant colonel. Concurrent with his promotion, he was personally recommended by General Conrad for decoration with the Order of the Iron Crown, Third Class. To justify this unusually high decoration, Conrad submitted a citation which stated that Redl

> . . . is excellently qualified for his post as Deputy to the Chief of the Intelligence Bureau; during the Balkan Crisis he showed exemplary effort and striking capabilities; upon the order of his Chief he independently supervised the operations of several Bureau sections—such as the supervision of the transit of war matériel through the Monarchy, the dealings with major civilian bureaus, and the representing of the General Staff at conferences to create a new Civil Code of Justice, by which he has safeguarded the military interests of the State fully and completely. It is due to his devoted duty and co-operation that the supremely important duties in the Intelligence Bureau could be smoothly discharged in this difficult time of crisis.

This citation, along with eighty others, was submitted to the Emperor's Military Chancellery via the Minister of War. Baron von Schönaich found Conrad too generous and cut the number

* My italics.

of recommended officers to thirty-seven. Alfred Redl's citation and proposed decoration were left unchanged for consideration by the Emperor.

The end of the Annexation Crisis did not terminate the prevailing tension in the Imperial and Royal Army. General Conrad interpreted Serbia's surrender as a defeat for Austria-Hungary. In his mind a golden opportunity had been lost to strike at the enemies who were gradually encircling the Central Powers with the express intent of destroying them. Foreseeing that the situation would finally result in a European war, Conrad continued in his effort to build up his Army. He did not neglect the Intelligence Bureau, for here was the only source of information which he needed both to formulate his own strategy and to defend his arguments for a higher budget that this strategy necessitated. Although his every attempt to gain the Bureau more money proved in vain, he continued to support it in any other fashion as best he could. At the same time, his demands upon it were so great as to keep its operations at a peak.

Nothing could have pleased Alfred Redl more. Not only did the tension continue to provide relatively easy access to information on which he based his reports to the avaricious Batjuschin in Warsaw, but it also guaranteed his personal spot in General Conrad's sun. As much as his promotion and pending decoration pleased him, Alfred was already concentrating on a greater success. Colonel Hordliczka had served nearly six years in the Intelligence Bureau; his imminent transfer was common knowledge in the General Staff Corps. If he, Alfred Redl, were to be named the new Chief of the Bureau . . . the total vista was too grand to encompass with the mind. The mere thought of the appointment was sufficient to erase fatigue, to drive him to fresh efforts as each passing month brought nearer the promised relief of Colonel Hordliczka.

Certainly there was plenty of work to claim him. Internal unrest accompanied by a new influx of spies meant that most of the counterintelligence measures implemented during the Crisis had to be continued during 1909. In the previous year, sixty persons had been arrested on suspicion of espionage. *In 1909 over eleven hundred suspects were arrested.* Each case had to be investigated, some taken to court. Farming out what cases he could to civil agencies and to local military commands, Alfred turned the trials in Vienna over to Captain Ronge who in May, 1909, appeared in court for the first time as military expert witness. Alfred's own attention went increasingly to the positive-intelligence effort. Frequent briefings were demanded by Conrad and by the Military Chancelleries of the Emperor and Francis Ferdinand. New field intelligence posts had to be staffed and supervised. Everything seemed to hinder the collection effort, nothing to help it. Finances were the sorest point. Ronge later wrote that "the best-paid intelligence posts received 1750 crowns quarterly, those in Galicia nothing. In 1908 after my repeated recommendations the latter were given 200 crowns in the second quarter along with orders to revive the dormant intelligence effort [against Russia]. . . . [Agents received] monthly payments of 60–150 crowns—as a result not many volunteered for the work which meant risking many years at hard labor or deportation to Siberia." To supplement the collection effort, the Bureau had been sending out its own officers on secret reconnaissance trips. The arrest of a number of these had caused protests to reach the Ballhausplatz from the foreign countries concerned. In the summer of 1909 the Foreign Office was further embarrassed when the Austro-Hungarian military attaché in Belgrade, Major Gabriel Tánczos, was justly accused of secret espionage and had to be recalled. The situation, as Conrad later wrote, "led to controversy between Count Aehrenthal [the Foreign Minister] and me. Apropos of the indispensable nature of such [officer reconnaissance] trips, I pleaded to His Majesty in an audience on November 27, 1909, the necessity of the intelligence service as well as increased funds for it. It was thus a sharp blow when Count Aehrenthal caused His Majesty to agree with the prohibition of such trips. We were from then on militarily blind, limited only to the observations of military attachés and uncontrolled agents."

The Intelligence Bureau had one more ally: Germany. When the Annexation Crisis had made war a possibility, General Conrad had begun an exchange of letters with the Chief of the German Great General Staff, General von Moltke, that dealt with joint tactics and strategy to be used in case of a European war. It was now decided to extend the reciprocity to the intelligence field by formalizing the co-operation which had existed between the two Intelligence Bureaus for well over a decade. The mission was given to Alfred Redl. In the autumn of 1909 he traveled to northern France and England and, after reconnoitering the railway systems in those countries, proceeded to Berlin for lengthy conferences with the Chief of German Intelligence, Colonel Brose, and his able assistant, Major Wilhelm Heye. Returning to Vienna with a complete joint intelligence plan in his pocket, he learned that Emperor Francis Joseph had awarded him the Order of the Iron Crown, Third Class. After making the command appearance at Court to thank the Emperor, he left for two weeks of troop duty with the Fourth Infantry Division where he commanded a battalion and a regiment before reporting as umpire to the annual maneuver in Moravia. Hordliczka later noted that during these troop exercises "all superiors designated [Redl] as an 'excellent Staff officer who will become a striking regimental commander.'" He returned to Vienna to receive still another honor. On September 18, 1909, he learned that as a result of his performance at the Berlin conference the German General Staff wished to decorate him with the Royal Prussian Order of the Crown, Second Class, a decoration that was formally awarded to him a month later and one that was rarely bestowed on any rank less than general.

In Alfred's mind there was just one end for his personal comet of these months, and that was the chair occupied by Colonel Hordliczka. He of course offered no outward sign of his ambition. A new officer in the Bureau, Captain von Hubka, remembered him that autumn. Von Hubka had taken rooms beneath Alfred's apartment on Floriani Street. They frequently walked to work together and Redl occasionally invited Von Hubka to his table at the Volksgarten restaurant. "Despite the work load he carried and the enormous responsibility of his position," Von Hubka recalled a half century later, "he remained the friendly if dignified officer whom everyone liked and respected. Sometimes we would spend an evening in the Volksgarten restaurant. Several officers of the Bureau—Captain Kovačević in particular—were generally present, then a public

attorney [Pollak], and on two occasions at least, young Hromodka who we all thought was Redl's nephew." Stefan
Hromodka remembered their meeting that October when he
was given two weeks of leave upon graduating from the Wiener
Neustadt Academy as a second lieutenant: "I saw Redl nearly
every day. He was furious when he learned that I was to be
posted to a regiment down in Hungary. The next day he told
me that he had talked to the Minister of War and that my
orders were to be changed to Brünn [in nearby Bohemia]. He
was very nice to me during my leave—took me everywhere
and paid for everything. The night before I left for Brünn he
told me that he was giving me an allowance of fifty crowns a
month. We talked some about my future. He warned me about
all the pitfalls that faced a young officer and told me especially
to have nothing to do with women. He said that he hoped
soon to be in a position where he could help me get ahead
faster. . . ."

9.

HE had rehearsed the scene a hundred times. He would
appear completely at ease, would joke a little with Colonel
Hordliczka. Then the Colonel would tell him. He would
register surprise, ask Hordliczka to repeat the words, falter a
reply to show humility and gratitude. And then . . . then he
was in Hordliczka's office that November morning and they
were laughing, and as Alfred Redl puffed on a cigar Colonel
Hordliczka scratched his nose and looked serious.

*Exactly, Colonel, the atmosphere is appropriate to the business
at hand.*

"You have perhaps heard, Redl, that I am soon to be relieved
as Chief of the Bureau?"

"A few rumors to that effect, sir," Alfred said. "I hope there
is nothing to them."

"I can tell you now that there is," Hordliczka said.

"Damn sorry to hear that, sir."

"We have worked well together, Redl. But six years in this billet—that is a long time."

"Six years, sir. Time certainly flies."

And now you are to give way to a younger man who you hope will follow in your footsteps.

"That is just what General Conrad was saying yesterday when he pointed up the necessity of a younger officer who was sufficiently qualified to carry on where I perforce am leaving off. As I told the General, many of my ideas are yet to be implemented, and that makes it doubly important for my successor to be acquainted with them."

"To follow in the Colonel's footsteps, so to say."

"Exactly, Redl. Very well put. And I am pleased to tell you that both General Conrad and I agree that you are the logical choice to remain in the Bureau so that this may prove the case."

Alfred moved forward in his chair. "I beg your pardon, sir?"

Hordliczka sighed. "I knew that you would be disappointed. I told Conrad that you would prefer troop duty . . . that you *deserved* troop duty."

I am glad he didn't take you seriously, Colonel.

"Any officer would, sir," Alfred said. "But I shall try to do my best."

"I know you will, Redl, you always do. Nevertheless I was disappointed when General Conrad first told me that he was keeping you on here. Oh, I was not in the least surprised, mind you. Just between us, had there been war last winter you *would* have taken over the Bureau."

Yes. Baron von Schönaich told me as much.

"I can hardly believe that, sir."

"I saw the letter myself. The Chief has often said that he has never seen a younger officer with such an amazing grasp of intelligence work. I agree."

"Thank you, sir."

And now let us get down to business, Colonel.

"In fact, Redl, if the Chief were not so interested in you I would have spoken up much more strongly yesterday. But he has given considerable thought to this situation. As usual, he is right. He freely admitted the desirability of giving you a battalion command. The experience, he feels, would make you more assertive than you are. But he emphasized that you are still very young—thus there is plenty of time for troop command. His final consideration, of course, was that the best interests of the service would be met by keeping you here for another year."

What is that? Something has gone wrong.

"Another year, sir?"

"I knew you would be disappointed. But you see it had to be one of us, and with my having been here over six years he would not hear of an extension. Neither of us believes that Ronge is quite mature enough to carry on without your supervision, but the overriding consideration is Lieutenant Colonel Urbanski. He will need all the help that you can give him in getting settled in this chair."

Urbanski? In this chair? But he will be Chief of the Bureau.

"Colonel Urbanski, sir?"

"Yes, my replacement. A splendid choice, I think. Brilliant record in Macedonia and certainly a fine performance here with us the past year. He is quite senior, too—up for promotion to colonel this spring. As General Conrad said, he has every qualification for running the Bureau except actual experience."

This is impossible. Qualifications? You mean he comes from a good family, he and Conrad are close friends. Of all the filthy tricks.

"He is a fine officer, sir," Alfred said.

The Bureau is mine! It is mine!

"None better," Hordliczka said. He stood up. "I know you will do everything within your power to make his job easier."

"I shall certainly try, sir."

Alfred met Lieutenant Colonel Urbanski on his way out.

197

"Colonel Hordliczka has just informed me of your appointment, sir," Alfred said. "I would like to congratulate you."

Colonel Urbanski shook the proffered hand. "Thank you very much, Redl. I am delighted that you are to stay on as my Deputy."

You will remember those words one day, Urbanski.

"I must leave," Alfred said. "You will excuse me, sir?"
Urbanski closed the door behind him and sat down.

"I think he was rather disappointed by not going to troop duty," Hordliczka said. "But he is a good soldier, he understands."

"Solid fellow, isn't he?"

"He certainly is," Hordliczka said. "Nor will you ever find a more loyal subordinate, Urbanski. Well, I suggest we get down to work. . . ."

A week later Alfred was again closeted with Colonel Hordliczka in a final audit of confidential funds. "There," Colonel Hordliczka said, "that checks." He signed the report. "All right, these can go to Urbanski in the morning. What else do we have?"

"Nothing more until this afternoon, sir," Alfred said. He suddenly smiled. "There is one other thing, sir. A personal matter."

"What is it?"

"Some months ago, sir, an old uncle of mine in Galicia died. His will was finally probated." Alfred removed some papers from his pocket and handed them to Hordliczka. "I have been left rather a large sum of money."

Hordliczka glanced at the papers. "I would say you had. I am sorry that tragedy had to accompany your gain." He handed the documents back to Redl.

Alfred laughed. "I scarcely knew the old man," he said. "It came as a great surprise. No one thought he was very wealthy." Alfred stood up. "I just wished to tell you, sir, in case you want to enter it in my records."

Hordliczka laughed at the candor. "I had better treat you

with more respect, Redl. What do you plan to do with the money?"

"I am still so surprised, I do not really know," he said. "I shall probably invest most of it. But I am going to buy an automobile. I have been wanting one for a long time."

"You do not seem very pleased, Stevie." Alfred fitted a cigarette into an ebony holder. "If you would rather *not* have the transfer . . ."

"No, Fredl, it isn't that," Stefan said. He got up from the bed and put on a robe over his pajamas. Helping himself to a cigarette from a silver chest on the bureau, he held a match to Alfred's, then lighted his own.

"What is it, then? I have gone to some trouble to arrange this transfer to the cavalry. Nobody ever did that for me. If *I* could have served in the Seventh Ulans, *I* would have been in War College long before I was. It is not an opportunity to be taken lightly!"

"I am not taking it lightly, Fredl," Stefan said. "Only, I don't know . . . just because you like army life so well . . . I am not at all certain that I shall make a good officer."

"Absolute rot," Alfred exploded. "Stevie, I have told you a hundred times, if you do not have confidence in yourself, no one else will." He went to the bureau and took a letter from one of the drawers. "Here. I had not intended to mention this. Your commanding officer wrote to me last week. He has given you an excellent fitness report. Under General Remarks he states that you are 'cheerful, good-natured, still in the process of character development, somewhat easily excitable, very good mind with good comprehension, industrious with good success. Leads a platoon well, independent leadership yet little tested. Well suited for field service, not always reliable in patrol service, but shows initiative. In general has a very good knowledge of riflemanship, is himself a good shot, and a good fire leader. Good horseman in field.' Now listen to this, Stefan. 'His entire personality is that of a highly gifted subaltern. In the opinion of the Officer Corps, meets the conditions of Point One of the promotion instructions.' There! What do you think of that?"

"Did Major Schwarzkopf write that about me?"

Alfred laughed. "He certainly did. I have written him that in my opinion it is a very acute judgment of you. You *are* impetuous but that is not necessarily bad if you learn to control it."

"But the cavalry, Fredl. I do not have the . . . well, you know what I come from, and those officers are real rich and . . ."

"There you are, a good example of what Schwarzkopf meant. You jump to a conclusion without having all the facts that are available. I know what you come from, but who else does? Forget about your past, Stevie. If anyone asks about your father, just say that he is in banking. We are not poor, you know— thanks to my Uncle Helmuth. I would not have arranged the transfer unless I could meet the financial requirements. I am giving you an increase in your allowance, I shall buy you two more full-blooded horses and I . . . well, I have a little surprise for you if you transfer."

Stefan looked up quickly. "What is it?"

Alfred sat on the bed and put one hand on Stefan's shoulder. "Who would have thought six years ago that you would be an officer in the finest cavalry regiment in the world? That is what hard work does, Stevie. Together, we can do much more. That cavalry uniform can be replaced by the *flaschengrünen* blouse of the General Staff." Alfred took Stefan's hand and placed it to his lips. "That lieutenant's insignia can be a general's. That name could one day bear a title. I am not young, Stevie, but you are. You have the world before you, an easier one than I have had. I have made it that way for you because I love you. Everything I own will be yours, everything I am doing is for you. I will give you everything. But you must promise to work hard. Promise me, Stevie."

Stefan turned his eyes away. "I will do what I can, Fredl. Fredl, what's my surprise?"

"Are you going to transfer to the Seventh Ulans?"

"Yes, certainly."

Alfred took a small box from his dressing gown and handed it to Stefan.

"Oh, Fredl! Fredl, it is beautiful." He put the diamond ring on his finger and played it in the light.

Alfred ruffled his hand through Stefan's hair and pulled him close to him. "If you work hard," Alfred said, "it is only the beginning."

The room in which Alfred Redl sat talking to a guest a few nights later was the most flamboyant of the several expensively decorated rooms in the Floriani Street apartment. It was his favorite room. He had personally chosen the red-rose brocade that lined the walls, the thick red oriental rug that covered most of the waxed parquet, and the red velvet drapery that hung over the wide front windows and the heavy sliding doors on either end. On this night the doors were locked; the room seemed sealed from its world like some kind of a living tomb, the sepulchral effect heightened by two wax-encrusted candles that burned in silver candelabra on the center table, and by soft warmth that seeped from a white porcelain stove in one corner, a *Kachelofen* whose shiny brass door had warped enough to show the room a thread of orange glow.

The two men sat in comfortable armchairs with their backs to the curtained windows. Between them was a smoking table which in addition to ash trays and a cigar humidor held a crystal carafe of cold white wine. The guest, a younger man, was smoking a cigarette from a long, ivory holder. He was as brunet as Alfred was blond. The most distinguishing mark of his handsome face was a Roman nose that bespoke his heritage as well as did his name. He was Count Albergo de Alvanti, an Italian officer diplomat in Vienna. He had been sitting in the room for nearly a quarter of an hour. Although quite certain that Colonel Redl had invited him for something more than a social drink, he had carefully masked his impatience by a practiced bonhomie of polite conversation. He was not surprised when his host broke a pause in the conversation by reaching for his wallet and saying: "I have been meaning to ask you something, Count Albergo." He removed a photograph from the wallet. "I am ashamed to admit that I have never been in Rome. I wonder if you could tell me where this snapshot was taken in your beautiful city."

Major Albergo leaned forward to let the candlelight flicker on the photograph. He saw two men standing in serious conversation before a monument. "Yes," he said, forcing his voice to remain casual, "that is the Goethe Memorial. A lovely structure."

"How stupid of me," Alfred said. "Of course that is it—the memorial built to commemorate the splendid cultural relationship between Germanic and Roman peoples. A fitting symbol for our great Triple Alliance, would you not agree?"

"Precisely, Colonel." Count Albergo tossed the picture carelessly to the table and raised his glass. "And a fitting subject for a toast."

Alfred's eyes did not leave the face of his guest as he sipped the excellent Gumpoldskirchner. "About the photograph—do you recognize either of the men?"

"I don't actually, no."

"Oh? Perhaps if you were to look more closely . . ."

Count Albergo again squinted at the picture. "No, Colonel Redl, both are strangers to me."

"You must have a short memory, my dear Count." Alfred removed a second snapshot from his wallet. "Perhaps this will refresh it."

Count Albergo stared at a picture of himself in company with one of the two persons in the other snapshot.

"That is the Votivkirche here in Vienna in the background," Alfred said. "This picture was taken two weeks ago."

Albergo stiffened. "I was not aware, sir, that Austria-Hungary kept diplomatic representatives of an allied nation under surveillance."

"Austria-Hungary does not," Alfred said. "Colonel Redl does—particularly when the representative is in covert contact with a man named Kretschmar who happens to be a ranking civilian official in the Imperial and Royal Arsenal."

Count Albergo handed the picture back to Alfred. "I assume that you have lodged a formal protest?"

"If I had, I would hardly invite you here. There are certain facts about your friend Kretschmar that you may not know. Perhaps you believe yourself to be his exclusive employer? Actually, you come last on the list. He has been working for Russia since 1889 and for France since 1902. You have operated him for only three years, I believe."

Albergo's surprise was evident. "How do you know this?"

"We arrested him yesterday," Alfred said. "House search last night. I spent today sifting the material. Kretschmar was a bureaucrat—he kept accurate records of his avocation as well."

"Are you going to request my recall?"

"Not unless you force me to," Alfred said. "I was after the Russian military attaché and I have more than enough on him. I rather hate to do this to poor old Martschenko. It will mean a cavalry regiment for him. From what he tells me, his liver is no longer up to field service."

"Why are you picking on him?"

"Two reasons. One is to embarrass our Foreign Minister who seems intent, as you know, in bedding with the Russians. The other is Martschenko himself: he thinks he has been fooling me." Alfred picked up his silver goblet and sipped some wine. "As you think you are fooling me, Albergo."

"I beg your pardon, sir!"

"I told you, Albergo, that Kretschmar kept detailed records. Your last transaction with him cost Italian Intelligence two thousand lire. Is that correct?"

Albergo hesitated. "Yes, it is."

"No, it is not," Alfred contradicted. "It cost four thousand lire and Kretschmar gave you back two thousand. He wrote it all down, Albergo. Your dealings with Kretschmar have proved very profitable to your own purse. That is why your nonchalance about your own recall does not impress me. I could smash your career in twenty-four hours." Alfred leaned back in his chair. "You have surprised me, Albergo. I thought that you were rich."

Count Albergo ran a finger down the ridge of his nose to rest it on his upper lip. "I was wealthy, Colonel, or rather my father was. My brother—he is dead now—brought the house nearly to ruin. I began gambling. I lost. I had to get money somewhere. I saw no harm in this method. It cost my government no more. The spy bears the loss." He dropped his hands between his legs. "What do you want of me?"

"Not nearly as much as I am prepared to offer you. You are really a very fortunate man, Albergo."

Albergo looked at him suspiciously. "What do you mean?"

"Simply that you may best serve me by remaining at your present post."

"And giving you information when you want it?"

"*Au contraire,*" Alfred said easily. "By buying information much desired by your General Staff. Information so valuable that it may prevent the dissolution of the Triple Alliance."

"What kind of information?"

"Plans of our fortresses, mobilization and deployment plans, reports on secret arrangements between us and the German Great General Staff. They will be very expensive documents, Albergo, but you alone will be told the price. What you add to it is your own affair."

"I understand, Colonel. I am to purchase false information with which to fool my General Staff."

"You are in no position to object, Albergo, but to ease your conscience—the documents are genuine. If Italy is aware of our impressive strength, not to mention our joint war plans with Germany, she will be more amenable to continuing the Triple Alliance. On the other hand, her evident knowledge of our plans will make certain Austrians less desirous of a war with her. In that sense, you see, you will be performing nothing short of a patriotic role."

"If I am exposed?"

"I alone hold the proofs that incriminate you."

"I don't mean that. If our counterintelligence should discover that I am buying documents from your Intelligence Bureau?"

"But my dear Albergo, whatever gave you that idea?" Alfred suddenly smiled. "Oh, you think that this is an official plan. No, my dear Albergo. My associates are much too unimaginative for that. It will be exactly as if you were dealing with a spy. That is why you must be very careful. If the spy should fall, so would you."

"Do you mean that these reports would be mailed to Italy? That payment would be made only after their authenticity was established?"

"That is what I mean."

"With whom shall I be dealing?"

Alfred removed a paper from his wallet and handed it across the table. "Here is his code name and cover address."

Albergo scrutinized the paper. "K.K.," he read. "Very well, I shall arrange to meet him on the first and fifteenth of each month."

"And where is he to send his reports?"

"I would prefer to deal directly with him on such matters," Albergo said. "It is much safer."

"That is why you are dealing with him now," Alfred said quietly. "It *is* much safer."

Albergo's surprise changed slowly to a tight smile. "I understand," he said finally. "Very well. The address is: Aliverti, Corso Garibaldi 17, Milano."

Alfred stood up. "I believe, then, that is all for the moment?"

"I can think of nothing more," Albergo said.

Alfred showed his guest to the door and returned to the room. Sitting again in his armchair, he relit his cigar. One of the candles sputtered and burned out. He made a note to tell Joseph to attend to it in the morning. He would be entertaining again the following night. This time his guest would be from the French Embassy.

The two men were stamping snow from their feet when the door opened. "Good evening, Joseph," Colonel Redl said. "There you are, Viktor. After you." He stepped aside to let Doctor Pollak enter the apartment before him.

Pollak removed his gloves and Joseph helped him off with his coat. He rubbed his hands together. "Warm enough in here," he said.

"It heats very well," Alfred said. "But you have something warmer while I change. Joseph, show the *Herr Doktor* to the drawing room. Pour yourself a brandy, Viktor."

When Alfred reappeared in civilian clothes, his friend stood up and handed him a glass. "Happy birthday, Alfred."

"Thank you, Viktor. It is good of you to join me for a quiet dinner on such short notice."

"I wish I had known that it was your birthday. I would have arranged a party."

"I much prefer this," Alfred said. "I can accept being forty-six . . . but I cannot celebrate it. The years, Viktor, where have they all gone?"

Pollak laughed. "Wait until you are facing fifty as I am."

"My dear Viktor, that will call for nothing less than a semi-centennial in your honor. Here, let me fill your glass."

As Alfred returned it, a bell tinkled. "Now who the devil . . ."

"Pardon me, sir," Joseph said. "Special delivery, sir."

Alfred took a small package from the tray.

"Secret admirer, Alfred?"

"No," Alfred laughed. "My nephew, Stefan. He never forgets my birthday." He tossed the wrapping on a table, opened a small box and removed some tissue paper. "Now that is thoughtful," he said. "A pocket knife. I am always losing mine. The last time he was here I kept borrowing his and he remembered. That *is* thoughtful." He removed the knife from a gray suede sheath to examine its chased surface. He handed it to Viktor. "In excellent taste, I would say."

"Very nice," Viktor said. He knelt to the floor. "You dropped the sheath. Ah, here it is." He handed the knife back to Alfred. "You are fond of that young fellow, aren't you, Alfred?"

"Indeed I am," Alfred said. "He is a promising young officer, Viktor. The 49th Infantry Regiment submitted a fine fitness report on him. He transferred to the Seventh Ulans at Stockerau, you know. They will keep him on probation for several months yet."

"What does that mean?"

"That the Regiment is looking him over. If he is finally approved, then he is made a permanent officer in it. His squadron commander, *Herr Rittmeister* Gilnreiner, is so far very pleased with him. I do hope that he makes it—the Seventh Ulans is the smartest cavalry regiment we have. It would be a great help when he applies for War College."

"Is he General Staff material?"

"I would say so, yes. He has an excellent mind. Of course he is still young—inclined to be impetuous. But, then, so was I at that age."

"Oh, I saw Heinrich today, Alfred. We no more than shook hands, but he sent you his greetings."

"I was there for dinner last week," Alfred said. "For brothers, we have amazingly little to talk about. What I know that is interesting I cannot discuss, and what he knows is not interesting. At least to me. Farmers! Bah!"

Viktor laughed at the face he made. "Someone has to raise the potatoes your soldiers eat."

"Yes, but do we really need officials in the Ministry of Agriculture to talk about them? Anyway, Heinrich knows as much about raising potatoes as Frau Sacher."

"Have you heard from Oskar lately?"

Alfred's face clouded. "Only indirectly. He is still with the 71st Infantry. He has not fully recovered."

"Riding accident, wasn't it?"

"Yes, and a bad one. His mount pinned his right side. The operation was apparently botched. I am told his mind is . . . that he is in a highly nervous state."

"That is a pity. Queer chap, Oskar."

"We have never been close, Viktor. I shall never forget— he was *so* furious when I was appointed to the General Staff." Alfred finished his brandy and looked at the clock. "Colonel Urbanski has asked us to stop by his club for a glass of wine," he said. "He wants to talk about the Kretschmar case. Do you mind? I have a table later at the Riedhof."

"Not in the slightest."

As they left the apartment, Alfred suddenly stopped. "I knew I had forgotten something," he said.

"What is it?"

"That lovely knife Stefan sent me." He half turned, then paused and shrugged. "Oh, never mind. We are late now."

10.

CAPTAIN RONGE lay on one side of the large bed, his hands folded behind his head. "I know, dear," he said, "he was somewhat expansive. But you must admit that he was also amusing."

His wife placed her hairbrush on the dressing table and

half turned to him. "No! Not when he is *so* cynical. I saw nothing amusing in that remark he made about our having two emperors. Why, it was positively treasonous!"

Ronge chuckled. "Now, my dear, he meant no more than the rivalry between Schönbrunn and Belvedere. Everyone knows that the Emperor is going one way and the Heir Presumptive another. It causes a great deal of confusion. That is all Colonel Redl meant."

"He doesn't have to go around saying so!"

"Oh, that is only his way. Poor fellow, he has no beautiful wife to do the talking for him."

"Don't *you* try to be amusing, Maximilian. Anyway, why hasn't he a wife?"

"Everyone says he is the most intelligent officer in the General Staff."

"Maxl!"

"Well, if you would come to bed . . ."

"Colonel Redl annoyed me very much this evening. He used to be so quiet and modest. Ever since he received that inheritance he has been different. I wish he would stop acting so . . . so *nouveau riche!*"

"Oh, darling, you make him sound like an ogre. He was only relaxing. He has been under enormous pressure lately. Without doubt he is the hardest-working officer I have ever known."

"You work hard."

"Yes, dear, but I do not have his responsibilities. Since Urbanski was promoted to full colonel, he has been on detached duty so often that Colonel Redl is practically running the Bureau. At a time like this, too. One crisis after the other."

"But he was positively *critical* of . . . of things."

Captain Ronge sighed. "He was merely stating the truth, my dear. Don't forget, he has been in the Bureau for years. The work tends to make one realistic."

"Oh, Max. You won't become that way?"

"Do I ever discuss military affairs in my home?"

"No."

"Well, I don't plan to begin. But I do wish you would understand that I owe a great deal to Colonel Redl. He has been

and will continue to be our friend." Captain Ronge rolled
over. "Do come to bed. It is very late."
"All right. But Maxl . . ."
"Yes."
His wife put down the brush and sighed. "Oh, never mind."

Lieutenant Güssel flung the letter to the desk and swore.
"Now what is the matter?" Lieutenant Hausmann asked.
"This billet. Why did I ever get assigned to Headquarters
of the General Staff? Lists, bulletins, orders."
"If you would finish reading those letters, we could have
coffee," Hausmann reasoned.
"An artillery orientation course. You aren't going to it. I
am not going to it. Why must *we* sit here and worry about it?"
"Behave yourself," Hausmann said. "If The Trumpet hears
you we shall really be in for it."
Güssel thumbed his nose at the closed door of the Adjutant's
office. He picked up the letter he had just manhandled and
straightened it. "Ready. Aim. Fire. In accordance with General Staff memorandum of 8 April, 1910, *Herr Major* Stefan B.
Hüttsohn of the Imperial and Royal General Staff Corps
requests permission to attend the Artillery Firing and Orientation Course for Troop Commanders at Bruck an der Leitha
from 31 June to 9 July." Güssel laughed. "It sounds like a
damn party."
"*Herr Major* Hüttsohn," Hausmann repeated, writing the
name on his list.
Güssel opened the next letter. "In accordance with General
Staff memorandum of 8 April, 1910, *Herr Oberst* Heinrich
Fuchs of the General Staff Corps regrets that he is unable to
attend the Artillery Firing Orientation Course for Troop Commanders at Bruck an der Leitha from 31 June to 9 July."
Güssel sailed the letter across his desk. Stiffening his face he
intoned: "On behalf of the Supreme Commander and the
Chief of the General Staff, I can only say, *Herr Oberst* Fuchs,
that we of the High Command shall miss you. Perhaps next
year, *Herr Oberst* Fuchs, or the year . . ."
Despite himself Hausmann laughed. "Come on, do finish
those damn letters."

Güssel abandoned his wit with obvious reluctance to open the next letter. "Reference General Staff Memorandum of 8 April, 1910, subject: Artillery Firing Orientation Course for Troop Commanders, 31 June to 9 July, 1910, Bruck an der Leitha. I shall report!" Güssel whistled. "This fellow means business. Redl, Alfred, *Oberstleutnant* of the General Staff Corps."

"He generally does mean business," Hausmann said, writing in the name.

Güssel shook his head. "Forty-four officers request permission to attend. Redl will report!" The young officer shrugged. "Now that we have signed up God, let us move on to the peasants. Next! Ready. Aim. Fire. In accordance with . . ."

"Your taxi is ready, sir," the head waiter told him.

"Thank you, *Herr Ober*." Alfred stood up, said good night to the officers at the table. Aside he handed the head waiter a large note. "Take care of the check when the gentlemen leave. Keep the change."

On his way from the crowded night spot he tipped the wardrobe woman, the doorman and in the street the old pensioner who held the door of the taxi for him.

The driver smiled at the familiar fare. "Good evening, *Herr Oberstleutnant* Redl."

"Good evening, *Herr Taxichauffeur* Scharer." He settled in the seat. "Home, please."

"*Jawohl, mein Herr.*"

The cab ground slowly out of Annagasse and turned left up Kärntner Street. Alfred leaned forward and slid the glass partition open. "I have been meaning to ask you, Scharer. This job you have, are you satisfied with it?"

The driver shrugged. "It is a living, sir."

"What are you paid?"

Scharer slowed and heaved against the wheel for the right turn into Ringstrasse. "One hundred and ten crowns a month, sir."

"I shall soon need a chauffeur. Can you drive an Austro-Daimler touring phaeton?"

"Yes, sir."

"One hundred fifty crowns a month and uniforms. The car will be kept in perfect order."

"That would be very agreeable to me, sir."

In front of his building, Alfred paid the driver. "I shall tell you when to pick up my automobile. Good night."

"Ah, Ronge. Come in. Mrs. Ronge received my note, I trust. Good. That was a splendid dinner." Alfred lighted a cigarette. "What do you have this morning?"

Ronge handed him a paper. "Came in last night, sir. It was just decoded. It looks as if our musician tooted his horn quite effectively."

Alfred read the paper half-aloud: "After performance in Kiev cabaret, Subject made a pretense of drunkenness and boasted of acquaintance with heavily indebted Austrian General Staff officer in Prague. Subject contacted by Russian Army Intelligence, Kiev, on following day." Alfred rubbed one side of his mustache. "The description of Colonel 'Marinsko' fits our friend, Major Galkin," he said. "Series of meetings between Subject and Marinsko ensued. Marinsko apparently satisfied. Has ordered Subject to effect contact between the officer and one Fräulein Mitzi Hartmann in Prague. Woman is suspected Russian resident agent, real name Tanya Ludocović. Await your instructions." Alfred handed the paper back to Ronge. "Interesting," he said. "I only wish we had such an informant network in this country."

"Do we arrange the rendezvous, sir?"

Alfred looked thoughtful. "As a rule I do not favor such operations. The only successful one that we ever ran was against the former Italian military attaché here, Lieutenant Colonel Delmastro."

"In 1905, sir?"

"Actually it began in 1904 when I let Delmastro 'recruit' one of my best agents. He soon won Delmastro's complete trust. Finally Delmastro—more to show off his own cleverness than anything else—sent this man to Lugano, at the time headquarters of their intelligence effort against us. I forged some impressive documents for him to take along. The Italians were very impressed and babbled their fool heads off to him.

We never did learn how much our documents confused them, but we found out several interesting details of their organization. That was how I later caught Peter Contin—the case that forced Delmastro's recall."

"A brilliant operation," Ronge said.

"More fortunate than brilliant," Alfred said. "For every one of such cases that succeeds, a hundred fail. They are in every sense 'luxury' operations. They require an enormous amount of time and effort, and of course the perfect agent to carry them through. You run a double risk with the agent. The minute he is placed in such contact with the enemy, you have sacrificed your control."

"You mean, sir, if he is doubled . . ."

"Exactly. You can never accept his report without confirming from other sources and that is often impossible. Even if he is trustworthy, you will sacrifice him if you continue to run him. Sooner or later their counterintelligence will trap him."

"In other words, sir, the result rarely justifies the effort."

"Yes, but three factors intervene here." Alfred's forefinger tapped the paper. "The operation will be held in our territory and the 'agent' is one of our own officers. Even without these advantages, our intelligence effort against Russia is so miserable that we are forced to try anything. At the very least, if we can blow this network in Prague, it will give General Conrad another argument for the funds we need to open a field post there."

"Lieutenant Ulmansky can leave for Prague tonight, sir." Ronge smiled. "If I may so, sir, he is a natural for the role of a dissipated General Staff major."

"Yes, he should do very nicely. Bring him in this afternoon for final instructions. You plan to accompany him to run the surveillance. I want some photographs, if that is possible." Noting Ronge's frown, Alfred asked, "What is the matter?"

"The Jeczes trial, sir. It opens the day after tomorrow. I am expert witness."

"I had forgotten. We can hardly ask for a postponement now." He rubbed his eyes tiredly. "Oh, the devil. Prague is more important than that wretched little Jew, Jeczes. I will substitute for you. Telephone over there this afternoon and tell them. Bring me your brief when you come back with Ulmansky this afternoon. I can study it tonight."

"Sir, it is none of my business, but . . ." Ronge's voice trailed off.

"But what, Ronge?"

"Well, Colonel Redl, you are working too hard, sir. I am not the only one who says so either. You just cannot continue at this pace, sir. No one can."

Alfred laughed. "*Lieber* Ronge, you should know by now that intelligence work is either feast or famine and we are going through a feast. As such we are special soldiers fighting a special war. If we can win . . . that is more important than our personal welfare." Seeing Ronge about to protest, he held up his hand. "No more about it, Ronge. We have a job that must be done. What little I can do will be more than repaid if for once we can turn the tables on that damn Batjuschin up in Warsaw."

Colonel August Urbanski von Ostrymiecz leaned awkwardly over the bed to kiss his attractive wife. "It was a lovely christening," he said, "but you must be very tired."

"How is Hansi?" she asked.

"Sleeping as only a three-day-old baby can," her husband answered. "Utterly carefree. I wish his mother would do the same." He sat carefully on the edge of her bed.

"His mother is still much too excited for sleep." She took her husband's hand in her own. "August, I am glad we decided to do this. Did you see Mother's face when you were holding Hansi? She looked so pleased. To me it would have been worth double the rush we went through to have the christening before she left Vienna."

"Just so you aren't too tired, my dear."

"I am exhausted—but very happy." She suddenly giggled. "Do you think we shocked our friends? My appearing like this in the living room?" She straightened her pink silk bed jacket.

"Not severely, my dear. Most of them have been married longer than we have."

"I don't think Colonel Redl was very pleased, August. It

was the strangest thing. I noticed him when he first came in. When he saw me—in bed like this—he stopped dead and stared. Just for an instant. The most peculiar look on his face."

Colonel Urbanski laughed. "He was probably embarrassed. Bachelors are unduly modest in such matters—or they pretend to be."

"No, it wasn't a look like *that*. As he stared at me, his face completely changed—somehow disdainful. If I did not know better, I would almost say a look of loathing came over it."

"Oh, my dear, really! Colonel Redl is one of your most faithful admirers. He always asks about you. Why, just yesterday he sent you that enormous bouquet. And look at his gift for little Hansi."

"August, do you *like* Alfred Redl? Personally, I mean?"

"That is a difficult question, my dear. I certainly don't dislike him. Professionally, I admire him very much and I even envy him his knowledge of intelligence. I could not ask for a more efficient deputy. My being away from the Bureau so much has placed an extraordinary amount of work on his shoulders. He has had to work nights and Sundays and holidays, but he has never complained and has always kept up. I wish I could tell you some of the things he is responsible for—well, you remember last spring when the Emperor refused to acknowledge the presence of the Russian military attaché at the *Hofball* and he was recalled to St. Petersburg on the following day. Don't you dare tell anyone, but if it were not for Alfred Redl, Colonel Martschenko would still be here doing his best to learn our secrets. He was responsible for the recall of Martschenko's predecessor, Wladimir de Roop, as well, and if I were the present Russian military attaché, I would stay out of Redl's way. His knowledge of Russian intelligence, indeed of Russian behavior, is simply uncanny. But there, I am not answering your question. Perhaps I cannot answer it. I like him, so do my colleagues. I wonder, though, if any one of us really knows him. I know that I do not. But that look of his you mention . . ."

Seeing that his wife was dozing, Colonel Urbanski broke off the sentence. He was going to say that perhaps the beautiful room and the baby and the mother had made Alfred Redl suddenly realize what he was missing from life. He was going to say that he sometimes wondered if Alfred Redl were not a very lonely man. Instead he rose carefully from the bed, smiled at his sleeping wife and walked quietly to the crib of his son.

The air meet had started early that morning, and the green meadow on the right of the private enclosure had soon been spotted by ordinary Viennese who with numerous progeny and large picnic baskets had come down on the special excursion train. The more fashionable spectators had not begun to arrive until midmorning. Their carriages, one after the other, had wound laboriously up the narrow, twisting road, picked up speed on the plateau of the flying field, rumbled past hangars and shops and a dirt apron crowded with monoplanes and biplanes to come to horse-snorting stops by the tents that formed a demilune around the private enclosure.

The Emperor would not appear today, but Archduke Karl was there to represent him, and as he had stood chatting over a glass of champagne with Archduke Max and Count Ledochowski, the arrival of the Prince of Parma and his party had been announced and minutes later the ornate carriage of Count Montecuccoli had appeared, and before the noon hour a host of lesser aristocrats and important civilian officials and ranking military officers had filled nearly all of the tables in the private enclosure. Taken all together, a festive scene: the ladies, their parasols unfurled against the sun, gathered in small groups exchanging gossip and offering coy glances to the handsome young men whose rakish opened helmets and scarved necks testified to their hazardous profession; the bearded gentlemen, heavy binoculars slung about their necks, smoking expensive Havana cigars, standing and sitting also in small groups to offer their sparse, usually erroneous knowledge of matters aeronautical; white-jacketed servants hovering over the tables to fill a glass, clear a plate, uncork a bottle of chilled wine; the flash and glitter of the *Hoch-und-Deutschmeister* regimental band whose stirring music seemed to make almost a dance of the waving colored flags overhead; the rumble of an approaching carriage, the grand entrance, the *küss die Hand* formality of greeting. And now and again a new sound, a sputtering en-

gine that sometimes died, sometimes lived to grow to a tenor
whine that halted conversation and claimed eyes until it had
propelled a lumbering thing of fabric and man and wire down
the dirt strip and ever so slowly into the air.

Captain Baron von Seiller of the General Staff had been
watching a circling monoplane whose pilot had spent the last
ten minutes trying to beat the day's altitude record of 2800
feet. He lowered his glasses and turned to his wife. "He is
starting down. I suspect his fuel is running low." He looked
at his watch. "Viktor said that he was coming out with Colonel
Redl. They are late." The Baroness smiled and nodded; she
was listening to a general at the next table.

"Yes," he was saying, "General Conrad is very air-minded.
He himself has flown. If I am not mistaken, he plans to use the
airplane in next year's maneuver. Indeed, gentlemen, I believe
that you will find most of my General Staff associates to be
well up on this development."

Several of the men nodded approvingly. "What will be the
primary military employment of the airplane, *Herr General?*"
one of them asked.

"Reconnaissance, sir. The airplane will open a new perspective of vision to us. Of course it will never replace cavalry but
it will augment it."

"What is your opinion of the bombing tests this morning,
Herr General?"

The general toyed with his *pince-nez.* "That trial, sir, was
purely an academic one. Our Emperor has made it quite clear
that aerial bombing can play no part in warfare as gentlemen
know it."

"I was surprised," one of the auditors remarked, "that only
one sandbag fell in the target area."

The general smiled tolerantly. "Well, sir, I am no airman
myself but I daresay that when one is flying at six hundred
feet of altitude, a circle of only one hundred feet in diameter
does not offer too precise a target. Leaving ethical considerations aside, I would say that this points up the impracticability
of the bombing theory. In a combat situation, a plane would
have to bomb from the fantastic altitude of two thousand feet
or higher. Even if a satisfactory bomb were produced, its use-

216

fulness would be confined as a hindrance to shipping operations in a crowded harbor. A bomb powerful enough to destroy bridges, for example, would be so heavy that no airplane could leave the ground with it."

"But if you employ the airplane for reconnaissance, *Herr General,* won't you need an observer in addition to the aviator?"

"You will, sir, and that is our chief interest: a more reliable machine that can easily carry two persons."

"Faster as well?"

"No, sir," the general said. "Any airplane that flies from fifty to sixty miles an hour is completely adequate for military purposes." He stood up. "And now, gentlemen, if you will excuse me, His Royal Highness has asked me to view the next event with him."

At his words, Baron von Seiller focused his binoculars on the apron. Seeing no activity he raised them to the far hangar. Suddenly he sat forward.

"What is it?" his wife asked.

"Look at that automobile coming past the hangar! Viktor is in it, so is Colonel Redl." He placed the binoculars on the table. "Excuse me, my dear, while I meet them."

Behind the tents Von Seiller watched the automobile roar down the road and slow as the uniformed chauffeur neatly turned it toward the private enclosure. The long body of the open phaeton was lacquered red, the same color as the leather upholstery of the front and rear seats. The brasswork was shined to a high polish and on each front door was a monogram, a five-pointed crest in gilt with the initials A.V.R. below it. The middle initial was dwarfed so that one who did not know might have thought it to signify the aristocratic "von."

The first person to descend from the automobile was the chauffeur who hurried to open the rear door for Alfred Redl's exit. "Ah, Von Seiller," he said, shaking hands. He flicked a spot of dust from his flannel jacket. "Rather grimy off the main road. We made splendid time, though."

Captain Kovačević laughed at Von Seiller's surprised face. "What is the matter, Von Seiller? Don't tell me that you came down in an ordinary carriage?"

"I am afraid I did." He stepped back to examine the automobile again. "It is really magnificent," he said.

"It only arrived a few days ago," Colonel Redl said. "I had Austro-Daimler build it to specification."

"Doesn't anyone want a bottle of wine?" Stefan demanded. "I am utterly parched."

"Come along, then," Alfred said. "We shall do something about that."

"Is it really his, Viktor?" Captain von Seiller asked his friend when they were alone.

"Yes, it is," Captain Kovačević answered.

"But how in the world . . . Viktor, that automobile must have cost twenty or thirty thousand crowns."

Viktor shrugged. "His inheritance . . . oh, of course, you were not in the Bureau when *that* happened. Some uncle of his in Galicia left him a packet."

Captain von Seiller took a last look at the automobile and turned away. "It must have been a considerable sum," he said.

"It was," Viktor replied.

Colonel August Urbanski stared with fascinated horror at the last page of the neat typewritten manuscript. "You leave little doubt as to the accuracy of your findings," he said to the officer seated opposite him.

Lieutenant Colonel Redl crossed one leg over the other and said, "As sure as I sit here, sir, I am convinced of the accuracy. So is Captain von Hubka." Von Hubka was Chief of the Italian Section in the Bureau.

"But this totally negates General Conrad's assumption that the Italian Army would deploy west of the Livenza. It renders Deployment Plan 'I' useless."

"Better now, sir," Redl said dryly, "than later."

Colonel Urbanski riffled the top-secret pages of Redl's report. "So that is what they did with the twenty-six million lire provided for 'fortress construction' in their 1909 budget."

"I am certain of it," Alfred said. "Every fact points to it. By fortifying the Tagliamento Line and screening the southern side of Gemona, they can move their pre-invasion deployment

218

thirty miles closer to us. Even if we discovered their intention in time, we could never breach modern fortifications with our present artillery."

Urbanski shook his head sadly. "I shall take this up today with the Chief. He will not be pleased." He placed the report on the side of his desk. "What is next?"

"More bad news, sir. I have had to close the Prague case. After such a promising beginning, too."

"What happened?"

"Marinsko or rather Major Galkin failed to keep his last appointment with Ulmansky. At my instructions, Ulmansky met the alternate rendezvous but with no success. Then yesterday the Prague police reported that Tanya Ledocović alias Mitzi Hartmann eluded surveillance and left Prague." Redl looked at his superior. "Our friend, Batjuschin, again."

"Undoubtedly," Urbanski agreed. "Well, we should not be too upset. Our associates in Berlin just lost their two top agents in St. Petersburg. Those damn Russians are difficult."

"And will remain so until we are given more funds to fight them with," Alfred said.

"Little chance of that," Urbanski said. "General Conrad has done everything possible with no success. Oh, I forgot to tell you, Redl—he said yesterday that he was going to keep you in the Bureau until spring." Urbanski smiled kindly. "Don't blame him. It is my fault. I know you want a command and you should have one. But do understand my side of the picture. No one in the Army has your experience in intelligence."

Alfred smiled wanly. "Sometimes I curse that fact," he said. He added in a resigned tone, "I will do the best I can."

Alfred smashed his fist down on the table. "Never mind how I found out! Is it true, Stefan?"

"Well, what if it is?"

Alfred wheeled to glare at the young officer. "Don't you be impudent with me. I asked you if it is true?"

Stefan threw up his hands in exasperation. "Yes, Fredl, it is true. I do have a girl in Stockerau. I have seen her quite often. I shall see her this evening, as a matter of fact."

PART II

"Why have you not told me of this?"

"For heaven's sake, why should I? You do not own me. I do not raise a fuss when you take that woman of yours out."

"You know perfectly well why I am seen with Vera. Who is this wretched girl?"

"She is not wretched. She is kind and sweet—she understands me."

"You will get rid of her!"

"I can't do that, Fredl. It would break her heart. She is in love with me, she wants to get married."

"Married! You can't get married. The *Kaution*. Where will you get the money for that? Do you think I am going to give it to you . . . even if I had that much? The *Kriegsschule*. You have to be single. You have to remain single for five years after graduation."

"Hilda wants me to leave the Army."

"Oh, Hilda wants you to leave the Army, does she? I am very glad to hear that. I appreciate that very much after what I have done for you." Alfred snapped his fingers together. "Just like that, Hilda wants you to leave the Army."

"Well, she said—"

"Spare me that, Stefan," Alfred said. He put his hand to his forehead. "You will pardon me, I do not feel well. It is quite something to have my faith and love in you so instantly destroyed. I think you had better go now."

"But, Fredl—"

"No, there is nothing more to say. I bear no hard feelings. I of course wish you every success."

"It would be different if I were getting somewhere in—"

"Getting somewhere? Why, you little fool. Twenty-two years old. A permanent officer in the Seventh Ulans. The best mounts that money can buy. Two diamond rings. A large allowance. Your own automobile. What do you think I had at twenty-two years of age? You are nothing but a spoiled, ungrateful—"

"What do you mean, my own automobile?"

Alfred looked pityingly at him. "I really see no reason to discuss the matter further, Stefan. But if you insist . . ." He searched briefly in his desk. "Here it is," he said casually, "my order to Austro-Daimler for a second automobile. It was to

220

be a surprise for you. I shall cancel it tomorrow . . . along with your allowance."

Stefan was silent.

"You should have no difficulty resigning your commission. It may not be so easy to find a satisfactory position. But then, your future bride is undoubtedly very wealthy."

"She is not wealthy," Stefan said petulantly, "and I wish you would not refer to her as my 'future bride.' "

"You are the one who is talking about love and marriage."

"You started it," Stefan said.

"With good reason, apparently. You know what I have told you about women. If you choose to ignore it . . ."

"I have not either ignored it. But damn it, Fredl, sometimes I get lonely out in that Godforsaken place."

"You can always come here, Stefan. Besides, it would not hurt you to study more than you have been."

"But the examinations are so far off."

"I thought you had decided to leave the Army."

"I did not say that, Fredl."

Alfred listened to the clock chime the hour. "I must dress now, Stefan. Doctor Pollak and I are driving to Semmering for the afternoon."

"Wait a minute, Fredl." Stefan walked to him and put his hand on Alfred's arm. "I am sorry. I did not think there would be any harm. You know that I do not really care about anyone else."

"I would like to believe that, Stefan."

"I can prove it, Fredl. I won't see that girl any more."

"Very well, then," Alfred said. "I shall be back from Semmering early. You will have dinner with me. About eight."

"About eight, Fredl. All right."

11.

FOR the sake of good drama, the life of Alfred Redl should have ended in the spring of 1911 when he was transferred from the Intelligence Bureau to Infantry Regiment Number 99. This was the point of natural climax, the correct moment for denouement. The international scene was quiet and would have offered no competition to the event. All but one of the characters to appear in the actual finale were on hand. Redl's own character was established, his terrible crimes were committed, his success in practicing them apparent. As Nature's peccadillo against Society, Alfred had come full bloom in this spring, and any of a number of factors could have worked to satisfy poetic justice by his undoing. Society should now have exposed him, repaired its wounds with a self-righteous tongue of revenge, and emerged victorious—glorious and immutable.

In fact, nothing of the sort happened. Alfred Redl was to live for another two years, he was to spend the next eighteen months in Vienna and the previous pattern of his life was to be altered only by its enlargement. When he left the Bureau in 1905 he was duly honored for his work, and in 1911 this was repeated. Colonel Urbanski wrote on his final fitness report that his

> . . . great knowledge of human nature, likewise his knowledge of all service conditions in the General Staff, his superior mind, his tactfulness, and his skill in human relations make him appear especially suited for Chief of the Personnel Bureau as well as for Chief of the Intelligence Bureau and General Staff Chief of a corps.

In summary, Urbanski judged Redl "a very educated, excellent General Staff officer who will fully qualify for any post."

General Conrad obviously agreed. A General Staff document dated January 9, 1911, shows that of several score General Staff officers all but two had served only one to three years of duty in Vienna during the last decade. One officer had served six years and was to be forthwith transferred to another location. But Redl had already served ten and one-half years in Vienna and now, as commanding officer of the 4th Battalion, would remain in Vienna. Conrad further specified that Redl would stay in the General Staff Corps and would be, so to speak, on loan to Infantry Regiment Number 99. And shortly before Redl's transfer, Conrad recommended him for the important Military Service Medal with the following citation:

[Redl] has proved outstanding as executive and policy officer during three and one-half years in the Intelligence Bureau; as Second Staff officer [he has] furnished reliable support for the Chief of the Bureau. [He] has expanded the Intelligence Service and has fully protected the interests of the Army in countless espionage cases.

Conrad's recommendation was disapproved by the Minister of War who noted that Redl "has already received an extraordinary Supreme decoration—the Order of the Iron Crown, Third Class—for his activities in the Intelligence Bureau. The award of another such decoration appears impossible to the War Ministry." Undeterred by this action, Conrad at once nominated Redl for an honor called the "Expression of Supreme Satisfaction," a personal citation awarded orally by Emperor Francis Joseph and carrying with it a special medal. This award was made on April 18, 1911.

Similarly, he repeated his early success as a troop commander. His triumph in Infantry Regiment Number 99 was apparent from the moment he arose in the Regimental Mess to deliver a message entrusted to him by the Emperor during his recent audience: "Give my greetings to the beautiful 99th—I can always count on this Regiment." A young regimental officer later recalled that "in two or three weeks, Colonel Redl was by far the most popular officer in the regiment. Always dignified, he was very friendly to junior officers. He went out of his way to help us and we worshiped him." During the autumn maneuver, the regimental commanding officer, Colonel Krasel, became suddenly ill; regimental command reverted to Alfred. According to his fitness report, he "qualified strikingly in every respect both as a battalion and regimental commander." The Brigade Commander, General Hordt, wrote that Redl was a "strikingly gifted, very informed staff officer who proved himself outstanding as battalion commander and who, during the maneuver, demonstrated much skill and common sense as regimental commander." And General Mansuet von Versbach, Redl's old commanding officer in 1906 and now Commanding General of Second Corps, noted that "during the corps exercise of this year [Redl] has handled himself excellently as Commanding Officer of an independent Group and carried through his decisions with consistency and energy. Strikingly fitted for regimental command."

This fitness report was read by a new Chief of the General Staff, General Blasius von Schemua, who had replaced Conrad in December, 1911, the latter being temporarily out of favor with both the Emperor and Francis Ferdinand. Von Schemua was obviously as impressed by Redl as Conrad had been. On May 1, 1912, Redl was one of eight lieutenant colonels selected from fifty candidates for promotion to colonel, an enormous honor in that there were only fifty-four colonels in the entire General Staff Corps. Two weeks later he was ordered to the General Staff "for special employment." That spring Von Schemua took him on a General Staff trip to Bosnia where the tactical problem of the invasion of Serbia was worked out. According to his 1912 fitness report, Redl "fully qualified as commanding officer of an independent infantry division. [He made a] correct estimate of the situation, [displayed] sharp talents; clear and simple in thought and command, consequently in execution. . . ." In the tactical exercises and maneuvers of that summer and autumn, Colonel Redl "displayed great mental decisiveness, handled himself easily and very well. . . ." On September 28, 1912, General von Schemua recommended his assignment as General Staff Chief of the Eighth Corps in Prague. On October 14—one week after the beginning of the First Balkan War—Emperor Francis Joseph formally approved the assignment. One morning shortly afterward, Alfred stopped at Regimental Headquarters to pay a formal call of departure to Colonel Krasel. As he left the building, he was suddenly surrounded by laughing and cheering junior officers who hoisted him to their shoulders and carried him to his waiting automobile.

Alfred's personal life also reflected the successful expansion familiar to former years. Soon after his transfer in 1911, he moved to an apartment at Number 10, Wickenburg Street, a four-story building of gray stucco not far away from his old residence. The elegance of the building with its numerous bay windows and balconies was immediately apparent from the stone-leaf decoration of the entrance and the luxurious foyer of black and white marble floors and gold marble walls. In this building, which housed the rare convenience of an elevator, Alfred claimed the top floor. According to one guest, he maintained "a luxurious establishment whose costly furnishings were definitely on the feminine side." An officer in the Intelligence Bureau recalled having been "invited there several times for champagne parties. They were stag affairs. The apartment, though scarcely masculine, was exquisitely furnished and Colonel Redl was an excellent host." On several occasions he entertained junior officers of his regiment at dinner, "not in his apartment, but in outlying restaurants where we drove in his splendid automobile." He continued to entertain his friends in the Intelligence Bureau, he was frequently seen at smart social affairs, he appeared now and then with a woman of the demimonde named Vera Schneider, and on Sundays he and Doctor Pollak frequently motored to Semmering or some other convenient suburb.

As was also usual, Stefan Hromodka continued to form an integral part of his life. A young officer in Alfred's regiment found Stefan "a nice enough sort. Colonel Redl often brought him to the Mess where he was introduced around as his nephew." An officer in the Intelligence Bureau recalled that Stefan was always present at Redl's parties: "I did not particularly care for him—a rather silly young cavalry officer, handsome, libertine type—but I thought nothing about his presence, nor did anyone else." Redl's chauffeur grew used to Stefan: "I would deliver Colonel Redl and his nephew to the Colonel's residence and would wait outside in the automobile. Sometimes late at night I drove the lieutenant back to Stockerau, but usually I was told to put away the automobile—he would spend the night."

It was not to make any difference at this time, but in his desire to hold Stefan, Alfred now began to display a definite irresponsibility of expenditure. In 1911 he not only gave Stefan the promised Austro-Daimler, but he also raised his allowance and sent his younger brother to Cadet School. Alfred had begun paying Stefan a personal allowance of fifty crowns a month in 1909. In 1912 he was paying Stefan six hundred crowns a month—more than his salary as lieutenant colonel—and towards the end of 1912 he raised this sum to nine hundred crowns. In 1912 he also gave Stefan a furnished apartment in Stockerau, but in return Stefan was forced to sign an agreement stating that if he married he would forfeit the apartment and furnishings.

The significance of this expenditure was not so much the immediate risk, which was not as great as it may appear. Although Stefan was personally unpopular in the Seventh Ulans, there was no question of his honor. A fitness report of 1912 judged him "cheerful, good-natured, solid character, ambitious, excellent mind, industrious. Is a very good . . . highly intelligent and dashing cavalry officer." He attributed his personal allowance to "his family." His regimental commander, Colonel Mold, later stated that Hromodka "lived on a grand scale and was regarded in the regiment as very well off . . . as the source of his wealth [he] gave his rich parents and also frequently mentioned his very wealthy Uncle Redl with whom he stood in active contact." According to *Frau Rittmeister* Gilnreiner, when Stefan received his automobile and private apartment "everyone was surprised, but when Stefan said that they were gifts from his rich uncle no one questioned it further. Colonel Redl had called on us several times and did appear to be wealthy."

The significance was rather that Alfred Redl had finally overextended himself. If he had broken with Stefan at this time, he might still have been able to survive. But he did not—he could not—break with Stefan, and he was not to survive much longer. To meet the enormous financial demands occasioned by both his own and Stefan's standard of living meant a constant sale of information to Russia, Italy and France. Here was risk of first degree, not so much in procuring the information as in the communications involved. Alfred Redl knew perfectly well that the Intelligence Bureau was becoming larger and better every day. He knew that the Bureau held some excellent minds and practiced some excellent techniques because he was responsible for the training of most of these minds and the perfecting of many of the techniques. He also knew that German intelligence operations were effective, and he himself had forged the agreement that was responsible for the joint counterintelligence plan operating between Germany and Austria-Hungary.

And now in the late autumn of 1912, the crisis was approaching, the denouement not far distant. But there was to be no poetic justice for Society. No one was going to expose Alfred Redl as much as he was going to expose himself. He would be punished, but Society would not be pleased. There would be no victory.

Part III

THE CURTAIN

1.

THEY shook hands and lighted cigars and settled in the leather chairs of the comfortable office to talk about themselves and their mutual friends and the old days in the Intelligence Bureau. Only after an orderly brought coffee did General Baron von Giesl, commanding Eighth Army Corps in Prague, change the conversation to the immediate.

"You have a large job, Colonel," the elderly man said. "I know no one else in the Army whom I should wish to trust with it."

"I appreciate that very much, sir," Alfred said.

"Colonel von Stanoilovic's untimely death has left us a chaotic situation at a bad time," the General continued. "I want you to post yourself on routine matters just as soon as possible. I think you will find your Military Secretary competent but, of course, you may choose anyone you wish. I am giving you a very free hand—what I expect soon is the smoothest-running corps in the Army." The General smiled and went on, "In your spare time you can treat our other problem."

"Yes, sir," Alfred said, "General von Schemua briefed me in Vienna. I have a number of ideas for that."

"That situation is really rather serious. As you undoubtedly know, Russia has been pouring money in here for a good many years. The pan-Slavs, the pan-Serbs, the Czech nationalists—they all are operating out of here."

"I know, sir—we have many enemies, but limited funds."

"I think that we shall find Vienna more than willing even on that delicate subject, although why they will not establish a field intelligence post here . . . well, perhaps the Government is waking up. I see the Intelligence Bureau did gain additional appropriations."

Alfred shrugged. "A total 165,000 crowns, sir. Ridiculous compared to the German's 450,000 marks. And Russia! One of the officers in the Bureau told me not long ago that Russian

Intelligence is spending thirteen million rubles this year. Imagine that, sir."

"Fantastic," the General said. "Will we ever wake up?"

"I sometimes wonder, sir," Alfred said.

A buzzer interrupted them. General von Giesl spoke briefly on the telephone, hung up and said: "There is a flat for you, Redl, should you want it. It is next door here. Completely private, of course. Stables in back, servant quarters below. It would come to you *gratis* so you could count your quarters allowance as gain."

"Thank you very much, sir," Alfred said. "That is a pleasant surprise."

"Little enough," the General said. "I believe that is all for now. Any questions?"

"Just two, sir. I can see there is some hard work ahead and I wonder if I could take classified material to my quarters overnight. I would keep it in a safe, of course."

"Certainly," the General said. "There are sentries posted in any event."

"I would also like to avoid social obligations, within reason. The last months in Vienna have been rather strenuous."

"You look tired, Colonel. I see no problem there. Naturally we hope to see something of you in our local group here and of course certain functions you must attend with me. But you will be excused from the usual calls. I shall have my Adjutant notify the junior officers not to call on you except when you so request." The old man stood up, took Alfred by the arm. "It is splendid to have you with me again, Redl."

"Thank you, sir. I am very pleased to be here."

The apartment off the Headquarters building was neither large nor luxurious, consisting as it did of a small vestibule, a living and dining room, two bedrooms, a tackroom and a servant's room. Alfred moved in at once and in another three weeks the rooms were redecorated to his taste. For the walls, drapery and upholstery he chose a burning-bright red sharper even than that of his automobile. He filled the rooms with baroque furniture, massive walnut pieces with brass fittings and overstuffed chairs and sofas. Numerous alabaster and bronze knickknacks were strewn about the rooms. On one of these, an ermine-clad figure of a woman, a concealed button could be pushed to make the wrap drop and reveal her nude figure. For one side of the living room, Alfred bought a new military library of expensive calfskin bindings. In a corner of the room stood a large desk, on top of it a bronze bust of Napoleon. In the next room a four-poster bed was made up with silk sheets covered with red and rose silk quilts. A dressing table held a manicure set, hair dyes, pomades, perfumes, a curling iron and a generous selection of cosmetics. Three closets were filled with his wardrobe that included 195 dress shirts, 10 uniform greatcoats that were silk-lined, 10 mackintoshes and raincoats, 10 civilian fur-trimmed overcoats and ulsters, 25 pair of specially tailored uniform trousers, 400 pair of suede gloves, 8 sabers, 10 pair of patent-leather shoes. A special section, to which only Redl held the key, contained silk kimonos, embroidered women's shirts and silk stockings. The tackroom held six new saddles with bridles, boots and spurs to complement the three horses—a full-blood white and two half-blood roans—stabled in the rear. On the window side of the tackroom stood a large worktable covered with the most modern photographic equipment. Throughout the rooms was a peculiar odor, a strong smell of sweet perfume combined with the heavier fragrance of Oriental incense.

Very few persons saw this apartment during Redl's occupancy. The servant Joseph lived there and several young officers who shared Alfred's affections came to it. But the chauffeur and grooms were not allowed in it, nor were Alfred's professional associates. When Captain von Hubka, a former subordinate in the Intelligence Bureau, visited Prague early in 1913, Alfred received him pleasantly, spent an hour or two with him discussing Conrad's reappointment as Chief of the General Staff as well as the dangerous Balkan situation (Von Hubka had just come from Montenegro where he was the military attaché), but did not invite him to his quarters.

No one apparently thought much about Colonel Redl's secluded life, particularly in view of his heavy work load. As General Staff Chief of an army corps he was charged with formulating and implementing policy, supervising instruction of commissioned officers, heading countless commissions and boards and reviewing the thousand and one details occasioned by administration and operation of a large headquarters, two infantry divisions, a cavalry brigade and an artillery brigade. He had also to gain a detailed familiarity with Eighth Corps war plans, which meant study of all mobilization and deployment orders including supply and replenishment details. In addition, there being no intelligence post in Prague, he had to organize and direct an intelligence effort, which in itself was a major task.

And as in the past when his performance of duty and exemplary social behavior quelled fleeting suspicions, so now added to his rank they served to guard him well. On those rare occasions when he accompanied Baron von Giesl he displayed his usual charm and tact, with the result that invitations from both civil and military circles flowed in a steady stream to his desk. All but the most important were sent to his Military Secretary with orders to regret. Each morning early he appeared in his office, turned to the mountain of work with his usual good-natured if quiet gusto, handled his juniors with tact and firmness and produced more from them than others ever had. He ate his luncheon either in the mess where he was cordial to his fellow officers (he always ate simply, drank a little wine) or sometimes he ate in his apartment, the wife of the porter cooking for him. He remained at his desk until late afternoon when his chauffeur drove him downtown along the Graben to the Café Continental where he sipped coffee and read the newspapers of Europe. Then he returned to his office, signed the last letters, filled a briefcase with documents, walked to his apartment, bathed, dressed and once again was driven across the Moldau River where he dined with various senior officers. After coffee and a liqueur, Alfred returned to his apartment, removed his expensive uniform in favor of silk pajamas and robe . . . and turned to the night's work.

The night's work, indeed the other lives of Alfred Redl, centered around the large desk with the special English locks that stood in one corner of the living room. The contents of this desk were varied. In one small compartment was a package of strychnine with the date 1902 written on it; a larger drawer held packets of bills, most of them large and unpaid: a tailor's bill for 9,000 crowns, a large stabling bill, a bill for the new library, furniture, linen, interior decorating and automobile repair bills. He owed between forty and fifty thousand crowns and his assets were about 4,000 crowns' worth of securities, his personal property and 14,000 crowns in cash that lay in a sealed envelope next to the bills. Another drawer contained small, neat notebooks that explained where some of the money went and from where some of it came. In these were listed various reports that Alfred had sold to Russia, Italy and France, the payments for each sale, money-order receipts recording his payments to various officers, a record of the extraordinarily high wages and extra payments he gave his servants, and curious little notations like the one in a calendar notebook under March 25, 1912: "Nik. Nzt." In still another drawer were packets of invitations, personal calling cards and letters, many entirely decent, friendly communications, but many also of a different nature, many from men, mostly officers, that began, "Dear Fredl: What joy it was to hear from you . . ." and ended with veiled demands for money. One envelope held Stefan Hromodka's signed agreement not to marry. The entire correspondence was saturated with a cloying perfume that permeated the photographs lying next to them. The photographs were Alfred's particular delight. There were many of them and they showed Alfred and his lovers singly and in pairs and in groups, and some were nude and some dressed in women's clothing—the figures in the photographs were indulging in varying perversions.

Alfred usually began the night's work by going to his desk, unlocking the compartments and drawers and looking through these papers and photographs. This act was very sacred to him; it formed the beginning of an exciting ritual that played fear against security. On the one hand he knew it was exceedingly dangerous to keep this material in his possession; on the other hand he knew his position to be such that he *could* keep it. And it was such because he was smarter, had always been smarter than the rest.

Alfred extended the ritual by leaving his desk for the photographic table where he unlocked his briefcase, sorted the classified documents and photographed them. The work was difficult because photography was still new and he was not yet proficient in it. Two letters in his desk, as a matter of fact, were complaints from his extracurricular employers: his pictures had faded so badly as to make his work nearly useless. So he was careful and worked hard and long, often late into the night, but always before retiring he went to the desk, recorded his night's work, wrote a letter or two and completed the ritual by looking through the photographs. Then he locked the desk and went to sleep in the four-poster bed with silk sheets and red quilts.

Once or twice a month he had his chauffeur drive him to Vienna where he stayed in the Hotel Klomser in downtown Vienna. He used these weekends to contact his cutouts and letter drops in order to mail the work of nights and collect the payments due him. For pleasure's sake Stefan usually came in from Stockerau and on Sunday Alfred often drove his old friend, Doctor Viktor Pollak, to the resort of Semmering for a quiet afternoon of beer and conversation.

This was the unrelenting pattern of Alfred's service in Prague. It lasted through the winter into spring, but even before the cold March wind had ceased to whine over the Moldau River small incidents, seemingly remote from it, had taken place.

Early in April, 1913, Major Maximilian Ronge of the Intelligence Bureau received an official letter from his counterpart on the German Great General Staff, Major Walter Nicolai, Department III-b, Intelligence. Acting under the counterintelligence agreement that Redl had helped to arrange between Austria and Germany, Nicolai enclosed a suspicious document, a letter that bore the address:

> Herr Nikon Nizetas
> c/o General Delivery
> Vienna, Austria

This letter, according to Nicolai's report, had lain for some weeks in Vienna and when no one claimed it the postal officials had returned it to the place of its postmark: Berlin. There secret police as part of the covert censorship effort had opened it. It held about 6,000 crowns and the addresses of two known foreign espionage centers, one in Paris and one in Geneva. Nicolai was turning the case over to Ronge because it obviously involved Austria.

Ronge persuaded his Chief, Colonel Urbanski, to let him use the slight funds at his disposal for the case. He painstakingly compared the typewriting on the letter with specimens laboriously collected by Redl and added to by himself. He could do nothing with the Paris address but investigation of the Geneva address led to a French Intelligence agent, one Monsieur Larguier, and before long Ronge placed irrefutable evidence of Larguier's espionage against Austria before Swiss authorities. Then as today the Swiss expressed sublime indignation, expelled Larguier, counted their profits and loudly reaffirmed their neutrality.

More important to Ronge, of course, was the identity of Nikon Nizetas. The letter and the money suggested that this person was an important spy, a fact that could jibe with the General Staff's suspicions that a leak in high officer circles of the Army did exist. Accordingly, Ronge set a trap. In cooperation with the Chief of Police, *Polizeirat* Gayer, Ronge installed two detectives, Ebinger and Steidl, in a room some distance from the General Delivery counter but connected to it by an electric bell signal. The detectives sat in this room from eight to six daily. They sat for days and then for weeks and no one came to call for the planted letter.

But the case did not die. Early in May two more letters addressed to Nikon Nizetas arrived in Vienna. The second of these, written in German, read as follows:

May 9, 1913
Most Esteemed Herr Nizetas!

You will already have received my letter of May 7 in which I apologize for the delay in writing to you. Unfortunately it was impossible to send you the money earlier.

Herewith I am honored, sir, to enclose 7,000 crowns which I shall risk sending in this simple fashion.

With reference to your proposals, they are all acceptable.

> Most respectfully yours
> (signed) F. DIETROCH

P.S.: I ask you to write me at: c/o Frau Elise Kjernlie; Rosen-borggate Number 1; Kristiana; Norway.

Together the two letters held 14,000 crowns in notes.

Thoroughly convinced now that he was on to something big, Ronge substituted these letters for the earlier one and sat back to wait. After six weeks more of inaction, the detectives and finally *Polizeirat* Gayer began complaining. Ronge soothed them appropriately and persuaded them to keep the case open. Ronge had served in counterintelligence for six years. He had been taught that any good counterintelligence officer must practice patience, and Alfred Redl had been his teacher.

A week after the letter addressed to Nikon Nizetas arrived in Vienna, Alfred Redl received a request from a young officer serving in his old regiment, the 99th in Vienna. This officer wished to take a bath treatment in Marienbad, an installation under Eighth Corps jurisdiction, and asked Colonel Redl if he could arrange it. Alfred remembered the officer well—he was a nice young man, always neat and courteous—and he sat down and wrote him a personal card:

> General Staff Chief of the Eighth Corps   May 16, 1913
> DEAR TAUMANN: Unfortunately you have missed the deadline for applications and also you have written me too late to enable me to do anything for you. All the spaces are assigned and the recipients notified. I will hold your request on file, however, and you will be given first consideration in case someone cancels which very often happens. I hope in this way to procure you the desired place. I certainly will give my attention to it. In any event hold yourself prepared to receive a place at a later date. Eventually I shall notify you by telegram. I am sorry that I am unable to grant your request which I would have been very pleased to have done.
>
> I send you and the gentlemen of the Regiment my best greetings.
>
>> Yours affectionately
>> (signed) REDL
>> Colonel

A few days later Alfred received another letter, this one from Stefan, a letter that like the others from Stefan brought a slight pounding in his breast, a tingling in his body. He opened it slowly, sat back to savor the words. He instantly swore. Red from fury, he read it through again, stared at the words, the vile, calculated words—he did not know what to do. For Stefan, as he had threatened in the past, had now decided to leave the Army in favor of marriage. He knew this would anger his dear Fredl but now he was really, truly in love, he was going to leave the Army and marry this girl. After all, Fredl had to understand, he was twenty-four years old, scarcely young, and he did not really like the Army or he did not like it the way he loved this girl and he was going to resign and leave the Army and get married and that is all there was to say.

Later a half dozen drafts of Alfred's reply were discovered in his desk drawer. One began, "Stefan, darling," another "Dearest Stefan," and each of them showed, in the later words of Colonel Urbanski, "evidence of the severe inner conflicts in which his passion had ensnared him." Alfred finished none of these drafts. He could not find the right words to express his outrage. Didn't Stefan know the sacrifice that had been made to give him what he had, to give him a career of honor leading to fame, to offer him luxuries never dreamed of by other young officers? Women? Didn't the young fool see what they did? How they infected a man with disease, chained him to poverty, to a small flat, to screaming brats?

He wrote, crossed out, inserted . . . no, no . . . wrote again, "Stefan darling," waited until a tear cleared his clouded eye, his trembling hand quieted. Draft, cross out, new letter . . . until he crunched his cigarette, straightened his uniform, washed, locked the correspondence away and went to General von Giesl.

"I would like permission, sir, to drive to Vienna for the weekend. I . . . there is some difficulty with my nephew."

"I am sorry to hear that, Colonel."

"He . . . the young fellow wants to leave the Army. He . . . wants to get married."

"Possibly a passing fancy," the General said kindly. He chuckled. "I nearly resigned once myself. We all go through it. Go on down and talk to him. Tell him I said there is no hurry—he has his whole life."

"Exactly, sir. I would like to leave early in the morning."

"Certainly, Redl. And good luck."

Back in his office Alfred ordered the Military Secretary to put through a personal call to Stefan at Stockerau. He turned to the day's mail, noted from a report that a place had become open in Marienbad. He drafted a telegram to the young officer in Vienna informing him of this, ordered it dispatched immediately and returned to his quarters. The call came through at the noon hour. Stefan, at first obdurate, finally agreed to meet him the next afternoon in the Hotel Klomser.

"Joseph," Alfred called. "Tell the chauffeur we shall leave at six A.M. for Vienna. Yes, you fool, tomo.row."

That night he finished processing some photographs, sealed his treachery in thick envelopes and addressed them. He would mail them in Vienna.

2.

AS USUAL, Stefan entered without knocking. Alfred rose from his chair, flung the newspaper carelessly on a bed, said, "My boy . . ."

"Good trip, Fredl?"

"Fine, yes, thank you. I came—"

"Hot for May," Stefan interrupted.

"A little something cool is on the way," Alfred said. He reached for Stefan's hand, grasped it in both of his. Stefan pulled it away. "It is pleasant in here," Alfred said.

Stefan turned to the room, sniffed. "Yes, it's all right."

A porter knocked and entered with a silver tray holding a champagne bucket and two glasses. Alfred tipped him and excused him. He felt the bottle, swirled it rapidly and took it from the bucket, unwound the wire, worked the cork out and tipped the neck hurriedly to one of the glasses. He filled them both and replaced the bottle in the cold bucket. He reached for a glass. His hand jerked and it spilled. He swore silently, righted the glass and refilled it. "Here, Stefan."

Stefan took the glass and held it high. "A drink to my future," he said.

"Yes," Alfred said. He touched his glass to Stefan's. "To the General Staff, Stevie, and your admission into it."

"No," Stefan said. "No General Staff. No Army career. I am finished . . . sick of the whole business."

"That is a nice way to speak after what has been done for you. That plainly shows your gratitude to those who have helped you. Oh, yes, that is very nice."

"No one has helped me but for himself, Fredl. I have given just as much as I have got. The Army will not miss me and I will not miss the Army."

"I shall miss you, Stevie."

"I am sorry, Fredl. I have warned you many times."

"Stevie, listen to me. This little thing—this . . . girl." He almost spat the word. "What can she give you?"

Stefan laughed. "Plenty, Fredl—not that you would understand."

"This . . . girl," Alfred repeated. "Look what you have now. 900 crowns a month, a 20,000-crown automobile, a beautiful private apartment. Almost no officer in the Army lives in your fashion. When I was your age, Stevie . . . I had nothing. I have sacrificed to give you these things. Your own horses . . . diamond rings . . . beautiful clothes. I have given you those. I will give you anything I have. I have—it has not been easy . . . there are debts."

Stefan drank his champagne and lighted a cigarette. He looked bored. Alfred refilled their glasses. "Listen to me. You think this girl . . . this creature . . . can offer you anything? You know what she will offer? A small flat, poverty, hard work, screaming, demanding children. Responsibility, Stevie. Responsibility with no happiness."

Stefan said nothing. Alfred moved to him, put his hand on his arm. "Stevie," he almost whispered, "I have a little money. I was . . . well, a trip for both of us, I thought."

"No, Fredl," Stefan said, but not harshly. "I cannot live this life. I worry, I go into debt, I get into trouble. . . ."

Alfred stiffened slightly. He said more sternly, "What is it this time?"

"Well, I . . . now don't scold me, Fredl. It was a card game. I was winning and then I began losing. I thought I could win it back and I—"

"Lost!" Alfred said. He stood and faced the younger officer. "How much did you lose?" he demanded.

"Quite a lot," Stefan admitted.

Alfred lighted a cigarette, drank his champagne, refilled his own glass. "How much?"

"Almost 8,000 crowns."

Alfred sat his glass sharply on the bureau. "Eight thousand crowns? Preposterous! You stupid little fool, haven't I told you a million times not to gamble? Where do you think I can raise 8,000 crowns? Do you think the money is in the streets?" He paced the room quickly. "So there is no girl, no marriage. You wanted me to pay your gambling debts. Is that it?"

"There is too a girl. I want to pay my debts, leave the Army and marry her."

"Oh, no, my boy. Not your cake and eat it, too. Have it one way or the other. As a matter of fact, I am tempted to let you get out of this mess yourself. That little debt would mean about three years in jail!"

Stefan paled. "Would you let that happen to me, Fredl?" he asked anxiously.

Alfred rubbed a hand over his face and sat down. "No," he said tiredly, "no, not this time. But so help me God, this is the last of it. If I pay this, you stay in the Army and make something out of yourself. And no more women!"

Stefan had lowered his head into his hands. Alfred's face softened. "Stevie, why must we always have these scenes?"

Stefan gripped Alfred's hand and moved to him. Alfred stroked his hair and sighed, "I will raise the money. But, Stevie, there has to be a stop—I have a great many debts now."

"I try to be careful," Stefan said. "I drink some wine and I don't know what happens." He tightened his grip on Alfred's hand.

"You must not gamble any more." Alfred held him tighter,

kissed his ear. "I only want you to be happy, Stefan. You are all I have in the world. I only want your happiness."

Stefan pressed his body closer. "I know you do, Fredl."

I have to get the money. I shall have to go directly to the postoffice now. Alfred patted the young officer's hand. "No more girls," he said.

"No more girls, Fredl. Fredl, could you give me the money this weekend?"

I have to get the money. I shall have to pick it up myself. That means a risk. With reluctance Alfred pulled himself away and stood up. "I am meeting Doctor Pollak for dinner, Stevie. There are a few things I must take care of first. I should be back from Semmering about four tomorrow afternoon." He sat on the wide arm of the divan, his arm around Stefan. "Why not pick up the money tomorrow evening? Around six. We could have dinner." He smoothed his hands over Stefan's muscular chest. "We can have dinner here in the room."

Dressed in a gray flannel suit, Alfred Redl left the Hotel Klomser at a quarter to six that evening. He walked a block away and engaged a taxi. At five minutes to six he entered the main postoffice and strode swiftly to the General Delivery counter.

"Nikon Nizetas," he told the clerk.

"Eh?" The clerk pushed the button under the counter. "The name?"

"Nikon Nizetas. I am in a hurry."

"Yes," the clerk said. "Nizetas. Nikon Nizetas." He pressed the button hard.

"Well, what is the delay?"

"Yes, yes," the clerk said, grinding the button. "Yes, here they are." He placed two bulky letters on the counter. "Sign here."

Alfred signed, slid the letters in his pocket, turned and walked rapidly to the waiting taxi. As he closed the door of the machine the two detectives rushed into the postoffice through a side entrance. "Where is he, quick?" Ebinger demanded.

"Too late," the clerk said, pointing to the street. "I rang the—"

The detectives ran outside only to see the taxi already some distance away. Ebinger read the license number which Steidl jotted down. "What the hell do we do now?" Steidl asked.

Ebinger cursed. "All we can do—try to run down the owner of the taxi."

"We can say the bell did not ring," Steidl suggested.

"We're going to be fired in any case," Ebinger said. "Might as well make it a good story."

"Maybe the clerk can tell us something," Steidl said.

The clerk answered with that insolence gained from special knowledge. "Medium height, he was, low voice—Austrian all right. Couldn't see his face because his hat was pulled down."

Outside once more the detectives looked down the street, then looked at each other. "Christ," Steidl said, "we ought to do *something*."

"What?" Ebinger said.

"Life is sure funny," Steidl said. "We wait all this time for it to happen and when it does you're out for coffee and I'm sitting in the privy."

"Why don't you shut up?" Ebinger said.

Alfred's heart slowly stopped pounding. "Café Kaiserhof," he told the driver. He leaned back in the leather seat to open his topcoat and to pull a knife from his jacket. The knife was encased in a gray suede sheath—it was the knife Stefan had given him years earlier. He took the knife from the sheath, opened it, slit the flaps of the two envelopes addressed to Nikon Nizetas. Snapping the blade shut, he slipped the knife back in his pocket and examined the contents of the letters. He thumbed the crisp notes rapidly, smiled and thrust them in his topcoat pocket. He felt the taxi slow. He turned and leaned forward, one hand on the door.

He paid the driver quickly, waited until the taxi rumbled down the street, then walked across the square to a cab rank. He climbed in the first machine and said, "Hotel Klomser." When the taxi started forward he looked through the back window, saw no one following and, for the second time, smiled. *It is very easy*, he thought.

As the detectives stood helplessly in front of the postoffice, a taxi labored up the street toward them.

"Quick," Ebinger ordered, "flag him."

The two detectives then made a discovery more appropriate to fiction than to real life: *The taxi was the same one that a short time before had carried off the man they were after.*

Both men ran to the taxi. Ebinger flashed his credentials. "Special Police," he said, "where did you take your last passenger?"

"Café Kaiserhof," the driver said, "but—"

"Fast," Ebinger commanded, "Café Kaiserhof."

Automatically the detectives began to search the back seat. "Hello," Steidl said, "what's this?" Between his thumb and forefinger he held a gray suede knife sheath.

Ebinger briefly examined it. Greatly excited he said, "If we can find the man with the knife . . ." his voice trailed off. Then he said, "He sat there, Steidl, where you are and took his knife to open the letters. He was nervous—he closed his knife, forgot the sheath. This is a piece of luck." Ebinger put the sheath carefully in his pocket.

No, the head waiter in the Café Kaiserhof had seen no one answering the description within the last half an hour.

But outside by the cab rank a very old man was important. He flicked a feather duster against a smoothly lacquered taxi and he told the detectives, "*Ja, ja,* such a man arrived here thirty minutes ago. Took *Herr Chauffeur* Blumbaum's taxi. Where did he go? Why, to the Hotel Klomscr."

"Special Police," Ebinger told the concierge of the Hotel Klomser. "Who has arrived in this hotel within the last forty-five minutes?"

The concierge examined the proffered credentials and scowled as if he were disappointed to find them genuine. "*Na, ja,* gentlemen. There is the salesman from Budapest, Herr Felsen, the two ladies, *Frau Präsident* Kleinemann and *Frau Direktor Doktor* Lüchow, there is *Herr Professor* Zank and our new guest, *Herr Doktor* Widener. Oh yes, there is, too, our old guest, *Herr Oberst* Redl."

"*Herr Oberst* Redl," Ebinger said.

"*Ja*, the famous *Herr Oberst* Redl," the clerk said proudly. "He stays with us always when he comes to Vienna. There is no finer gentle—"

"Ebinger," Steidl said quietly, "why don't we consult the *Herr Oberst?* There is nothing he does not know about such a matter."

Ebinger bit his lip. "Our orders were to tell no one. On the other hand . . ." His fingers interrupted his sentence by feeling the suede sheath in his pocket. He pulled it out and handed it to the clerk. "As your guests come down, ask them if they have lost this *füttertal*."

"Very good," the clerk said.

The detectives retreated to a small bench in the lobby from where they could easily watch the desk.

In his room Alfred counted the money a second time, much more slowly, his fingers tracing each crisp surface. He counted it twice. 14,000 crowns. He examined the envelopes, noted from the postmarks that more money should soon be delivered. Then he crumpled the envelopes and burned them in an ash tray. When the glow faded he crushed the ashes, opened a window and fed them to the breeze. He went to his suitcase, pressed a button. The top opened out to reveal a small hiding place which now received the crisp notes.

Alfred undressed, washed and put on his General Staff uniform. He dressed carefully, flicked some dust from his polished boots, smoothed and waxed his mustache and left the room. It was a quarter to seven.

He walked casually down the hotel corridor, down the winding balustrade. Crossing to the desk, he placed the heavy key on the counter and smiled at the clerk.

"Oh, good evening, *Herr Oberst*," the clerk said. The clerk did not see the negative shake of Ebinger's head. "Pardon me, *Herr Oberst*," the clerk asked, "would this *füttertal* belong to the *Herr Oberst* by any chance?"

"Why, yes," Alfred said, "I was wondering where I had . . ."

He felt the unconscious force of four eyes drilling his back. He turned quickly, instantly recognized the source for what it was. At that moment he knew he was caught, but like anyone beginning a reflex action he had to finish a reflex action and so he said, ". . . misplaced it." He took the sheath and stuffed it into his pocket and without a further glance at the enemy and with a perfectly straight, normal face he slowly turned from the desk, walked through the entrance and joined the busy hurrying street of evening.

Down Strauchgasse he walked and before a large glass window full of hats he paused and he saw the detectives coming after him. He did not know that Steidl had called *Polizeirat* Gayer and had said, "This is Steidl. The gentleman in question is Colonel of the General Staff Redl. Yes, sir: Redl. Everything is in order." But he did know that he was caught, that he had been caught most stupidly and that he had to have time to think.

At the corner of Strauchgasse, Alfred turned to the Freyung Passage which offered him a choice of three exits. Once in the Passage he groped in his inner tunic pocket, found some papers, tore them savagely and flung them to the air.

"Pick up the papers and report at once with them to the *Polizeirat*," Ebinger told Steidl. "I will stay with him."

At the end of the Freyung, Alfred hesitated, then chose Tiefen Graben. He turned to see Ebinger behind him. Their eyes briefly met. Ebinger smiled.

I must think. I have to think. I am walking down Tiefen Graben in Vienna on the evening of May 24th in the year 1913. I am a colonel of the General Staff Corps and I am heavily decorated, widely respected and certainly above reproach. I am, but for that man behind me. The end for me is very near unless I can think well. For some reason I do not seem able to think very well and now I must force myself to think well. Now I am on Heinrichs Gasse going to the canal. It is the evening of May 24th and it is twenty-two minutes past seven o'clock and where am I going? I should be going to Prague because it is in Prague that my apartment is located and in that apartment are a great many incriminating papers. From Prague—could I get over the border? I could try. I must get to Prague. I should be going to Prague. Instead I am going to dinner with Viktor Pollak.

Alfred reached the end of Heinrichs Gasse. He stared a moment at the dirty water of the Danube Canal, then turned left along the wide Franz Josef-Kai.

Viktor Pollak is a friend of mine. What could Viktor Pollak do for me? I must lose this detective who is following me. Where is his partner? Yes, the papers. He will turn those in. I must hurry. Viktor Pollak. How can he help me? The one with the papers will report to Gayer. Viktor knows Gayer. Now what could he do? I must think. But I must hurry.

Alfred turned up the Ringstrasse. He looked behind him. Ebinger was there. Alfred flagged a taxi, climbed in and told the driver the address. Ebinger was close behind him. Ebinger noted the number of the taxi, heard the address Alfred had given. He was calm. He waited a minute or two for another taxi.

Polizeirat Gayer was pacing his office when Steidl arrived. "Redl," he said, breathing hard. "He threw away these papers in the Freyung Passage. Ebinger stayed on his tail." Carefully he put the scraps of paper on his Chief's desk.

"Good work," Gayer said. He picked up the telephone. "Get me Major Ronge. Immediately." He turned to the scraps and with Steidl's aid began fitting them together. A buzzer sounded and he picked up the phone. "This is Gayer, *Herr Major*. The pickup has been made and the person identified." Gayer paused, then said: "Colonel Redl. Yes, that is correct—Redl. Almost no doubt. I think you should come here, but I wish you would stop by the postoffice to pick up the receipt he signed. Fine."

The two men worked at the jigsaw madness without talking. The buzzer sounded. "Gayer here," he said, picking up the phone.

"Ebinger, sir. I am at the Restaurant Riedhof in Josefstadt. The subject is dining with *Generaladvokat Doktor* Pollak. They are sitting at an alcove table. I have them under surveillance. Subject is talking rapidly and nervously."

"Stay with them. Steidl will report to you with further instructions." Gayer hung up, spoke briefly to Steidl who left immediately. Gayer was working on the papers when Major Ronge was shown in. Without formality Ronge placed the postoffice receipt showing the signature "Nikon Nizetas" on the desk. "I would know the handwriting anywhere," he said. "His all right."

Gayer told him to sit down and then shoved some pasted scraps toward him. One was a money order receipt for nine hundred crowns payable to First Lieutenant Stefan Hromodka. The other was a registered letter receipt. Ronge tapped the latter. "The cover address of Doctor Katz—Batjuschin's best operative."

Gayer nodded. "There," he said and handed two more papers to Ronge. Ronge looked at them, whistled through his teeth. They were receipts for registered mail sent to other Russian cover addresses. Gayer took a bottle of brandy from his desk, filled two glasses and gave one to Ronge.

"Thank you," Ronge said. "I . . . it is awful." Ronge drank quickly and said, "I must call Colonel Urbanski at once."

Gayer ordered the call. When the buzzer sounded, Ronge lifted the telephone. "Good evening, sir. Ronge here. We have the man." Ronge's jaw muscles knotted to force the single word from his lips. "Hello, sir—are you there? No, sir, there is no doubt at all. Right, sir. Grand Hotel in fifteen minutes." He hung up and turned to Gayer. "The Chief is at the Grand Hotel. I am going to meet Colonel Urbanski there. The Colonel wonders if you would stand by here. He wants Redl back in his hotel after he finishes dinner—if necessary, by force."

Ronge took his hat and walked slowly to the office door. When he closed it behind him, he was a much older man.

Viktor Pollak was hungry. He was glad when he saw the uniformed figure of his friend enter the restaurant, the familiar face search the room to light on his table. He put down his *apéritif* and stood to welcome him. He saw instantly that something was wrong.

"No, no," Alfred brusquely refused the offer of a drink. He sat down. "I must talk to you, Viktor. I am in the most terrible difficulties. They are after me, you see."

Viktor looked into his friend's eyes and said gently, "Who are after you, Alfred?"

"They are all after me, everybody."

"You look tired, Alfred. Perhaps if we eat at once . . ."

"I am tired. Yes, let us have dinner. I am very tired and I think your idea is excellent. Perhaps dinner . . ."

A waiter took their order. They sat silently until thick soup was ladled from a silver tureen and placed before them.

"Every man sins," Alfred suddenly said. "There are many ways to sin."

For the love of God, Viktor thought, *what is wrong?*

"Every man sins in one way or the other. When you think about it, what are morals really? It is a matter of degree, that is all. It is all a matter of degree."

"Eat some soup," Doctor Pollak said.

Alfred raised a spoonful of soup to his mouth, then abruptly lowered it. "Certainly I have sinned," he said. "Every man sins. I have sinned because I am a human being like the rest. You did not know, did you," he said almost proudly, "that I am infected with syphilis?"

"Alfred, really," Pollak protested.

"Oh, yes, I am," Alfred said. "She was a circus rider in Lemberg and I was in love with her. After that I hated and I sinned because every man does. It is a matter of degree, that is all."

"Do try to eat something, Alfred," his friend said nervously.

Alfred placed his spoon in the soup and stirred vigorously. He left it there to grip the table with both hands and Pollak watched the candle gleam on his manicured nails and wondered what he should do. Alfred stared in the face of his friend and said, "You think I come from a good family, Viktor? Well, I do not. I come from nothing, absolutely nothing, Viktor. And when a man comes from nothing and is something . . . why, then, he must have sinned."

"Alfred, stop it. You are tired. I have told you many times, you cannot work on and on like—"

"Viktor, listen to me. I met this man. He knew about me. He caused me to . . . Viktor, that inheritance. There is no inheritance. Well, did you hear me? Why don't you—"

"Alfred! Sit down! I am your friend, Viktor Pollak."

Alfred sank back in his chair and looked at his friend. He lowered his eyes to the small whirlpools he was making in the soup. "I do not feel very well, Viktor. I am most awfully, enormously guilty. Viktor, please help me. Will you help me?" He bent over the table to plead, "Will you get me a pistol?"

"I want to take you to a friend of mine," Viktor said. "A doctor. He will help you."

"Listen to me, Viktor. There is a doctor in Prague who has a sanitarium. I am under his treatment. I want to see him. Tonight! Listen, I have an excellent idea. You tell them that I am ill and must be rushed to Prague. They will listen to you. They will send someone with me."

"Who are 'they,' Alfred?"

Alfred scowled at his friend's stupidity. "The police, of course. I am in trouble with the police. *Polizeirat* Gayer, Viktor—your friend. He will believe you. Telephone him."

"There is no need for that," Pollak said patiently. "I can go with you to Prague, Alfred. We can leave right away."

"Quite impossible, Viktor. You do not believe me. Look there in the foyer where I am pointing. See him? Dark suit, heavy, balding—he is a detective . . . he is trailing me."

Viktor saw the man. He pushed back his chair and stood up. "You stay here, Alfred. I shall get to the bottom of this."

As Viktor walked past Ebinger to the telephone, the detective pretended not to notice him. "Hello," Viktor said, "*Polizeirat* Gayer? Viktor Pollak is speaking. I am . . ."

". . . at the Restaurant Riedhof dining with Colonel Redl."

"Why, yes, how do you know this?"

"What is it you wish, *Herr Generaladvokat*?"

"Colonel Redl is very upset, *Herr Polizeirat*. In my opinion he is suffering a nervous breakdown. He has delusions of persecution, says one of your men is following him. He . . . has been speaking strangely . . . has asked me for a revolver. I have persuaded him . . . he is willing to go under medical care . . . I want to . . ."

"There is nothing to be done tonight," Gayer said abruptly. "I want you to get him back to the Hotel Klomser as soon as possible."

"But what is—"

"I am sorry, *Herr Doktor*. I can not explain. But nothing can be done tonight. Everything will be arranged in the morn-

251

ing." Some of the harsh quality left the voice. "It is a very serious situation. I most strongly urge you to do as I say."

"Is there no way I can help him?"

"The best way is by seeing him to the Hotel Klomser. Good night, *Herr Doktor*."

Pollak returned to the table. Alfred stared dully at him. "Nothing can be done tonight, Alfred." He tried to make his voice easy. "I really think the best thing for you is a good sleep. You will feel much better in the morning."

They finished the meal in silence. Despite Viktor's protests Alfred paid the bill. At his suggestion they walked back to the Hotel Klomser. The large clock in Parliament Tower showed half past eleven as they reached the door. Viktor shook his friend's hand. "You will feel better in the morning, Alfred. Good night."

Alfred held the hand a moment too long. Then he dropped it as though it hurt him. "Good-bye, Viktor," he said.

Major Ronge met Colonel Urbanski at the entrance to the Grand Hotel on Ringstrasse. Off in a corner he briefed him quickly on the developments. Urbanski asked several questions, then said, "Come on." They walked into the palatial lobby and through it to a dining room of chandeliers and shining crystal and white linen and soft silver and the gypsy band of Rigo, and they walked over the soft carpet to the prosperous, happy table of General Conrad von Hötzendorf, Chief of the General Staff.

"Pardon me, sir," Colonel Urbanski said, touching the General's elbow.

"Well, what . . . Urbanski, Ronge!" The General arose. "Do sit down for a—" He noticed the tight set of Urbanski's mouth.

"I must speak to you privately, sir," Urbanski said.

"Of course," Conrad said. He excused himself from the two ladies dining with him and led his officers to a small alcove room.

"You will pardon me, sir," Colonel Urbanski said, "but you had better sit down. The man we have been waiting for picked up the letters at four minutes to six this evening. The man was

252

followed and his guilt has been established almost beyond question."

"Good, excellent," Conrad said. "Who is he?"

Urbanski wet his lips. "Alfred Redl."

"Redl," Conrad gasped.

Urbanski hurriedly briefed him. When he finished he clicked his heels together, stood at attention and said, "I await your further orders, sir."

"This is completely fantastic," Conrad whispered. With hands clasped behind his back, he began pacing the room. "Our enemies will greatly relish this," he said aloud. "They will enjoy this very much indeed. They will say, 'We told you about the *flaschen-grünen* corps. Elite corps, indeed. Traitors right within this elite corps.' Our German allies will appreciate this. The world, the entire world, will eat this crumb with great delight. They say we are rotten, the Empire is dying, our Army unworthy. Now they will say, even a General Staff officer, Chief of Counterintelligence, deputy in the Intelligence Bureau, General Staff Chief of our most important corps, even he sold out. Oh, yes, this places us in a grand position."

"Sir—" Ronge started to say.

"Don't interrupt me," Conrad said. "The situation is terrible. This will mean a shock to our Army that it cannot stand. Now, what is there to do? Don't interrupt me. I am thinking aloud. Redl. I have given him everything. *Gottverdammtes Schweinhund!*" He suddenly wheeled to face Urbanski and Ronge. "There is one way," he said. "If we can keep it a secret, we can spare our Empire, our Army, this indignity. Who knows about this to date?"

"Gayer, of course," Urbanski said. "Two detectives. Doctor Pollak knows something. I, of course, and Major Ronge."

"All right. These people will be sworn to blood secrecy. Then form an arrest commission—my deputy, General Höfer, will head it, pick up a legal officer, you and Ronge complete it. You will go to the Hotel Klomser and arrest Redl. Interrogate him to discover the extent of his treachery and his accomplices. He will then die. Do you understand?"

"Yes, sir," Urbanski said.

"After he is dead you will report to me in person. Is that clear?"

"Yes, sir," Urbanski said.

"Very well, that is all."

Conrad von Hötzendorf watched the two officers leave. He lighted a cigarette, forced his hand to stop trembling. Walking slowly across the soft carpet toward his table, he was able to twist his face into a smile.

3.

ON THE surface nothing looked amiss.

Alfred turned from Doctor Pollak, crossed the small lobby of the Hotel Klomser, asked for his key at the porter's desk. "Call me at eight," he told the porter.

He walked up the stairs and down the corridor to Room Number One, inserted his key in the door, opened it, flicked the light switch. Just as if he had been out for an evening, just as if he were now back for a night's sleep.

Once inside the room, however, his straight body sagged, his fingers groped to unhook the choke collar of his tunic. More carefully he worked with the tight buttons on its front. He flung it on the bed. *"Mein Gott,"* he said aloud, "what went wrong?"

His eye fell on the champagne bucket and the two glasses.

That was a mistake. I should never have gone to the postoffice.

He pulled the small gray suede sheath from his pocket, found the knife in his other jacket and replaced it.

I should never have opened the letters in the taxi. I should never have used this knife. I should never have received this knife, never have helped Stefan in the first place.

He lighted a cigarette and sat in a chair to think about Stefan and their first meeting. Then he thought about Arthur Schnitzel, his cadet friend, Hans, other men he had loved, about his childhood in Lemberg and the poverty and hand-me-down clothes and cabbage soup, he saw his father with a pipe hanging from his mouth and saliva bubbling from one corner of it, the filthy railroad uniform, heard him quarreling with his sagging, hand-wringing, bleating, pious wife. He pulled up faces and pulled out names he thought forgotten. He remembered Maria's beautiful body lying in the sun bed of that afternoon and felt almost at once the crushing pain of silver nitrate and the soft kneading hands of Arthur. He remembered the War College examinations, the promotions and decorations and compliments, the espionage trials where each word of his was listened to, respected, accepted. He interrupted his race of years by clearing his throat and saying, "Good God Almighty, what *did* go wrong?"

Fear closed in. He rose from the chair.

They will be coming soon. Conrad will have learned by now. An arrest commission.

"The thing is," he said aloud, "I must die. But I must take first things first." His forehead wrinkled, he sat at the small desk to write two letters. He wrote one to General von Giesl, one to his brother Heinrich. In each he explained that he had been a victim of life, a pawn that fate had moved to play an ugly game. He signed the letters, sealed the envelopes, wrote twelve o'clock midnight on each envelope.

Well, they have forced me to die. They will come here to stand supreme, to judge me in the eyes of their own righteousness. They are men, men must judge. Very well. I shall thwart them. I will die now.

He took the knife that Stefan had given him, removed the sheath that had betrayed him, opened the blade that would save him. He sat in the large chair that faced the wardrobe mirror. He clenched the knife in his right hand and held it before him.

One clean plunge and it will be over. The blade? Is it long enough to reach the heart? The heart. Where exactly is the heart?

The knife fell to the floor. "To miss," he said aloud, "would

255

be terrible. It would hurt me terribly. It would mean hospital, prison."

"There is more than one way to skin a cat," he said next. He stooped, picked up the knife and cut a long piece from the pull cord of the window drapery. Dragging a chair to the window, he stood on it, tied the cord to a wall fixture, tied its other end around his neck. He kicked the chair from beneath him. The fixture ripped away, he fell heavily to the floor. He loosened the cord that hurt his neck and rubbed his hip. Tears came to his eyes.

The quarter hour signal of the clock in Parliament Tower sounded. Alfred checked his own watch against it, set it up a minute to make things right. "They will be coming soon," he said. Ronge, he knew, would be among them, undoubtedly Urbanski; there would be a legal officer.

He stood up, went to the washbasin, washed his red eyes and damp forehead, brushed his close blond hair, cut a stray whisker from his mustache. He put on a silk dressing gown.

It will be my only chance. If I tell them too much, they will hold me. If I tell them too little, they will hold me. I must play this one well. I must win this one. I shall let them kill me.

He smiled at the thought. He began to want them to arrive.

At twelve thirty a knock sounded on his door. Alfred opened it, stepped back to let the four officers in. He stood nearly at attention and he said, "I know why you have come. I am guilty. I want only to judge myself." Less formally he said, "I would like to speak to Major Ronge alone."

General von Höfer nodded to Urbanski and Vorlicek and the three officers left the room. Alfred sank to a chair. "It is all true, Ronge," he said. "Ronge, I do not know how it started but it is all true." He turned his haggard, lined face to the eyes of the other officer. "I am sick, Ronge. For the love of God, help me."

"What do you want?" Major Ronge asked.

"A weapon. Get me a pistol." When Ronge made no reply, Alfred implored, "Get me a pistol. Please get me a pistol." He fell forward to his knees. "Please dear God, get this for me."

Ronge went to the other three officers waiting outside. After a brief discussion, General Höfer agreed to the request. He then discovered no one had brought along a pistol and he sent Ronge to fetch one. Upon Ronge's return, the officers again entered Redl's room. Redl was sitting in a chair facing them. He did not stand.

"For whom have you worked, Redl?" Colonel Urbanski began.

"Russia," was the reply. "Not a long time, though. I . . . those terrible debts . . . I . . . about a year ago . . ."

"Who are your accomplices?"

Alfred shook his head. "I have none," he said tiredly. "Only a fool would use accomplices." He liked that—thought it had just the right tone. To his own surprise he heard himself adding, "Lieutenant Hromodka—my nephew—he was here this afternoon with me—he has nothing at all to do with my—my activities."

Each of the four officers scribbled notes as Redl talked.

"What have you betrayed?" Urbanski demanded.

"Not very much," Alfred said. He dug a thumb and forefinger in his eyes. "A General Staff manual, it was restricted, an Order of Battle, some supplements . . ." His voice trailed off.

"And?" Urbanski prompted.

"And the Eighth Corps mobilization plan—no, I am not sure. I remember photographing it . . . but did I . . ." He crushed his head in his hands. "My desk in Prague . . . you will find everything in my desk in Prague."

Urbanski looked at Von Höfer who nodded. Alfred lowered his hands from his head, saliva flecked the corners of his mouth. "Let me alone to die," he begged.

Von Höfer nudged Ronge. "The pistol," he muttered. Ronge placed the pistol on the desk beside the letters of farewell. The officers filed from the room.

Alfred looked up when he heard the door click. Staring at the pistol, he said aloud, "Thank God." For a moment he remained motionless. He had won again and he wondered why he felt no jubilation. He stood up, lifted the small pistol from the desk and hefted it. "I must die soon," he said aloud. He laid the pistol down, its muzzle pointing away from him.

He wondered what it was that kicked in his mind and in an effort to discover what it was he sat down again and pressed his hands tightly to his head. His knees, he noticed, were trembling and he closed them together. Suddenly he tensed. His hands came from his head and he looked down at the shiny points of his boots and in a voice of great surprise he said, "Of course that is it. I *am* guilty."

Alfred Redl stood up to proclaim his discovery to four walls and a room full of smoke. "I *am* guilty," he repeated. This was very good; this settled the stomach and stilled the mind and the emotion of joy brought a tremble to his hands and he all but burst with the thought of his own guilt.

Why, I have been guilty for a very long time. I have been guilty for years and years and years. Now why have I never told a priest of this?

He would liked to have had a priest at this moment but he knew that the four officers in the street below would not permit him a priest. Instead he went to his desk, took a piece of paper and began writing.

The four officers loitered self-consciously on Herrengasse. Now and then one would glance at the peep of light showing from the front windows of Room Number One. "I wish he would hurry up," Ronge said.

"Yes," General Höfer said, "we stick out here like sore thumbs."

"Perhaps we should change to civilian clothes," Colonel Urbanski said.

"A very good idea," the General said. "Colonel, you and Vorlicek go home now and change. When you return, Ronge and I can go."

Colonel Urbanski took a taxi to his home. While he changed clothing, he told his wife of the horrible events. When he returned with Vorlicek the other two officers left. By four A.M. the officers were dressed in mufti. Now and again two of them went to the corner café for coffee.

Alfred was satisfied with what he had written. It was his last will and testament and his confession and he read it aloud: "Passion and levity have destroyed me. Pray for me. I repent my sins by my death." He signed this simply, "Alfred." He liked it very much, read it through again, looked at his watch and underneath his signature wrote, "It is one forty-five. I shall now die. I ask there be no inquest held on my body. Pray for me."

He read the entire document aloud, propped it on the desk with the two sealed letters, repeated its message while dragging the divan in front of the wardrobe mirror. He took the pistol in his right hand, stood before the mirror and stared at himself. "Passion and levity have destroyed me," he said.

He put the small muzzle of the pistol inside his mouth until the cold metal pressed against the bone of its roof. He pulled the trigger. The body slumped awkwardly, missed the couch and fell to the floor. The right hand relaxed, the pistol slipped to the carpet. In the small room nothing moved except blood that trickled from the left nostril. Alfred Redl was dead.

At four thirty-three A.M. a jangling telephone awakened the night clerk in the lobby of the Hotel Klomser. "*Na, ja,* what then?" the clerk sleepily answered.

"This is Army Headquarters in Vienna. The Commanding General wishes to speak to Colonel Alfred Redl. Urgent business."

"I must call him," the clerk said. "Hold on."

Muttering to himself the clerk slowly climbed the stairs, walked to Room Number One. He knocked lightly on the door. He knocked again and a third time before he timidly turned the knob and pressed the door open. The room was still lighted. He saw the body at once, recoiled, then saw the blood. "*Mein lieber Gott,*" he said, "the *Herr Oberst* is dead."

He ran downstairs to the phone. "Hello, hello," he shouted. "The Colonel is dead."

A steady hum answered his words. He blinked, realized that no one was on the other end. He pressed the cradle, then called the police.

Epilogue

1.

THE police notified Army Headquarters. Early Sunday morning the Commanding General of Second Army Corps in Vienna sent a hastily composed investigating commission to the hotel. Doctors Tauss and Schild studied the corpse, the wound and the room to conclude that Colonel Redl had stood before the mirror, shot himself through the mouth with the bullet passing through the roof of the palate and plunging deep from right to left in the brain to end in the left skull crown. Colonel Redl's effects were sequestered and sealed and the body sent to Army Hospital Number One in Vienna for routine autopsy. The examination required only a few hours; at ten minutes to eleven on Sunday morning Second Corps telegraphed the Military Chancellery of the Emperor:

> Colonel of the General Staff Corps Alfred Redl, General Staff Chief of the Eighth Corps, has this night killed himself in Hotel Klomser for reasons up to now unknown. Letters left behind.

Later in the day the Military Chancellery of the Heir Presumptive telegraphed similarly to the Archduke at Castle Konopischt and to Colonel Bardolff on holiday in Styria.

Simultaneously a more secret action took place. When General Conrad learned from the arrest commission that Redl was dead, he ordered Urbanski and Vorlicek to Prague for an investigation of Redl's apartment. These officers took the nine o'clock train from Vienna, lunched with Baron von Giesl and turned at once to the task. Because Redl's apartment was locked, Von Giesl sent for a local locksmith. This man, Wagner, was reluctant to accompany the officer sent to fetch him. But the military was a powerful instrument and Wagner in the end, albeit complainingly, went with the officer.

Years later Colonel Urbanski wrote that "the apartment was

two rooms whose furnishings to be sure had a light feminine touch. . . ." In fact, he told his wife shortly after the investigation that the minute he walked into the apartment he knew the truth because of the very strong odor of perfume and the feminine and outrageous furnishings. And in a later official report he noted that the entire apartment was "peculiarly sickeningly sweet, [a] disgusting impression."

The apartment was jammed with evidence of Colonel Redl's guilt. As Wagner's skill unlocked each drawer of the desk, the cabinets and closets, Urbanski and Vorlicek soon realized that Redl had "confessed" precious little the previous night. Not only did the drawers disclose Redl's hitherto unknown perversion, but they also proved treachery on a far higher plane than the relatively minor work admitted by Redl. Further, "a search of the desk in Redl's office produced a service manual of provisioning instructions; this, as well as a few of the documents found in the iron safe, showed wood impressions of the sort originating from clamps [of a photographic stand]."

When Colonel Urbanski returned to Vienna that night he took with him two large suitcases filled chiefly with "documents and photographic films, besides first drafts of letters whose content showed an unnatural spirit of the writer, likewise a collection of obscene pictures which were also sequestered." Major Ronge later wrote that "Colonel Urbanski returned with enough material from Redl's apartment to fill a room—the books and papers were saturated with perfume." (Some years later Ronge was forced to leave a crowded tram when he smelled the same perfume.) This did not complete the investigation, for which purpose Wenzel Vorlicek stayed on in Prague.

The general public learned of the suicide in the Monday morning edition of the *Neue Freie Presse*. Tucked as it was between two ordinary accidents in an inner column, "Day's Events," it did not look very important:

> Suicide of a General Staff officer. Severe nervous tension yesterday drove a highly placed General Staff officer to his death. He is Colonel Adolf [sic] Redl, General Staff Chief of the Eighth Army Corps in Prague. On Saturday night in a Vienna hotel he shot himself in the mouth. Colonel Redl had worked devotedly . . .

In view of the coverage given to the mounting tension between Serbia and Bulgaria, the acrimonious budget debates in Parliament and the description of nobility present in Berlin for the wedding of Kaiser Wilhelm's daughter to the Duke of Cumberland, it is probable that many a reader missed the brief announcement entirely. The evening edition of the same newspaper, however, carried the story under a separate heading:

> Vienna, May 26. One of the most excellent and best-known officers in the General Staff, Colonel Alfred Redl, General Staff Chief of the Eighth Corps in Prague, committed suicide Sunday night in a hotel in the inner city. The highly gifted officer, who was on the verge of a great career, killed himself by a shot in the mouth, an act prompted, it is believed, by mental overexertion resulting from severe neurasthenia. Colonel Redl, who served for a long time in a military capacity in Vienna, and who was equally popular in civil and military circles, had only arrived from Prague on Saturday night and taken quarters in the hotel. . . .

On the same day the Army announced that Colonel Redl would be buried with full military honors, a statement that sent shivers of anticipation to the populace whose love of ceremony, particularly where death was concerned, was as great then as it is today. The burial battalion of the Vienna Command was alerted and while it shined instruments and practiced drill, various civil and military organizations submerged local florists with orders for fancy wreaths. This would be a fine funeral— not as magnificent, of course, as one of the Habsburgs': "Will you ever forget Archduke Otto's funeral in 1906? Such a beautiful corpse . . ." but a substantial one none the less with miles of black bunting, several intoning priests, a squadron at least of resplendent cavalry, muffled drums and solemn salvos over the open grave.

But now a tuft of rumor appeared in the pacific sky painted by officialdom. It probably started with Redl's servant, Joseph, who indignantly told a reporter that the pistol found in the room was not Redl's, that therefore Colonel Redl must have been murdered. Although the police quickly frightened Joseph into silence, the damage had been done: word started around that "something was wrong." The word was enlarged by the hotel clerk. He was also silenced but only after he had told more people of the strange happenings in the Hotel Klomser that evening and night.

Another tuft of rumor sprang from the discrepancy inherent in the announcement of Redl's insanity. A young officer in Redl's old regiment, the 99th, asked how Redl could have been crazy when a day earlier he so thoughtfully and efficiently wired this officer that the place in Marienbad would open in July and was reserved for him. He told a few of his comrades about this, showed the telegram Redl had sent him. A few more people talking—the rumor began to snowball. Then, too, reporters interviewed Redl's chauffeur before the police got to him and the chauffeur said that Redl was no more crazy, no more tired, than anyone else. Up in Prague the officers of Eighth Corps thought exactly the same—they had talked to and worked with Redl a day earlier. General von Giesl, himself, spoke to Colonel Urbanski of Redl's "usual easy attitude" that day—"one could not notice in him the slightest sign of any abnormality or depression." Both Francis Ferdinand and his aide, Colonel Bardolff, had reason to join this queue of disbelief. They had been in direct communication with the victim for some months; in April, Redl had sent Bardolff a lengthy and brilliant analysis of an article on the Montenegrin Army that had been proposed for dedication to the Emperor; again, on May 7th Redl had forwarded an anti-Habsburg article taken from a confiscated Prague newspaper along with relevant and confidential background material on its author. Hardly the acts of an insane man.

Other isolated suspicions developed that kept the rumor alive and added to its burgeonings. "Why," some asked, "if Redl's suicide is on the up-and-up, doesn't the *Military Review* make mention of it? And what is the reason for Baron von Giesl's sudden appearance in Vienna?" Others wanted to know: "If Redl were not insane, why did he commit suicide?" And a young cavalry officer in Stockerau, Stefan Hromodka, asked himself, "Did he do it because of me?" Whereupon, to gain an answer, he wrote a special-delivery note to Heinrich Redl, Alfred's respectable civil-servant brother, saying it was urgent they meet. Stefan subsequently told Heinrich of their quarrel.

Even while Stefan was talking to Heinrich, an order for his arrest had gone out from Second Corps on grounds of incriminating evidence found in Prague. Captain Gilnreiner, Stefan's squadron commander, was enjoying a set of tennis at Stockerau with his wife and another couple when he was suddenly summoned to Regimental Headquarters. He returned to the court, his handsome face pale and serious. Without a word he picked up his racket, bowed and excused himself. After the game his wife returned to their quarters and was informed by a servant that the captain had left for Vienna. Later she learned that he had been ordered to arrest Stefan.

Taken singly, none of these incidents amounted to much yet each served the easy cause of rumor. In a surprisingly short time the air of Vienna resembled that so well captured in Sir George Aston's quoted rhyme about 1917 London:

> Absolute evidence have I none,
> But my aunt's charwoman's sister's son
> Heard a policeman on his beat
> Say to a housemaid in *Downing Street*
> That he had an uncle who had a friend
> Who knew *for a fact* when the war would end.

But rumormongering is a normal expression of psychological behavior in time of stress. Usually it dies away or, if continued, does not necessarily harm the concerned subject or institution. And this probably would have been the case now except for one of those incredible coincidences that God seems to arrange to protect the general public from the machinations of its officials.

Wagner, the Prague locksmith hurriedly summoned to open Redl's apartment, had shown reluctance because he was a star halfback on the football team D.B.C. Sturm I which was scheduled that Sunday afternoon to play a very important game against the rival club SK Union-Holleschowitz. The team captain of Sturm, Egon Erwin Kisch, was also a reporter for both a Berlin and a Prague newspaper, a young man of outstanding intelligence and journalistic ability. When his star player failed to show for the game, Kisch became understandably furious and when Sturm lost to Union by seven-five his fury grew. He was still burning the next day when a disconsolate Wagner appeared in his office. Kisch later described the scene:

> "I have come to tell you that I couldn't make it yesterday."
> "So I noticed. Get out!"
> "It was really impossible. I had—"
> "It is all the same to me, what you had to do," I interrupted him.
> "I was all dressed when a soldier came to our shop and said that one of us must come to corps headquarters to open a lock."
> "Don't give me that! So it took five minutes. And we waited an entire hour before the kickoff."
> "It took three hours. I had to break into an apartment and then into all the drawers and closets. Two gentlemen from Vienna were there, one they called 'Colonel.' They were looking for Russian documents and photographs of plans."
> "Whose apartment was it?"
> "I think it belonged to a general. A large apartment on the first floor."
> "And the general was not there?"
> "The one the apartment belonged to? No, he wasn't there. But the Corps Commander was."

Although I was captain of a football club which had yesterday lost a game through the disloyalty of this halfback, I now forgot my anger with him. Instead of "Don't give me that," I let him tell me exactly what had happened yesterday afternoon, how the colonel from Vienna had handed photographs of plans and documents to the Corps Commander and how each time the latter shook his head and said, "Terrible, terrible! Who would have thought this possible!" Wagner said that the apartment was remarkable, "like that of a woman," with actual toilet articles and curling irons and perfumed letters and pictures of young men.

> "How do you know that both officers were from Vienna?"
> "They said they had to return to Vienna that evening. They thought I did not understand German. Whenever they wanted a lock opened the Corps Commander translated to me in Czech."

It could only have been the apartment of Colonel Alfred Redl, General Staff Chief of the Prague Corps, about whom the official Telegraph-Press Agency had today released a report. . . .

The reporter Kisch at once took the scoop to his chief editor. Together they worked out a plan—had the story been written straight, the edition containing it would have been confiscated. Instead, Kisch sent off the straight story to his Berlin newspaper while his Prague paper, *Bohemia,* published the following:

> We have been requested by official sources to deny the rumor particularly current in military circles that the General Staff Chief of the Prague Corps, Colonel Alfred Redl, who the day before yesterday committed suicide in Vienna, has betrayed military secrets and has spied for Russia. The Commission sent from Vienna to Prague which was accompanied by a colonel and which on the previous Sunday afternoon in the presence of the Corps Commander, Baron Giesl, broke open the apartment and the drawers and closets of Colonel Redl and undertook a three-hour search, was investigating discrepancies of quite another nature. . . .

Prague authorities, believing that Vienna officials had released this information, failed to confiscate the appropriate edition of *Bohemia,* with the result that the story was picked up by Vienna and provincial newspapers. To a citizenry inured to "reverse news" the words could read into one meaning only. There arose a public clamor too powerful to be denied. On Thursday, May 29, an official statement was published in the evening edition of the quasi-official *Military Review:*

> The existence of Colonel Redl has ended through suicide. Redl committed this act as he was about to be accused beyond any doubt of the following severe misdeeds:
> 1. Homosexual affairs which brought him into financial difficulties.
> 2. Sale of secret official information to agents of a foreign power.

Where once single clouds of rumor floated, massive thunder-heads of shock and indignation now appeared. While telegraph keys clicked the story to Paris and London, New York and Berlin, the citizenry of Vienna exploded. Excepting the *Military Review,* every paper in Vienna threw the story on the front page. Each issue fed the public "confirmed" details from "high-level" sources, reports often so ridiculous as to be ludicrous. Statements followed by official denials followed by new statements flowed hourly into editorial offices. Parliament flew into an uproar, political parties castigated the government,

Conrad's scalp was demanded. Editors gave the wildest allegation full currency and those stories not published were passed by word of mouth through *Stüberl* and *Büro*. On May 31, an enterprising theatre owner drew full houses by running the new and supposedly very daring film *Dorian Grey*.

The first move of a greatly shaken Army was to cancel the planned funeral of the traitor. While instruments were put away and wreaths returned, a second autopsy was performed. The body was then placed in a cheap pine coffin. Alone, without ceremony and at night the remains were taken to the Zentralfriedhof, Vienna's large cemetery, where in nonconsecrated ground they were interred in Grave Number 38, Row 29, Group 79. The Vienna public was cheated out of its pretty funeral.*

2.

A LARGE portion of reaction to the official announcement of Redl's crimes did not directly affect the General Staff. Even had the General Staff known that a young Austrian writer, Stefan Zweig, upon hearing the news in Paris felt terror clutching at his throat, it would not have cared, nor would it have been concerned with Joseph Redlich's diary entry of June 2 that "the case of Colonel Redl's treason shocks public opinion: but from my viewpoint it is only one of the many abscesses from

---

* Perhaps it was as well. The corpse could not have been an edifying spectacle. Here is an extract from the post-mortem:

Brain hyperplasia—chronic solidification of the hard and soft meninges—widespread adenomatous tissue in the chronically inflammatory changed thyroid gland—adhesions between the left lung and the pleura—enlargement of the heart myocardium and of the pericardium and endocardium—severe widespread chronic inflammation of the entire aortae extending from the heart to the bifurcation—echinococcus tumors in the liver—chronic manifestations of gallstones with chronic gall bladder inflammation—chronic adhesive peritonitis—hernia on the right side including parts of omentum—advanced chronic inflammation of both spermatic vesicles—new growth in the cortex of the right suprenal.

These extraordinarily severe and widespread diseased changes have doubtlessly for years influenced very considerably the correct evaluation by the subject of the importance of his acts. . . .

which the Habsburg State suffers. Anyway the Finance Ministry is in a mess," nor would it have been upset that on the night of June 2 Vienna police found a bleeding student who had shot himself because he thought he was being persecuted as Redl's accomplice.

But the General Staff was concerned with three elements in the storm of criticism that broke over it: the Austrian Court, the Austrian Parliament and the German Army. When it became clear to Conrad von Hötzendorf that he was faced with those adversaries, he acted immediately, adroitly and dishonestly.

Imperial and Royal Chief of the General Staff
to
The Military Chancellery
Of His Majesty, Emperor and King
in
Vienna, May 26, 1913
As directed by Part One of Service Regulations, I report that the investigation instituted immediately after the death of Colonel Alfred Redl, General Staff Chief of the Eighth Corps, has established with full certainty the motives of the suicide as follows:
1) Homosexual activity, which brought him into financial difficulty.
2) Has sold official orders of a classified nature to agents of a foreign power.

(signed) CONRAD
General of Infantry

Whether this document was submitted to the Emperor on May 26 is open to question. It was probably not submitted until May 28 when the true facts of the case could no longer be concealed. For Wednesday, May 28, is when the Military Chancellery of Francis Ferdinand received its copy. That up to this time neither the Chancellery nor Francis Ferdinand held any insight into the facts is confirmed by Colonel Doctor Bardolff's enclosing Conrad's brief report in the following letter to the Heir Presumptive:

For some time the Intelligence Bureau of the General Staff has pursued an espionage case whose leading person was not to be discovered.

268

Recently various circumstances, special deliveries made through the picking up of general delivery letters, pointed to Colonel Redl.

On grounds of this knowledge the arrest of Colonel Redl was imminent.

He evaded this through suicide.

After the suicide the Chief of the Intelligence Bureau, Urbanski, immediately traveled to Prague and undertook a search of Redl's apartment.

The results of this proved that Colonel Redl had sold most important military secrets to agents of foreign powers, the buyers being France, Italy, and Russia.

Redl produced photographic copies of documents that were available to him as Corps General Staff Chief at any time, of which a number were found still in his apartment; the expert compilation of these copies will perhaps make it possible to determine the extent, at least in part, of the treachery.

The motivation of the treachery was a need for money which grew out of his homosexual affairs.

An officer of Ulan Regiment Number 7, with whom Colonel Redl cultivated sexual relations, as noted in his papers, is already by order of the War Minister being legally prosecuted.

Prior to 1905, then from 1907 to 1911, Colonel Redl was assigned to the Intelligence Bureau of the General Staff and for a long period during this service was himself Chief of the Counterintelligence Section of the Bureau.

At one time he was very nearly appointed General Staff Chief of the Eleventh Corps (Lemberg).

Until recently he was also considered for Chief of the Intelligence Bureau, an idea given up a short time before.

Redl lived very modestly until a few years ago; since two to three years, however, he lived a very luxurious life and owned among other items two automobiles; he explained the source of his money by an inheritance.

So far as can now be determined, Redl's espionage activities appear to have begun originally after his appointment to General Staff Chief of the Eighth Corps—autumn of 1912. The Chief of the General Staff has ordered a strict investigation of the case, for which purpose the Eighth Corps Commander, General of the Cavalry Baron Giesl, is staying in Vienna.

By special order of Baron Conrad, no concealment of one sort or another will be tolerated.

The name of Redl will no longer be mentioned in the newspapers, at least by official sources; whether by this the secrecy of the affair will be achieved is a question.

Redl's corpse will be taken in the next few days to Lemberg for burial by his brother.

Most embarrassing!   May 28
                                              (signed) DOCTOR BARDOLFF

On June 2 a copy of Conrad's report to the Emperor, a document based on a précis of the case drawn up by Urbanski, reached Bardolff who immediately forwarded it to Francis Ferdinand. Conrad reported:

Through a report of the German General Staff, with which there consists a reciprocal working agreement in espionage matters, the Intelligence Bureau learned that large amounts of money and letters arrived in Vienna under a General Delivery address and that the content suggested espionage in favor of Russia.

The Intelligence Bureau arranged a permanent police surveillance of the postal counter in order to pick up the trail of the receiver of these letters.

This surveillance had already lasted roughly six weeks when on May 24 at approximately six P.M. the surveillance personnel confirmed that Colonel of the General Staff Corps Redl picked up the letters delivered to the address in question. Police Headquarters immediately informed the Chief of the Counterintelligence Section of the Intelligence Bureau, Major Ronge, who in turn reported to his Bureau Chief, Colonel von Urbanski. Both officers presented themselves at about ten P.M. to the Chief of the General Staff and reported the information.

The Chief of the General Staff ordered the arrest of Redl.

To carry this out General von Höfer and Major Vorliczek [sic] were summoned. Locating and orienting them took until midnight.

On the way to the Hotel Klomser where Redl was staying the Commission telephoned Police Headquarters about midnight in order to ask for the latest developments.

Regierungsrat Gayer told them that about an hour earlier— eleven P.M.—*Generaladvokat* Pollak had informed Police Headquarters that he had dined with Colonel Redl. The latter had been very excited and had disclosed to him that he must kill himself since he had done something terrible. Redl had wanted to go see the President of Police but could not get in touch with him.

When the Commission arrived in the hotel—about thirty minutes past midnight—Redl was in his room just attempting to carry out the suicide which he had obviously decided upon. One saw on the night table a heavy knife and on the bed a length of window-blind cord. Redl had already written farewell letters to His Excellency Giesl and to his brother—dated midnight.

Upon the entrance of the Commission Redl stated: "I know why you gentlemen have come. I am guilty. I ask only for enough time to justify myself."

In view of his imminent death Redl was asked what he had betrayed and if he had accomplices. At this interrogation Redl admitted his espionage for Russia. He emphasized that he had practiced it only recently, that he had been driven to it through his disastrous passion and he confessed in particular that he had sold to Russia a classified field manual, the appendices to the War Order of Battle and possibly the mobilization instructions of the Eighth Corps. The question, did he have accomplices and was the lieutenant seen often in his company also guilty, he denied most decidedly. He wished still to write a farewell letter to his servant.

The Commission granted this and gave him opportunity to judge himself.

Colonel von Urbanski along with Major Vorliczek left early on May 25 for Prague in order to report to the Corps Commander and to search Redl's apartment.

The papers that were found proved that Redl had doubtlessly practiced espionage, but also that he had cultivated homosexual relations and in particular had stood for a long time in this connection with Lieutenant Stefan H. of Ulan Regiment Number 7 —his alleged nephew—and that this passion had forced him without doubt to high expenditures.

From the discovered data the first clue to espionage is traceable to March, 1912.

Discovered addresses make it appear without doubt that espionage was practiced in favor of Russia, France and Italy.

The following were definitely betrayed:

Classified field and staff manuals.
War Order of Battle with supplements—border and rail transport security.

271

Field-base regulations.

Mining procedure plan for roads and communications.

Armament of fortified areas.

Observations of the 1909 Emperor's Maneuver.

Definite war preparations of recent times—deployment plans —could not have been betrayed because they were not distributed to corps and Redl could not otherwise have had access to them.

Bringing the most important of the documents that proved espionage and homosexuality along with those concerning his financial expenditures, Colonel von Urbanski returned to Vienna on May 25 while Major Vorliczek remained in Prague in order to make further investigation.

On grounds of the incriminating material against Lieutenant H., he was arrested.

High expenditures. During the espionage activity of Redl in the period 1912–1913—up to now nothing has been found to prove that he practiced espionage earlier—Redl had an apartment in the Corps Headquarters building which the Corps Commander had given him gratis along with a stable. This amounted to an annual subsidy of about 4200 crowns. The apartment was not extravagantly luxurious, but still it was furnished with a certain sybaritic sensuality. Redl had the wife of the porter cook him noon meals and ate here and there in the evenings in the company of senior officers. Otherwise he stayed mostly at home. One saw light in his room until late in the evening and supposed that he had a great deal of work. About every six weeks he went to Vienna for a short time, which in the case of a bachelor who had lived for a long time in Vienna was not striking.

The large expenditure of Redl resulted from the satisfying of his homosexual passion, which is shown most clearly from his costly relationship to Lieutenant H. to whom—as it is confirmed up to now—during the last seven months he gave about 900 crowns a month allowance besides horses, the furnishings of an apartment and an automobile. Redl also owned an automobile.

The large expenditure which Redl practiced was explained by him through an ostentatious display of an inheritance document.

In the papers left behind, a certified inheritance document was actually found which, however, awarded Redl only a slight portion of an estate willed to many heirs. Subsequently it was learned that Redl practiced a large expenditure when he was a staff officer on troop duty with Infantry Regiment Number 99—since May, 1911—which showed itself in generous entertainment of officers on various occasions, in ownership of an automobile, expensive horses and in other extraordinary expenditures.

In reference to the many circulating newspaper reports, a few facts should be stressed:

Espionage activity—up to now traced back only to March, 1912—the notes over delivered and paid-for material concern only the time he was Corps General Staff Chief.

No accomplices confirmed—also he was too sly for this.

Rumors of compromising of senior officers and a lady are false.

But the photographs pertaining to homosexual activities have still not been fully identified and further compromisings are yet probable—striking are the high wages and bequests for past and present servants.

A connection with the Jandrić and other recent espionage cases does not exist.

Generaladvokat Pollak, a friend of Redl's from the time of their common activity in espionage cases, dined with him on the evening of May 24; it was he who notified the police that Redl wished to commit suicide. Pollak thus had nothing to do with the arrest commission.

Several statements designed to confuse the issue and thus help to exonerate the General Staff are included in this report. The first of these is the misleading sentence: "The Chief of the General Staff ordered the arrest of Redl." He did. He also ordered Redl to be briefly interrogated. Much more to the point, he ordered Redl removed, and removed quickly, and lips sealed, too. In the statement, Redl emphasized "that he had practiced [espionage] only recently, that he had been driven to it through his disastrous passion. . . ." This is not true. Redl said he had been driven to it through the need for money to pay his pressing debts. The arrest commission had no idea of Redl's homosexuality until Urbanski and Vorlicek entered the Prague apartment. Conrad admitted this later when he stated that the papers in the Prague apartment proved homosexuality. More important: "From the discovered data, the first clue to espionage is traceable to March, 1912," an assertion immediately contradicted when "Observations of the 1909 Emperor's Maneuver" is listed under material betrayed. Why would anyone be interested in the 1909 Emperor's Maneuver in March, 1912? In a later book, Major Ronge described the espionage case of 1910 in which Lieutenant Ulmansky of the Bureau impersonated a drunken General Staff major in Prague, and concluded: "Why the promising connection between the General Staff major and the Russian colonel [Marinsko] was suddenly and abruptly broken off first clarified itself much later. We had a traitor in the Bureau who revealed the trap to the Russians!" This could only have been Alfred Redl. Again: "The large expenditure of Redl resulted from the satisfying of his homosexual passion which is shown most clearly from his costly relationship to Lieutenant H. to whom—as it is confirmed up to now—during the last seven months he gave about 900 crowns a month allowance besides horses, the furnishings of an apartment and an automobile." Redl did not give Stefan these presents "during the last seven months." He started giving Stefan presents in 1904 when he got him in Cadet School, he continued to give him presents during his student days, he began paying him a small allowance in 1909 and in the ensuing years he regularly increased the allowance and augmented it with costly gifts. "Subsequently it was learned that Redl had overspent heavily when he was a staff officer on troop duty with Infantry Regiment Number 99—since May, 1911—on such things as generous entertainment of officers on various occasions, in ownership of an automobile, expensive horses and in other extraordinary expenditures." Redl was extravagant from the time he was commissioned and everyone who knew him knew that as well. He was famous in the Army for dressing in the best military uniforms and civilian clothing, he had indulged in petty fraud back in 1898, he was short of money in Russia, he entertained often and well in Vienna, he owned beautiful horses and lived in splendid comfort in Vienna, and he bought his automobile in 1910, not in 1911.

Conrad presented this watered version of the facts to Emperor Francis Joseph in an audience on June 1. Although the eighty-three-year-old Emperor had been greatly disturbed upon first learning of the treachery, he soon realized that this was but one more tragedy in a life of tragedies and he accepted it as philosophically as he had the deaths of his son and wife. Conrad later wrote: "First of all I spoke to His Majesty about the Redl case. His Majesty was very much grieved by the incident, still he accepted it calmly and dispassionately. Nor was he indignant about the suicide."

The Austrian Parliament performed no more brilliantly than the Emperor. As it had done since its inception, this curious body of Empire nationals seemed intent only upon airing its indignation rather than seeking the real grounds for it. The first interpellation was placed by Member of Parliament Breitner on Thursday, May 29. Typically enough, it was placed against a minister having nothing to do with the case, the Minister of Justice. After lamenting the "medieval practice" of the *Vehmgericht* or secret court trial of Alfred Redl, it alleged that Doctor Pollak had been a part of this procedure and asked the Government:

> What part did the General Advocate of the Supreme Court have in this purely military proceeding?
>
> How will the Minister of Justice explain the co-working of his named high official in an action of a secret military court?

Another parliamentarian, Doctor Wilhelm Neumann, came closer to the point with an interpellation that asked:

> Is it correct that the colonel has betrayed the mobilization plans of the Austrian Army to the northeast neighboring state?
>
> Is it correct this has insured in case of war certain defeat of the Austrian Army and with it the death of uncountable thousands of soldiers?
>
> Is it correct that for many years the colonel practiced espionage for the benefit of the northeast neighbor state, that he carried on an exorbitant scale of living, trafficked with homosexuals . . . and of all this his superiors had no knowledge?
>
> Is it correct that the colonel was persuaded by officers to commit suicide?
>
> Is it correct that this action, besides impairing the complete investigation of this case, in itself is a severe offense against the law?
>
> Is it correct that other officers are involved in the case?
>
> What guarantees are there that such a crime will be prevented in the future?

Member of Parliament von Wassilko delivered a fiery denunciation of the Army's procedure and asked if the President of Parliament "will carry the context of the query to the Government and will do what is necessary so that Parliament receives an answer." Upon the reading of this question many cries of "Bravo! Bravo!" were heard. Interpellations continued to pour in, the Government continued to delay its reply. On June 4 representatives of the Czech Agrarian Club formally asked if a reply were to be made. The Government announced that Defense Minister von Georgi would if possible reply the next day.

The actual reply had already been written. Its basis was the same précis prepared by Urbanski and used by Conrad for his report to the Emperor that is quoted above. Urbanski later wrote that "this document was fully approved by the Chief of the General Staff and was forwarded to the Emperor via Francis Ferdinand. The latter's office changed it so violently and fundamentally that what the Defense Minister [von Georgi], speaking from it, said in Parliament could satisfy no one and gave more reason for people to say that vital details were being hushed up."

Urbanski was correct in saying that the text of the reply was radically altered. It was not, however, altered by Francis Ferdinand. Bardolff received the draft in the Military Chancellery *after* it had gone to the Emperor. In his report to Francis Ferdinand concerning this document, Bardolff objected to "the presentation relevant to the suicide [which] permits all kinds of interpretations and attempts to conceal the truth. The Commission, to be sure, did not directly cause the suicide but it certainly made it possible, otherwise it would not have left the revolver behind. This explanation will satisfy no one and should be changed to one that holds more with the truth."

Another paragraph in the draft read:

> The espionage activity of Redl can at this time be confirmed only from March, 1912. It is therefore quite impossible to consider that his activity could reach back many years; particularly during his many years of employment in the Intelligence Bureau where he repeatedly functioned as expert in espionage cases is this activity straightway contradictory to his active employment

as a spy of a foreign power, since Redl, who in the interpretation of each [espionage] case always showed himself very strict, would have had to run the danger of being betrayed by these very spies."

Doctor Bardolff commented: "One cannot say in one sentence that at present Redl's espionage activity can be confirmed only from March, 1912, and in the sentence immediately following that 'it therefore is out of the question that his activity could reach back many years.' Such stylistic and logic errors may not occur in a declaration by the Government." Concerning the drastic alteration of the document referred to by Urbanski, Bardolff in fact explained to Francis Ferdinand that "the Minister [of Defense] requests that no further shortening [of this proposed reply] be considered and that the draft be sent back as soon as possible. *This draft has been cut to about half the length of the one that was this morning submitted to the Emperor* [and cut] *on the order of the Emperor.*" * The Emperor's decision should surprise no one familiar with Francis Joseph's tactics. It was the old line of least resistance: muddle up the problem, play one force against another—and at the end still remain on the throne. The fact had to be admitted, so admit it, partially explain it, confuse it, let people grumble and finally the scandal would die from disinterest, the Empire would continue to struggle along.

On June 5, 1913, Minister of Defense von Georgi stood before a packed Parliament to deliver his carefully prepared and censored reply. If he had hoped for any soporific effect he was disappointed. According to the evening edition of the *Neue Freie Presse,* his reply "exercised no great calming effect . . . the over-all impression was dissatisfaction." One parliamentarian, Doctor Otto Lecher, said, "Mere denials and silences are no explanation." Another, Hueber, said, "I ask that this case be discussed and the facts determined so that it cannot be said: 'One hangs the little ones while the great ones go free.'" At the point when Von Georgi stupidly and illogically argued that Redl could not have been a spy when he was with the Intelligence Bureau because he interpreted the law so sternly, Member

* My italics.

of Parliament Habermann presciently interrupted with: "The fox among the geese."

Still the speech was given and Bardolff duly reported to Francis Ferdinand:

> General of the Infantry Baron von Georgi answered the interpellation over the Redl case in today's session of Parliament. The answer went smoothly, without any incidents.
> Subsequently Member of Parliament Nemeć moved for opening of debate.
> This proposal was refused.
> With this the Redl case seemed to be settled in Parliament.

Doctor Bardolff was wrong.

3.

ARCHDUKE FRANCIS FERDINAND was deeply affected by the official announcement of Redl's guilt. For one thing, it gave him reason to believe that Conrad had intended to keep the true facts from him. For another, it tended to confirm what he had long suspected: that the Army and especially the General Staff were in no condition to fight the "preventive war" Conrad seemed so intent on.

But overshadowing these thoughts was a greater one. Francis Ferdinand, an ardent Roman Catholic, knew that Redl by being forced to suicide had been forced to commit a mortal sin of such severity that he could well have doomed himself to eternal damnation. The ambiguity of Conrad's report to the Emperor at first caused the Archduke to conclude that the arrest commission alone was responsible for Redl's act. Pertinent portions of the report were personally annotated by Francis Ferdinand, who wrote at the end of his copy:

> The arrest commission thus consisted of:
> General Höfer
> Colonel Urbanski
> Major Ronge
> Major Worliczek

and was *commanded* by General of the Infantry Baron Conrad to arrest the criminal.

This was to be done; the arbitrary procedure of the commission, taken strictly militarily, was simply without discipline.

While Francis Ferdinand studied this report along with Bardolff's frequent communiqués, he fed his imagination on his own indignation. He would have all of the facts, and neither the Army nor the General Staff was going to stand in his way. On June 1, Bardolff wrote the Minister of War, General Krobatin, as follows:

> Urgent!
> By order of the Heir Presumptive I report that His Imperial Highness [Francis Ferdinand] in reference to publications in the press requests an explanation of the following questions:
> a.) The suicide of the former Colonel Redl, particularly an explanation of the report that the suicide was urged upon him or at least made possible to him;
> b.) Luxurious living standard of Redl, particularly if this point was not already earlier striking and why the same was not investigated.
> His Imperial Highness is pleased to express the wish that the legal investigation be forwarded in detailed form without consideration of any other factor.

On June 4, the Minister of War replied abruptly and rudely:

> Other than the documents sent by the Chief of the General Staff to the Imperial-Royal Minister of Defense for the answer of the interpellation in Parliament, of which a copy was sent to the Military Chancellery [of Francis Ferdinand] . . . the War Ministry has at this time learned no more—and is therefore not able to supply the desired explanations.
>
> (signed) KROBATIN

Perhaps having anticipated this barren reply, Francis Ferdinand had already ordered General Conrad to appear in audience on June 4. Conrad later wrote:

> One of the most unpleasant [audiences] during my time as Chief of the General Staff. His Imperial Highness was indignant over the Redl case, especially over the permission of suicide

which he could not accept on religious grounds. A flood of re-
proaches spilled over me. The Archduke said that I was too
good with the people [officers of the General Staff]; he would
make the General Staff feel it. Thereupon I answered: I took
the post of Chief of the General Staff only because Your Imperial Highness wished it; I do not enjoy it and am not suited
for it. Francis Ferdinand [said]: You must straighten out the
General Staff. I refused to accept this criticism, based as it were
on generalization from a single case.

The next day Conrad discussed this unpleasant interview
with Joseph Redlich, who wrote in his journal:

> June 6, 1913. To luncheon yesterday with Count and Countess
> Berchtold in honor of the Bavarian State Minister v. Hertling
> . . . then spoke with Conrad who very dramatically told me
> about the Redl case. . . . Conrad then quite frankly told me:
> it was he who had immediately said that one must give [Redl]
> a revolver. . . . Conrad then told me that yesterday he had had
> an hour's conversation with Archduke Francis Ferdinand who
> reproached him about the suicide as an injustice on both reli-
> gious and legal grounds. After a serious argument Conrad said
> to him: the religious side of the matter was absolutely unim-
> portant to him as an officer. Conrad told me further that Arch-
> duke Francis Ferdinand had said to him: You see how fortunate
> it is that we have not gone to war against Russia with a traitor
> in our rear. Thereupon Conrad had laughed and said: What
> Redl had betrayed was quite insignificant. Conrad explained
> to me that Redl had first sold himself fourteen months earlier,
> that he had left behind large debts and that the damage which
> he caused was slight. . . .

Conrad's line was clear: minimize the whole mess. Already on
May 31 the Foreign Minister, Count Berchtold, had written
Conrad his dismay over the case. Conrad "answered him [by]
saying that there was no reason for profound apprehensions
concerning our military position and I would have spoken with
him about it on the occasion of my earlier visit had this not
been interrupted by Duke von Arna."
It is simple to draw a clear picture of General Conrad von
Hötzendorf during these trying days. This small and nervous
man, this urbane and powerful officer, flitting from state lunch-

eons to groups in the Sacher Hotel to intimates at the Jockey Club—innuendoes here, denials there, all to throw doubt on the generally ridiculed Austrian Parliament and the generally disliked Heir Presumptive, all to exonerate the General Staff, all to minimize the importance of Redl's treachery. In his own way Conrad was not a bad actor. In fact both Conrad and the General Staff were deeply disturbed. This is shown in part by the many contradictions that exist in official and quasi-official documents still extant, in part by numerous grammatical errors in these documents, and finally by Conrad's classified Corps Order Number Six of June 11, 1913:

> Classified General Staff Number 2511. The shocking crime of Colonel Alfred Redl has filled each member of the Army with the most thorough disgust and utter horror, but I still cannot refrain from expressing personally my own sickening disappointment. I would never have thought it possible that an officer of the General Staff Corps, whose members I treated constantly with fullest confidence and chivalrous co-operation, could be capable of such a criminal act.
>
> But since this was the case, the gravity of the issue and the great danger accruing to the State from such a crime forces me to the following orders:
>
> 1. My Deputy and the Chief of the Personnel Bureau must concern themselves most particularly with the personal circumstances of the members of the General Staff Corps in order to discover any irregularities, to report to me immediately any improprieties, and to present to me on the occasion of change of duty or promotion their notes of any peculiarities.
> 2. All Corps and Division General Staff Chiefs, all Bureau and Section chiefs, prior to each promotion terminus—thus before October 1 and April 1 of each year—will submit to me a detailed report on any General Staff officer in his command in which appears everything either not included or insufficiently included of a recent nature in the Qualification List. Particularly to be included in this are the attributes of character and the private living standard—especially financial—so that the kind of striking events familiar to the Redl case cannot remain unnoticed or unmentioned. In view of the inexorable demands in the interest of the service which stand above all else, any other

consideration must be disregarded; and anyone making such a report has to bear the full responsibility.

3. The analogous duty is imposed on all other members of the General Staff who have, as commandants of schools and courses, etc., members of the General Staff under them.

4. All members of the General Staff must exercise immediate influence on those of their subordinates who threaten to fall into the danger of a frivolous life, but I also expect fellow officers to practice such influence on each other. It is especially contemptible to let pass on the one hand this sort of thing, but on the other hand to gossip about it, especially afterwards.

5. I forbid any concealment of irregularities.

Classified General Staff Number 2460. All General Staff officers, particularly all General Staff and Bureau chiefs, must urgently insure that service manuals, orders and documents of a highly restricted nature be used by everyone without exception *only in the official area* (therefore in no case at home).

Likewise it is to be observed that *full* knowledge of such restricted documents shall be held only by the planners entrusted with the work by pertinent sections. Any such very secret documents are to be kept locked up and issued only to the section personnel who wrote them.

I emphasize once again that not only off-duty discussions but also private correspondence of a confidential nature is most strongly prohibited.

(signed) CONRAD

Nowhere can Conrad's confusion of fact and fancy be more clearly illustrated than in his correspondence concerning relations with the German Great General Staff. On June 1 the Austro-Hungarian military attaché in Berlin wrote one of Conrad's aides a classified letter:

With regard to the Redl case I must write you the following. Understandably the matter has caused unrest here in the General Staff because of the question whether matters which concerned Germany were given away by Redl.

Above all else the content of the discussions between the two Chiefs [Conrad and Von Moltke] comes into consideration. . . . I have provisionally said here that in my opinion Redl could well have been informed over the *fact* and arrangements of such a conference, but not over the content of such correspondence. [Marginal note, presumably Conrad's: "No more than the general public knows."] I believe that it would be wise if I were to be officially authorized to make a reassuring statement here to the Great General Staff, particularly on this question.

On the whole I would like to suggest that the investigation also be conducted as to determine which important matters are compromised and, since this perhaps will scarcely be able to be answered, which questions in a negative sense—trench mortars, Triple Alliance arrangements, etc.—could Redl no longer have known about, thus which questions have in any event remained safe and undisturbed. A communiqué over the result of such an investigation should, in my opinion, then be given to the Great General Staff and perhaps to the Prussian Minister of War.

I am writing directly to you because, it is to be hoped, only you and the planners know of the thing mentioned at the beginning [the Conrad-Von Moltke conferences] and are able to form the text of a possible answer.

Yesterday the question was discussed with me whether the report in the press that military secrets of Germany had been betrayed should be denied. The view was taken that in order to quiet the German public a denial should be given, and in the meantime this has been done.

I am completely flabbergasted at the entire case and cannot really believe it. Also here in the General Staff, especially in Section III-b [Intelligence] one is not able to believe it. *From the standpoint of my own conscience I am glad that I have never discussed anything secret with Redl which could so easily have been the case. . . .** *

Having anticipated some difficulty with its German ally, the Austrian General Staff had already published in the *Military Review* of May 31 a "most determined" denial of "the rumor that Redl had betrayed mobilization and deployment plans of Germany." On June 3 a Berlin newspaper published a similar story of which the next to the last paragraph is an open lie:

The Prussian General Staff has released the following official statement:
In several newspapers the supposition has been forwarded

* My italics.

that the Austrian Colonel Redl could have betrayed secrets of
the German General Staff. Relations with our neighboring
Monarchy are, to be sure, the most conceivably favorable and
have led to neutral visits, but these have not resulted in an exchange of military secrets.

It is obvious that such material, which itself is known to only
a few persons on our own General Staff, would not be given to
even a friendly foreign power.

The information that during the Bosnian Crisis [1908-1909]
Colonel Redl had been in Berlin and had conferred there with
the Chief of the General Staff is false.

No reason for fear exists, therefore, that German war manage-
ment has been involved by the espionage of an Austrian officer.

To carry the lie further, General Conrad on June 17 sent a
personal and secret letter to his German opposite, General von
Moltke:

YOUR EXCELLENCY!

I take the liberty to most respectfully send you this letter
because the fantastic news in the papers over the scope of
treachery in the Redl case appears to me to necessitate a communication to Your Excellency.

My letter has been intentionally delayed, not only until existent material was confirmed and checked but also until it was
determined which mobilization and war plans were actually
available to the traitor and which ones he could have been able
to learn about.

The result of these official inquiries is that Redl neither as
division or corps General Staff Chief, nor during his service in
the Intelligence Bureau had acquired data over *specific* war
plans, such as collection and grouping in the deployment areas,
orders to army corps, intended operations and the like.

The sensational reports of the newspapers that the criminal,
particularly from his service in the Intelligence Bureau, would
have gained full insight into the "most secret" plans and dispositions are without further ado patently inaccurate to those
well versed in service operations because this Bureau for the
collection of information over foreign armies and for counterintelligence does not need and does not receive data on the
specific war plans of its own Army.

Moreover these plans are so handled that, for example, the
destinations of a corps in various war eventualities are not even

known in peacetime to the corps commander and his General Staff Chief.

As for the military arrangements common to the Triple Alliance or even of the conferences which I had the honor to pursue repeatedly with Your Excellency, Redl was in no way informed. Disregarding the common precautions between us for purposes of counterintelligence, which Redl was active in for a long period, he could know only so much of the fact of existent military arrangements as is known by the public at large.

The severe moral damage which this monstrous crime has caused the Imperial and Royal General Staff and with it the whole Army is of course not able to be lessened by the facts that I have taken the liberty of disclosing to Your Excellency, although they reduce the real damage to that extent which emerges from the treachery of restricted organizational data and mobilization measures.

Accept, Sir, the expression of my outstanding esteem. . . .

In a cover letter to his military attaché in Berlin, Conrad wrote:

You, Sir, are further authorized to explain to the Royal Prussian War Ministry that Redl was never oriented over connections which existed or do exist between the two Army staffs in technical-military questions (such as ordnance, trench mortars, pointed cartridges and the like), and therefore could have betrayed nothing over them.

The truth of Conrad's various assertions can best be judged by stating a few of the simultaneous and secret actions of his General Staff officers. Urbanski was busy and would remain so for weeks making investigations of Redl's known friends, most of whom were either kept under surveillance or actually interrogated (official sources denied that such investigations were being conducted). General Staff Captain Emil Ratzenhofer of the Railroad Bureau was sent to Prague to find out what secrets Redl had access to (his long report disclosed that Redl had used many important mobilization, transport and supply documents). On June 16 the Operations Bureau of the General Staff wrote the Army Inspector in Sarajevo that "in case the arrival and departure troop movement plans valid up to February 28, 1913, have not yet been called in by the Army Inspectorate and destroyed, they will be forwarded to the Operations Bureau. . . ." The Intelligence Bureau's code and cipher expert —Captain Andreas Figl—was ordered to make completely new codes for the Army "because Redl betrayed the existing ones." Altogether the investigation required several months; according to the War Ministry, the case, including the replacement of plans and orders that one supposed Redl to have betrayed, cost "at least 100,000 crowns."

Nor did the patent absurdity of Conrad's stand escape his various auditors any more than the Defense Minister's statements escaped Doctor Bardolff who objected to "such stylistic and logic errors . . . in a declaration by the Government." Everyone concerned knew that for years Redl had participated in General Staff exercises where high-level strategy was usually discussed, that he had participated at division, corps and army levels in the most important maneuvers, that he knew every officer of consequence in the Austro-Hungarian Army and that most of these could not say, like the military attaché in Berlin, "I am glad that I have never discussed anything secret with Redl, which could so easily have been the case."

Neither Von Moltke nor his officers were fooled. Not being a strong person and certainly not being disposed to quarrel with an ally at a critical time, Von Moltke replied courteously to Conrad's letter: "Now you have written me a letter over this tragic case and I would not like to thank you for it without adding how I sympathize with you. . . ." But Colonel Urbanski later wrote:

> Above all else the esteem enjoyed by the Austro-Hungarian General Staff was severely injured and the trust in the purity of its members was impaired. The arising mistrust finally spoiled the consistently good relations with the German Great General Staff. . . .

The arising mistrust also spoiled General Staff relations with Archduke Francis Ferdinand. On June 12 Doctor Bardolff telegraphed Conrad, who was conducting a General Staff exercise at Buczacz in East Galicia, that Francis Ferdinand wished each member of the arrest commission to furnish a written statement of the handling of the Redl case both in the Hotel Klomser and

286

in Prague. Conrad agreed but warned of some delay since the concerned officers were on various maneuvers.

Most of the information in the subsequent reports from Von Höfer, Urbanski, Vorlicek and Ronge has already been related. The chief importance of the documents to Francis Ferdinand was the proof of Conrad's direct order to the arrest commission "to determine Redl's guilt in connection with which the Chief of the General Staff had said to lay nothing in the way of Redl in case he voluntarily wished to judge himself." Once the Archduke learned that—and it was Conrad's own deputy, General Höfer, who wrote it—Francis Ferdinand began a systematic persecution of the General Staff. Urbanski later wrote that throughout the summer of 1913 the Archduke's "animosity against me made itself felt in oppressive pressure on my Bureau, whose output repeatedly incurred his urgent criticisms. At the Tabor maneuver [September, 1913] he was strikingly cooler than in past years. . . ." On September 30, 1913, Joseph Redlich entered in his diary:

> . . . I spoke privately with Conrad. He is fully preoccupied with the most recent events. He remains Chief of the General Staff only on order of the Emperor. His relationship with the Archduke has deteriorated since the sudden change in the political-military viewpoints of the Archduke after the visit of the German Emperor in Springe. The first important clash was caused by the Redl affair. The Archduke at that time was unsparing in his denunciation of the General Staff which Conrad defended to the full. At that time he offered to resign. Then on September 14 he came from the Breslau maneuver [in Germany to the Austro-Hungarian maneuver at Tabor] and with that came a scene without parallel. Conrad had not been informed that at nine o'clock, two hours after the arrival of Archduke Francis Ferdinand, a mass had been scheduled. In consequence he did not appear for it. At ten o'clock he was ordered to report to the Archduke who reproached his staying away from mass with unparalleled anger, even brutality, whereupon Conrad very excitedly replied that he was here to run a maneuver, not to go to mass. . . .

Francis Ferdinand then intruded in the command of the maneuver to the extent that Conrad returned to Vienna and submitted another letter of resignation. Francis Ferdinand replied to it in a very kind, almost contrite, manner and assured Conrad of his continued confidence. Conrad was forced to stay on by order of the Emperor, who did not want a change during the current Balkan crisis. Redlich continued:

> But the situation, as he [Conrad] says, is untenable. As highly as the Archduke formerly praised him to the skies, so now he hates him—Conrad. Conrad said that he suffered from delusions of Caesarian greatness. . . .

A few months after this episode, an auction of Redl's personal effects was held in Prague. Present was one Herr Langer who bought a camera. Noting a film still in it, Langer removed it and gave it to a young student to develop. The photographs were of the title pages and several pages of a classified field manual on mobilization for higher commands. The student immediately turned the films over to one of his professors who in turned passed them to the commanding officer of the 91st Infantry Regiment. After confiscating six more undeveloped films, the commanding officers sent them to Eighth Corps. In the meantime the story hit the newspapers. Colonel Urbanski later wrote:

> I was called on the telephone one day in the Bureau from Castle Konopischt [Francis Ferdinand's favorite residence]. The Archduke, himself, was on the phone and he screamed at me: "Have you heard of the newest filthy mess? The surrender of Redl's camera together with content to a high school pupil?" There followed a flood of reproaches and the threat to bring me to a legal investigation. I could not speak but I was extremely upset in presentiment of further unpleasantnesses. Conrad interceded for me but the Heir Presumptive would not be dissuaded from his belief that it had been my duty to take the photographic apparatus at the time of the first search in Redl's apartment. . . .

This episode culminated in the forced retirement of Colonel Urbanski in the spring of 1914. It was not to last very long. On June 28, 1914, Archduke Francis Ferdinand and his wife were murdered at Sarajevo. When World War I began a few weeks later, Colonel Urbanski was removed from retirement and promoted to brigadier general. Although he served throughout the war with distinction, his career had suffered a setback from which it was never fully to recover.

More vitally affected even than Urbanski were those persons closely related to the traitor. Shortly after Alfred's crimes had been confirmed, Heinrich's daughter was absent from her school. "We all wondered about it," a former classmate said, "but we were not allowed to discuss it. In about two weeks our little friend returned to school with a new name. This was very strange to us because here was the same person only with a new name. In a surprisingly short time we had forgotten about it. Of course, one never quite forgot."

Presumably on account of his family and his respectable civil position, Heinrich Redl wasted no time in legally changing his name. But his brother Oskar, whose final orders to military retirement were signed by the Emperor the morning of Alfred's suicide—an honest coincidence—did not apply to the Lower Austrian authorities until late August, 1913. "On grounds of the espionage affair concerning my brother, Alfred," he asked that his name be changed to "Rhoden." The authorities suggested that he take the new name already chosen by Heinrich. In an angry reply Oskar rejected the suggestion. He changed his mind a few months later and on February 11, 1914, accepted the name designated by Heinrich. (Oskar himself was a bachelor. In so far as can be determined, the family has survived only in the childless widow of Heinrich's son.)

4.

THE spring and summer of 1913 passed. A young lieutenant visited Alfred Redl's grave when it was a few months old. He found no formal marker. Instead, on the still-swollen rectangle of ground he saw a large wreath of evergreen boughs whose center branches were entwined to form the letter "R." The sexton did not know who had put it there. The general public would not have cared, for most people had soon lost interest in the Redl case. The Balkan War provided news to fill the yawning maw of the daily press; readers found themselves more interested in the living than in the dead, more interested in the "knightly satisfaction" demanded by Captain Gerö in a duel with Count Karolyi or in the impressive luncheon menu served to General Count Zeppelin at Schönbrunn.

Some thunder remained to peal but, excepting the auctioned camera, there was more rumble than clap, more drizzle than storm. Ernst Breitner spearheaded a group of parliamentarians that protested the Government's explanation of the case. After listing specific objections, Breitner perorated:

> . . . the proceedings which were applied against him [Redl] are so sinister, so very redolent of the darkest Middle Ages, that one is not able to comprehend them in our time. From whatever point of view one regards the inducing of Redl's suicide by the commission, it remains more and more misunderstood and damnable. It acted against the interest of the State, it made the full explanation of the matter impossible, it violated our sense of justice in that a human being contrary to justice and law was driven into death.

The Government answered Breitner and his associates by ignoring them and when one Doctor Ernst Weisl drew the attention of the *Neue Freie Presse* to a 1907 decision of the State Supreme Court that accomplices in suicide can be punished "with six months to one year of hard labor," the Government ignored him, too.

On July 29 the Army brought Stefan Hromodka to military trial, found him guilty of the crime of unnatural prostitution and sentenced him to three months of hard labor, discharge from commissioned rank and deprivation of the Military Jubilee Medal. An official report stated that "the intense and thorough investigation has offered no facts that Hromodka either participated in the espionage activity of the deceased Colonel Redl or had any knowledge of the activity." (Upon his release from jail, Stefan went to Captain Gilnreiner, his old squadron commander, for advice. Gilnreiner advised him to go to South America and begin a new life. Stefan did not heed him. Instead he married, produced children. He is alive today—an old man with not very attractive memories.)

A last attempt to explain the crime of Alfred Redl was never published. It was made by a "High Ecclesiastical Prince"—probably a cardinal—in the Roman Catholic Church in Rome. On July 30, 1913, the Austro-Hungarian military attaché in Rome reported to Vienna:

> I have recently had opportunity to speak with a Senior Ecclesiastical Prince who belongs to the closest circle of the Pope. The gentleman had interested himself very much in the Redl case and appeared to me to be very well oriented over it; he asserted that one can ascribe this case, exactly like the Dreyfuss case, only to the international tendencies of Jews who have never possessed and who will never possess at any time patriotic feelings.
>
> He stated further that Redl had been a Jew from both paternal and maternal sides; he had investigated the matter and had the most definite proofs for it. According to the Prince, his mother was a Sternberg from Moravia—either this name is that of the aristocratic family or else it is Jewish.
>
> The admission of these internationally minded elements to positions of high trust is a great danger for each state, for they are *never* trustworthy. With this, the Prince turned his conversation to Free Masonry in the civil-military-naval leadership of Italy and said that general public opinion had now already recognized the danger of Free Masonry to Italy and would eliminate it with all available means, at least from the Army and Navy. . . .

Here was an ideal answer! Had Redl been a Jew he could not have been considered a true Catholic and thus his suicide could not have offended this religion. Such was the anti-Semitic fervor of that day's Vienna that had Redl been a Jew public sentiment would have at once swung in support of the Army for its noble action although it would still have been criticized for allowing a Jew on its General Staff. Unfortunately for those officials concerned, Redl was not a Jew. His father's religion is plainly carried as Roman Catholic in railroad personnel records and all Army records show Alfred, Heinrich and Oskar to be Roman Catholic. Not a word in support of this allegation is found in the records, not a word later appeared in Ronge's, Conrad's or Urbanski's writings over the case.

But the idea was a good one and no less a person than Julius

Streicher resurrected it shortly after Germany had taken over Austria in 1938. Writing to an Austrian government bureau on one of those inflammatory letterheads of his Munich anti-Jewish magazine, *Der Stürmer*, Streicher quoted some Prague press reports which alleged that Redl's name before his baptism had been Redlich (and thus Jewish). Was Redl a Jew?

In a formal reply the Austrian Government stated that it had investigated the matter in its archives and that no proof of the allegation could be found. It must be assumed, therefore, that Alfred Redl was not a Jew.

Like the High Ecclesiastical Prince many years before, Julius Streicher was probably very disappointed.

Although World War I smashed the Austro-Hungarian Empire into the precarious bits that Adolf Hitler's German Reich later chewed one by one, the Austrian public has never entirely relegated the Redl case to the limbo of dead tragedy. From the summer of 1913 to the time of this writing scarcely a year has passed without a flare-up of public interest. On each of these occasions a number of old General Staff survivors and chauvinist monarchists have continued to deny that Redl performed treachery of any great importance.

Perhaps the strongest evidence of the seriousness of Redl's treachery has been offered by the actions of those who would minimize it. After World War I, a systematic whitewash of the case was undertaken. Various archives were plundered of documents relating to the case, official histories and important memoirs either ignored or lightly touched the matter. The campaign was not altogether successful. Internecine warfare among the whitewashers caused both too much information to be published and too many contradictions in alleged "facts" to appear. The plunderers also overlooked some important documents and these have brought out further contradictions and errors in official and quasi-official statements. Finally, contemporary voices, and some very competent ones, too, wholly contradicted the official line. A former Austrian Minister of War, General Auffenberg, later wrote that "there is not the slightest doubt about it that the damage which [Redl] caused through his criminal activity was enormous. . . ." On February 26, 1915, Joseph Redlich entered in his journal:

> Today Doctor Ivo Pilar from Tuzla called on me. He explained to me very clearly our disaster in Serbia. We were unprepared from the beginning on, our first war plan was betrayed by Redl, thus the Serbs were completely prepared. The latter ruined [General] Potiorek's plan and his simultaneous hooklike push to the Drina, Save and Belgrade, by bringing up 60,000 men by the West Railroad and throwing them against what they knew were the weak flank of the Austrian Drina Army. . . .

Count Sternberg said later in Parliament:

> Redl denounced each Austrian spy. He delivered our secrets to Russia and hindered our learning Russian secrets through spies. So in 1914 Austria and Germany remained unaware of the existence of seventy-five divisions, more than the whole Austro-Hungarian Army—hence our desire for war and our defeat. If we had seen clearly, our generals would not have driven the high Court officials into war.

Redl's diabolical, if ingenious, trading of spies with Batjuschin was confirmed early in World War I when the German Army captured Warsaw and with it the headquarters of Russian Intelligence Center West. An Austrian officer attached to German Intelligence read and later reported on the correspondence between Redl and Batjuschin that formed a part of the captured documents. In the subsequent course of the war this officer was told by a German associate that Batjuschin's agent, Pratt, when in a German prisoner of war camp described the Redl case as "my most beautiful success." (Pratt died soon after, Batjuschin and Pawlow continued to serve in Russian Army Intelligence during World War I—their ultimate ends are not known to the writer.)

The material effect of Redl's treachery is as difficult to measure as the effect of any treachery. It was probably not as great as Count Sternberg, for example, supposed, although his indictment is surely defended by Austria's terrible defeats by the Russians early in the war. Redl did paralyze Austro-Hungarian espionage inside Russia at a critical time and he did sell countless secrets of his Army and possibly a few of State. He was probably responsible for a large portion of the "120 secret Austrian and German documents" found in Russian headquarters in Warsaw in 1915. Part of the blame for the loss of Galician fortresses and thus tens of thousands of Austrian soldiers to Russian prison camps must be laid to him, and his actions help to explain the abortive Imperial and Royal Army effort in Serbia. On the other hand, he was caught over a year before the war began and remedial action in part was taken—codes and ciphers changed, war plans revised. The direct damage he caused was certainly great. It was probably not decisive.

But the indirect result of Redl's treachery was decisive. It was a moral result and it brought to the Austro-Hungarian Empire —to the monarchy and the military, the bureaucracy and citizenry—an almost helpless sense of fear. A General Staff officer with thirty-two years service, a gentleman welcome in higher military and civil circles, a colonel, General Staff Chief of the most important Army corps, a famous man wearing noble orders and decorations . . . and then, suddenly: a homosexual and a traitor! This was terror clutching at the throat of a nation. Never again was the citizen going to trust the Army, never again was he to feel really secure in his own land.

That was Alfred Redl's bequest to his country. It was infamy to a startling degree, but as infamy it was nothing new to the Austrian. And as infamy it was characteristically if unconsciously ployed with irony. Burial lots are not sold in the Zentralfriedhof; they are leased for ten-year periods. In 1923 when no one paid the rent for Redl's bones the grave was opened to admit a new coffin. It held the corpse of a woman.

> The grave's a fine and private place
> But none I think do there embrace. . . .

Bibliography

I. General

This is an arbitrary and sharply limited selection mainly intended to offer the interested reader some reference works which have not been included in standard bibliographies.

Aston, G. C., *Secret Service*. London: 1930.

Auffenberg-Komarów, Moritz Freiherr von, *Aus Österreichs Höhe und Niedergang*. Munich: 1921.

Baernreither, Joseph M., *Fragmente Eines Politischen Tagebuches*. Edited by Professor J. Redlich. Berlin: 1928.

Bardolff, Carl Freiherr von, *Soldat im Alten Österreich*. Jena: 1939.

Barton, George, *The World's Greatest Spies and Secret Service Agents*. London: 1917.

Bergler, Edmund, *Homosexuality: Disease or Way of Life?* New York: 1956.

Berndorff, H. R., *Spionage!* Stuttgart: 1929.

Bouman, P. J., *Revolution of the Lonely*. (Translated by F. S. Renier and A. Cliff.) London: 1954.

Brehm, Bruno, *Die Throne Stürzen*. Munich: 1951.

Bullock, Alan, *Hitler, A Study in Tyranny*. London: 1952.

Busch, Tristan, *Major Kwaplitschka*. Vienna: 1950.

Chlumecky, Leopold von, *Erzherzog Franz Ferdinand*. Berlin: 1929.

Conrad, Franz von Hötzendorf, *Aus Meiner Dienstzeit 1906-1918*. 5 vols. Vienna: 1922.

Corti, Egon Caesar Conte, *Vom Kind Zum Kaiser*. Graz: 1950.

————, *Mensch und Herrscher*. Graz: 1952.

————, and Sokol, Hans, *Der Alte Kaiser Franz Joseph I*. Graz: 1955.

Daniloff, Jurij, *Russland im Weltkriege 1914-1915*. Jena: 1925.

Das Infanterie Regiment Nr. 99 im Weltkrieg, 1914-1918. Vienna: 1929.

Die österreich-ungarische Monarchie in Wort und Bild. Vol: Galizien. Vienna: 1898.

Die Weltskriegsspionage. Munich: 1931.

Eid und Kriegsartikel, k. und k. Armee. Vienna: 1874.

Encyclopaedia Brittanica, 1953.

Franz, Georg, *Erzherzog Franz Ferdinand*. Brünn: 1943.

Friedjung, Heinrich, *Das Zeitalter des Imperialismus, 1884-1914.* 2 vols. Berlin: 1922.

Frischauer, Paul, *The Imperial Crown.* London: 1939.

Fry, Christopher, *The Dark Is Light Enough.* London: 1954.

Giesl, Wladimir Baron von, *Zwei Jahrzehnte im Nahen Orient.* Edited by Edward Ritter von Steinitz. Berlin: 1927.

Gollomb, Joseph, *Spies.* New York: 1928.

Görlitz, Walter, *The German General Staff.* London: 1953.

Grote, H. H. A. A., *Vorsicht! Feind Hort Mit!* 1930.

Grun, Bernard, *Prince of Vienna.* London: 1955.

Gurko, Wassili, *Russland, 1914-1917.* Berlin: 1921.

Hindenburg, Paul von, *Aus Meinem Leben.* Leipzig: 1920.

Iongh, Jane D., *Margaret of Austria.* (Translated by M. D. Herter Norton.) London: 1954.

Kann, Robert A., *The Multinational Empire.* 2 vols. New York: 1950.

———, *The Habsburg Empire.* New York: 1957.

Kern, Fritz, *Conrad und Berchtold.* Article in Europäische Gespräche, Number II. Berlin: March-April, 1924.

Kisch, Egon Erwin, *Der Fall des General-Stabschef Redl.* Berlin: 1924.

———, *Marktplatz der Sensationen.* Vienna: 1948.

———, *Prager Pitaval.* Berlin: 1952.

Kiszling, Rudolf, *Erzherzog F. Ferdinand von Österreich-Este.* Graz: 1953.

Krylov, Ivan, *Soviet Staff Officer.* New York: 1951.

Lehmann's Allgemeiner Wohnungs-Anzeiger nebst Handels- und Gewerbe-Adressbuch für die k.k. Reichs-Haupt- und Rezidenzstadt Wien nebst Floridsdorf und Fedlersdorf, 1900-1913. 28 vols. Vienna.

Lengyel, Emil, *The Danube.* New York: 1939.

Liddell Hart, Basil H., *A History of the World War.* London: 1934.

Ludendorff, Erich, *Meine Kriegserinnerungen, 1914-1918.* Berlin: 1920.

Ludwig, Emil, *July 1914.* (Translated by C. A. Macartney.) London: 1929.

May, Arthur J., *The Habsburg Monarchy, 1867-1914.* Cambridge: 1951.

Molden, Berthold, *Alois Graf Aehrenthal.* Berlin: 1917.

Moltke, Helmuth von, *Erinnerungen, Briefe, Dokumente 1877-1916.* Stuttgart: 1922.

Mylonas, George E., *The Balkan States.* Washington: 1947.

Newman, Bernard, *Epics of Espionage.* London: 1950.

Nicolai, Walther, *The German Secret Service.* London: 1924.

———, *Nachrichtendienst, Presse und Volkstimmung im Weltkrieg.* Berlin: 1920.

Österreich Staatsarchiv, *Serie-Inventare Österreichischer Archiv.* Vol. 2. Vienna: 1953.

———, *Inventar des Kriegsarchivs Wien.* Vienna: 1953.

Owen, Frank, *Tempestuous Journey.* London: 1954.

Ray, Oscar, *Espions et Espionnage.* Paris: 1936.

Redlich, Josef, *Das politische Tagebuch Josef Redlichs.* 2 vols. Edited by F. Fellner. Graz-Köln: 1953.

————, *Emperor Francis Joseph of Austria.* New York: 1929.

Ronge, Maximilian, *Kriegs- und Industrie-Spionage.* Vienna: 1930.

Rowan, R. W., *Spies and the Next War.* New York: 1936.

Schematissmus der k. und k. Armee, 1882-1913. 31 vols. Vienna.

Sedgwick, Henry Dwight, *Vienna, the Biography of a Bygone City.* Indianapolis: 1939.

Seeliger, Emil, *Spione und Verrater.* Berlin: 1930.

————, *Hotel Sacher.* Berlin: 1939.

Shepherd, Gordon. *The Austrian Odyssey.* London: 1957.

————, *Russia's Danubian Empire.* London: 1954.

Steed, Henry W., *The Habsburg Monarchy.* London: 1913.

Steinitz, Eduard Ritter von, *Rings um Sasonow.* Berlin: 1928.

Taylor, A. J. P., *The Habsburg Monarchy, 1815-1918.* London: 1948.

————, *The Struggle for Mastery in Europe.* Oxford: 1954.

Tremel, Ferdinand, *Kaisertum Österreich.* Graz: 1946.

Tschuppik, Karl, *Francis Joseph I.* New York: 1930.

————, *The Empress Elizabeth of Austria.* London: 1930.

————, *The Reign of Emperor Francis Joseph.* London: 1930.

Urbanski, August von Ostrymiecz, *Conrad von Hötzendorf.* Graz: 1938.

————, *Die Ausspähung und deren Abwehr.* Chapter excerpt, pp. 798-810. Source unidentified.

————, *Das Tornisterkind.* Private manuscript.

Walzel, Clemens von, *Kundschaftsdienst oder Spionage.* Leipzig: 1934.

Wassiljew, A. T., *Ochrana.* Vienna: 1930.

West, Rebecca, *The Meaning of Treason.* London: 1949.

Westwood, Gordon, *Society and the Homosexual.* London: 1952.

Wilde, Oscar, *De Profundis.* London: 1949.

Zweig, Stefan, *The World of Yesterday.* London: 1943.

————, *Ungeduld des Herzens.* 1938.

II. Newspapers and Periodicals

Allgemeine Schweizerische Militär-Zeitung. 13 vols. Basel: 1900-1913.

Fremden-Blatt. Vienna: May 26-June 30, 1913.

Le Figaro. Paris: May 30-June 13, 1913.

Le Petit Parisien. Paris: May 30-June 15, 1913.

Militärische Rundschau. Vienna: 1912-1913.

Neue Freie Presse. 56 vols. Vienna: 1900-1913.

New York Times. New York: May 30-June 13, 1913.

Streffleur's Militärische Zeitschrift. 26 vols. Vienna: 1900-1913.

The Times. London: May 30-June 13, 1913.

III. Commerce Archives, Vienna *

File Number 172. Subject: Imperial and Royal Carl Ludwig Railroad Company, Personnel and Death Records, Franz Redl.

* These documents have not been released heretofore.

IV. Archives of the Province of Lower Austria *

File Number XIII—4221/1 of October 23, 1913. Subject: Request for legal change of name by Oskar Redl.

V. Archives of the City of Vienna *

Legal Proceedings, Case of August Doré. 217 pages.
Legal Proceedings, Case of Alexander von Carina. 2 vols. 672 pages.
Legal Proceedings, Case of Doctor Bronislaus Ossolinski. 3 vols. 611 pages.
Legal Proceedings, Case of Bronislaus Dyrcz and Simon Lawrow. 3 vols. 924 pages.
Legal Proceedings, Case of Peter Contin. 2 vols. 924 pages.

VI. War Archives, Vienna *

A. Department of the Military Chancellery of His Imperial and Royal Highness, General of the Cavalry and Admiral Archduke Franz Ferdinand:
Number 14-24 of May 25, 1913. Folios 1-2. Military Chancellery to Franz Ferdinand. Subject: Redl's Suicide.
Number 14-24/2 of May 28, 1913. Folio 1. Chief of the General Staff to Franz Ferdinand. Subject: Homosexuality and Treachery of Redl.
   Folios 2-3. Colonel Bardolff to Francis Ferdinand. Subject: Homosexuality and Treachery of Redl.
Number 14-24/3 of June 1, 1913. Folios 1-2. Colonel Bardolff to Minister of War and reply. Subject: Request for details of Redl case.
Number 14-24/4 of June 5, 1913. Folios 1-16. Colonel Bardolff to Francis Ferdinand. Subject: Government's Reply to Parliamentary Interpellation in Redl case.
Number 14-24/5 of June, 1913. Folios 1-18. Chief of the General Staff to Colonel Bardolff. Subject: Chief of the General Staff's report to the Emperor and Government's reply to Parliamentary Interpellation in Redl case.
Number 14-24/6 of June 3, 1913. Minister of War to Colonel Bardolff. Subject: General Baron von Giesl's trip to Vienna.
Number 14-24/10 of June 11, 1913. Colonel Bardolff to Francis Ferdinand. Subject: Investigation in Redl case.
Number 14-24/11 of June 18, 1913. Folios 1-10. Colonel Bardolff to Francis Ferdinand. Subject: Personal reports by members of the Arresting Commission, Redl case.
Number 14-24/12 of June 28, 1913. Military Chancellery to the War Ministry. Subject: Secret Mobilization Plan of 1910.

* These documents have not been released heretofore.

Number 14-24/15 of July 30, 1913. Folios 1-3. Austro-Hungarian Military Attaché in Rome to Chief of the General Staff and the Military Chancellery. Subject: Conversation with Senior Ecclesiastical Prince.

Number 14-24/16 of August 5, 1913. Ministry of War to Military Chancelleries of the Emperor and the Heir Presumptive. Subject: Official costs of the Redl case.

Number 59-50 of May 8, 1913. Folios 1-13. Colonel Redl to Colonel Bardolff. Subject: Anti-Monarchy article in confiscated Prague newspaper.

Number 40-11/1 of April 19, 1913. Folios 1-6. Colonel Redl to Colonel Bardolff. Subject: Translation of and advice concerning article written by a private citizen on the Montenegrin Army.

Number 36-2/3 of January 27, 1914. Ministry of War to Military Chancelleries of the Emperor and the Heir Presumptive. Subject: Final Disposition of *corpora delicti* in the Redl case.

Number 60-6/2 of May 16, 1914. Folios 1-10. Minister of War to Francis Ferdinand. Subject: Relief from active duty of Colonel Urbanski.

Number 60-6/2-1 of June 10, 1914. Folios 1-4. Colonel Bardolff to Archduke Francis Ferdinand. Subject: Discovery of photographs of secret documents in the auctioned camera of Redl.

Number 60-6/2-3 of June 21, 1914. Folios 1-2. Chief of the General Staff to the Military Chancellery. Subject: Return of documents in case of Colonel Urbanski.

B. Department of the War College in Vienna:

File Number 23. Report of Tactical Student Trip, 1894, Alfred Redl.
File Number 23-84. Report of Mapping Exercise, 1893, Alfred Redl.
File Number 53. Entrance Examination Result, 1893, Alfred Redl.
File Number 11. Result of Chief Entrance Examination, 1892, all participants.
File Number 23-CL. Class Standing, End of First Year, 1893, all students.

C. Department of the Military Chancellery of His Imperial and Royal Highness, The Emperor Francis Joseph:

Number 13-3/27 of September 25, 1905. Folios 1-4. Subject: Award of the Military Service Cross to Captain Alfred Redl.

Number 13-2/2-2 of April 22, 1906. Folio 2. Subject: Award of the Royal Spanish Military Service Order, Second Class, to Major Alfred Redl.

Number 50-1/12 of October 14, 1912. Folios 1-2. Subject: Award of the Expression of Supreme Satisfaction to Colonel Redl.

Number 28-2/24 of May 25, 1913. Subject: Report of Redl's suicide to the Military Chancellery of the Emperor.

Number 28-2/25 of 1913. Subject: Reply to Interpellation placed in Parliament, and letter from private citizen.

D. Department of the Ministry of War Presidium:

Number 2-88/2 of 1907. Subject: Records of Alfred Redl, transfer of from the *Landwehr* to the Intelligence Bureau.

Number 17-67/68 of August 13, 1909. Folios 1-71. Subject: Award of the Iron Crown, Third Class, to Lieutenant Colonel Redl.

Number 6-8/25 of September 18, 1909. Subject: Award of the Prussian Royal Order of the Crown, Second Class, to Major Redl.

Number 76-7/17-2 of April 6, 1909. Subject: Composition of the General Staff in case of war.

Number 28-42 of November 23, 1910. Folios 1-2. Subject: Appointment of Lieutenant Colonel Redl as permanent military expert witness in civil trials.

Number 1-1/2 of April 27, 1909. Folios 2, 4-6. Subject: Promotion of Major Redl.

Number 40-10/24 of August, 1910. Folios 1-2. Subject: Appointment of Lieutenant Colonel Redl as military expert witness.

Number 5-9/2 of May 1, 1911. Folios 1-3. Subject: General Staff recommendation of Lieutenant Colonel Redl for decoration by the Emperor.

Number 2-101/2 of April 25, 1911. Folios 2-8. Subject: Transfer of Lieutenant Colonel Redl.

Number 1-1/5 of April 30, 1912. Folios 2, 29. Subject: Promotion of Lieutenant Colonel Redl.

Number 2-240/2 of October 10, 1912. Folios 1, 3. Subject: Transfer of Colonel Redl.

Number 10-18/2 of January 22, 1913. Subject: Retirement of Lieutenant Colonel Oskar Redl.

Number 2399. Subject: Qualification List of Alfred Redl.

Number 446-1/2/61-98. Subject: Personal Register of Alfred Redl.

E. Department of the General Staff:

Number 992 of April 1, 1896. Chief of the General Staff to Commanding Generals, all Army Corps. Subject: General Staff Trip of 1896 (Assignment of Alfred Redl).

Number 774 of April 1, 1897. Folio 3. Chief of the General Staff to Ministry of War. Subject: Promotion of Alfred Redl.

Number 5-1/6 of April 19, 1898. Personnel Bureau of General Staff to General Staff officers. Subject: Assignment to Language School, Kazan, Russia.

Number 5-1/7 of June 6, 1898. Alfred Redl to Personnel Bureau of the General Staff. Subject: Request for assignment to Language School, Kazan, Russia.

Number 5-1/8 of October 16, 1898. Captain Dokomal to Personnel Bureau of the General Staff. Personnel Bureau to Alfred Redl. Subject: Assignment to Language School, Kazan, Russia.

Number 46-16 of November 2, 1899. Chief of the General Staff to Alfred Redl. Subject: Language School, Kazan, Russia.

Number 5-1/1 of January 15, 1899. Chief of the General Staff to the Austro-Hungarian Military Attaché in St. Petersburg. Subject: Arrival of Captain Redl.

Number 5-1/2 of February 12, 1899. The Austro-Hungarian Military Attaché in St. Petersburg to the Chief of the General Staff. Subject: Arrival of language students in St. Petersburg.

Number 5-1/3 of March 1, 1899. Chief of the General Staff to the Austro-Hungarian Military Attaché in St. Petersburg and to Captain Redl and Captain Dáni. Subject: Language School, Kazan, Russia.

Number 5-1/4 of March 19, 1899. Chief of the General Staff to the Ministry of War. Subject: Travel of language students to Russia.

Number 5-1/5 of March 19, 1899. Chief of the General Staff to the regimental commanding officers of Captains Dáni and Redl. Subject: Transfer of records.

Number 7-2 of March 15, 1899. Chief of the General Staff to Ministry of War. Subject: Return of officers to the General Staff Corps.

Number 7-2/3 of April 16, 1899. Chief of the General Staff to the Ministry of War. Subject: Promotion of General Staff officers to Captain, First Class.

Number 47-1/3 of May 19, 1899. Personnel Bureau of the General Staff to Alfred Redl. Subject: Discrepancy in return of Redl's bedding.

Number 47-1/4 of June 28, 1899. Redl to Personnel Bureau of the General Staff. Subject: Redl's return of bedding.

Number 2-18/4 of April 30, 1900. Chief of the General Staff to all Army Corps. Subject: Assignment of General Staff officers.

Number 2-39 of October 3, 1900. Chief of the General Staff to all Army Corps. Subject: Change in assignments of General Staff officers.

Number 19-4 of February 1, 1900. Personnel Bureau to Alfred Redl. Subject: Arrangement of free apartment and hospitalization for Redl's mother.

Number 19-22 of April 20, 1900. Alfred Redl to Chief of the General Staff and to the Ministry of War. Subject: Request for leave.

Number 19-22/2 of May 5, 1900. Chief of the General Staff and Ministry of War to Alfred Redl. Subject: Arrangements for personal leave.

Number 66-1/1 of January 13, 1901. Chief of the General Staff to General Staff officers. Subject: Election of General Staff Horse Fund Committee.

Number 2-28 of August 17, 1905. Folios 1-2. Chief of the General Staff to the Imperial-Royal Ministry of Defense and to the War Ministry. Subject: Assignment of General Staff officers to the *Landwehr*.

Number 7-2/1 of September 29, 1905. Chief of the General Staff to the Ministry of War. Subject: Recommendation of General Staff officers for promotion to major.

Number 8-43 of September 13, 1905. Chief of the Intelligence Bureau to Chief of the General Staff. Subject: Recommendation of Captain Alfred Redl for decoration.

Number 14-1/7 of April 18, 1905. Chief of the General Staff to General Staff officers. Subject: General Staff Trip, 1905.

Number 5-2/3 of November 4, 1906. Folios 1-2. Military Chancellery of the Emperor to the Personnel Bureau of the General Staff. Subject:

Appointment of Alfred Redl as interpreter to visiting Russian funeral delegation.

Number 14-2/6-5 of 1907. Chief of the General Staff to General Staff officers. Subject: Appointment to the large General Staff Trip of June, 1907.

Number 19-16 of March, 1908. Doctor Hofer to the Personnel Bureau of the General Staff. Subject: Illness of Major Redl.

Number 66-1/3 of February 11, 1908. Chief of the General Staff to General Staff officers. Subject: Election of officers to General Staff Horse Fund Committee.

Number 66-8/5 of November 7, 1908. Major Redl to Chief of the General Staff and Ministry of War. Subject: Request for new service horse.

Number 2-77 of 1909. Chief of the General Staff to General Staff officers. Subject: Assignment to duty stations.

Number 7-1/2 of March 24, 1909. Chief of the General Staff to General Staff officers. Subject: Promotion of General Staff officers.

Number 8/17 of March, 1909. Chief of the General Staff to Ministry of War. Subject: Recommendation of Lieutenant Colonel Alfred Redl for the Order of the Iron Crown, Third Class.

Number 39-3/24 of July 5, 1909. Chief of the General Staff to General Staff officers. Subject: Appointment of General Staff officers as maneuver umpires.

Number 39-13/5 of June 22, 1909. Chief of the General Staff to General Staff officers. Subject: Troop maneuver assignments.

Number 28-6/2 of April 9, 1910. Folio 20. Lieutenant Colonel Alfred Redl to Personnel Bureau of the General Staff. Subject: Request for assignment to Special Artillery Orientation Course.

Number 28-2/3 of April 9, 1910. Chief of the General Staff to General Staff officers. Subject: Assignment to Artillery Orientation Course.

Number 2-4 of January 9, 1911. Folios 1-14. Chief of the General Staff to Intelligence Bureau. Subject: Reassignment of General Staff officers.

Number 8-17 of April 14, 1911. Chief of the General Staff to Military Chancellery of the Emperor. Subject: Request for Expression of Supreme Satisfaction to Lieutenant Colonel Alfred Redl.

Number 2-59 of September 28, 1912. Chief of the General Staff to Ministry of War. Subject: Recommendation of Redl for General Staff Chief of the Eighth Corps, Prague.

Number 7-1/4 of April 3, 1912. Chief of the General Staff to Ministry of War. Subject: Promotion of General Staff officers.

Number 18-14 of June 5, 1913. Folios 1-4. Chief of the General Staff to Ministry of War and to the Vienna Garrison Command. Subject: Disposal of Redl's private effects.

Number 18-14 of June 5, 1913. Folio 5. Operations Bureau of the General Staff to the Army Inspector in Sarajevo. Subject: Recall and destruction of secret war plans.

Number 18-14 of June 5, 1913. Folios 6-8. Austro-Hungarian Military Attaché in Berlin to the Chief of the General Staff and the Chief of the General Staff to General von Moltke. Subject: Extent of Redl's treachery.

Number 18-14/3 of June, 1913. Folios 6-7. Chief of the General Staff to Captain Emil Ratzenhofer and to Eighth Corps Command, Prague. Subject: Orders to Ratzenhofer to make investigation of documents that had been available to Redl.

Number 18-14/3 of June, 1913. Folios 8-14. Ratzenhofer to Chief of the General Staff. Subject: Report on classified documents that had been available to Redl.

Number 18-14/5 of July 12, 1913. Ministry of War to the Operations Bureau of the General Staff. Subject: Redl investigation.

Number 18-14/6 of October 2, 1913. Subject: Redl investigation.

Number 18-14/5 of July 18, 1913. Subject: Redl investigation.

Number 36-2/11 of June 11, 1913. Chief of the General Staff to General Staff officers. Subject: Corps Command, Redl case.

Afterword and Acknowledgments

THE origin of this book goes back some seven years to a rainy night in a *Schlösschen* or country house a few miles outside of Salzburg. I was working for American intelligence in Austria at the time, and that is perhaps why I had taken from the old library a leather-bound volume called *Spionage*, a history of Austro-Hungarian army intelligence written by General Maximilian Ronge. I was browsing through this work when I struck the chapter on Alfred Redl. Never having heard of the case, I was soon fascinated in it from an intelligence standpoint and, as I continued wading through the difficult German, I became just as fascinated in Redl from the human standpoint. Upon finishing the chapter I experienced disappointment—Ronge had told so little of what surely was a lot. Who was Redl, *really*—where had he come from, why had he gotten into such a wretched mess, how had he gotten away with it? I decided then that one day I wanted to write the story of Alfred Redl.

For the next three years my desire was frustrated. While I went from the Salzburg desk to another in Marine Corps intelligence I found myself in an active professional and social existence that precluded any more than taking notes whenever I ran across the name of Redl. A sudden illness changed matters: hospitalization allowed me to finish researching the case from American and English sources; retirement from the Marine Corps, which included a lump-sum payment of five thousand dollars, allowed my return to Europe. I went to Vienna thinking I would have the book written in a year. I was wrong.

Initial probing abroad brought study of what is the closest approxima-tion to a definitive work that existed on the Redl case: *Der Fall des General-Stabschef Redl* by Egon Erwin Kisch, the Prague reporter who broke the scandal in 1913. Most American and English sources—generally chapters in espionage anthologies—depended on this book, but now I discovered other and more valid secondary sources which either enlarged or contradicted Kisch's information. That he had made numerous factual errors soon became obvious, not surprising since he did not have access to official records and since he had published in 1924 and thus could not use material offered in the later memoirs of persons directly involved with Redl. Further, neither Kisch nor these other persons had concerned them-selves with Redl's background. But it was from a comparative study of all these sources that I was able to make a research "target list" and start trying to find the answers.

My overtures to the War Archives in Vienna were met by an instant rebuff in the form of a military director who assured me that neither I nor anyone else would ever be allowed to study the pertinent documents. To hurdle this obstacle, I began lobbying with the President of Austria, the late Theodor Körner (who told me in detail about his own friendship with Redl), and worked down through a bureaucratic maze which after about fifteen months came to an apparent blind end. To complicate mat-ters, I had just run out of money when my agent wrote me to forget the whole project, that no one in America would be interested in such a book. This annoyed me to the degree that I borrowed another five thousand dollars, fired the agent and went back to work. A month later I fortu-nately discovered an agent who welcomed the idea of this book (and who has constantly urged me to its completion). Three months later the bureau-cratic maze led me to a cabinet minister who held the necessary power and the courage to say yes. Armed with proper credentials I returned to the War Archives to be welcomed by a new director, a delightful and co-operative scholar named Dr. Krauss, who turned me over to his able assistant, Dr. Szaivert. Thus it was that I became the first private in-dividual to sift (and have photographed) the official documents which in turn led to the discovery of the heretofore neglected files of Archduke Francis Ferdinand as well as to files in other archives, all holding a plethora of new information on the case and on Redl himself (see Bibliography).

During my prolonged battle with Austrian (and French, Italian and Russian) bureaucracy, I was also investigating other original sources: per-sons who had known Redl. Most of the principals—officers such as Conrad von Hötzendorf, August Urbanski and Max Ronge—were dead, but in some instances, especially that of the Urbanski family, their survivors offered valuable information. Too, many junior officers of Redl's time were still alive and were often helpful, indeed essential to filling the gaps. That is not to say that frustration and disappointment were ever far re-moved from the effort of these years, and yet some form of compensation seemed forever present. Although, for example, I never did locate the

Redl-Batjuschin correspondence (which I am convinced was destroyed), a considerably lesser effort won me the helpful friendship of the scientist and author Tristan Busch, who as an Austro-Hungarian intelligence officer had personally read the correspondence when it was confiscated in Warsaw by German intelligence early in the Great War. Again, I spent months looking for the espionage treatises allegedly written by Redl only to learn that at the end of World War I the Chief of the Intelligence Bureau, General Ronge, had personally burned all such documents including lists of spies and informants; soon after, however, I found two retired intelligence officers who remembered the documents very well, had read and studied them, in other words verified their existence and Redl's authorship, a finding substantiated and enlarged by a fortunate poking into some remote archives that produced the official records of five complete espionage cases in which Redl was deeply involved. The matter of Redl's male paramour, Stefan, was especially difficult. Having heard that he was still alive, I had spent over a year trying to locate him when one night an anonymous telephone call gave me his exact name and address. (I subsequently found him, a large man who disquietingly clutched a meat chopper during our first interview.) I followed dozens of false leads; I was once threatened by a seventy-year-old madman, I have wasted hours with persons who wanted either money or—more sadly—just someone to talk to. But I spent as many hours with delightful persons who could tell me about Redl and his army and that incredible political entity, the Austro-Hungarian Empire. Taken altogether, my research effort was similar to a detective trying to reconstruct not only a crime but the motivation for it.

Writing the book was another problem. As my research had painfully disclosed, neither homosexuality nor espionage lend themselves to detailed recording, nor did the post-World War I destruction of certain case documents help. I lacked some information, and no one knew it better than I, and I knew further that until the Kremlin opens its historical files I had satisfied myself in the research task: I had uncovered a tremendous amount of new information in official archives, I had learned (and was often able to corroborate) other information from personal interviews, I had made a research synthesis of all important secondary sources and, perhaps most important, I felt that I had the necessary picture of Alfred Redl. To put it down and yet to keep the story human and thus alive, I decided that I would have to play high judge during the preparation. Accordingly the selection of facts is my own responsibility and so is the interpretation placed on certain contradictions in existing evidence. Because I can not offer positive proof for a few of my assertions and because this case is still living, I have used fictitious names where one or more of three factors are involved: where it would embarrass persons who have paid a penalty and who are still living or who have survivors; where there is doubt about the name of a person involved in any single incident; or where I have constructed a scene that may reflect adversely on one of the principals.

The reader should know that I am deeply indebted to the following persons who have so generously aided me in collection of source material: Doktor Alexander Lernet-Holenia, Frau Helene Scheu-Riess, Doktor Ernst Benedict, Professor Doktor Lorenz Böhler, Professor Doktor Erwin Stransky, Professor Doktor Heinrich Benedict, Professor Doktor Hans Hoff, Hofrat i.R. Oberst a.D. Andreas Figl, Oberst a.D. Gustav von Hubka, Oberst a.D. Baron Viktor von Seiller, Frau Doktor Heide Heiny née Urbanski, Frau Witwe General August Urbanski von Ostrymiecz, Direktor Doktor Hans Urbanski, Bundespräsident General a.D. Theodor Körner (deceased), Baron Johann A. Eichoff, Bundesminister Ferdinand Graf, Doktor Ludwig Jedlicka and personnel of the War Museum in Vienna, General a.D. Emil Liebitzky, Doktors Krauss and Szaivert and personnel of the War Archives in Vienna, Chauffeur Karl Scharer, Direktor Doktor Fritz Molden, Oberstleutnant a.D. Hermann Weise, Doktor Josef Reichelt, Ingenieur and Frau Doktor Howorka, Doktor Tristan Busch, Doktor Gideon Büro, Professor i.R. Doktor Hans Giebisch, Hauptmann i.R. Hermann Goriany, Doktor Oskar Dressler, Doktor Ludwig Bürgel, Frau General Witwe von Dragoni, Doktor Helmuth Peter, Oberst a.D. Doktor Johann Blumenthal, Doktor Max Vlad. Allmayer-Beck, Mr. Friedrich Torberg, Mr. Joseph Wechsberg, Colonel Olle-Laprune, Professor C. V. Easum, Doktor Dietrich Mende, Mr. George Bell Dyer, Major Anthony Aylmer, the personnel of the National and University libraries in Vienna, Doktor Edmund Bergler, the personnel of German archives too numerous to list, the personnel of the Wiener Institute, London, and of the Writers and Speakers Research, London. I am equally indebted to those persons who have offered valuable information but who have preferred to remain anonymous.

It is impossible to thank all of the persons who have otherwise contributed to the writing of this book, but in particular I would like to mention the following: in Vienna, Mr. and Mrs. John Meyer, Mr. and Mrs. William Busser, Mr. and Mrs. Robert Deans, Oberst Doktor and Frau Doktor Johann Blumenthal, Mr. and Mrs. Ronald Blackett, Mrs. Betty Alexander, Mr. Nigel Leigh-Pemberton, Count Jakob Coudenhove-Kalergi, Mr. William Carter, Miss Louise Raimey, the American Minister in Vienna, James K. Penfield, and Mrs. Penfield, Mr. and Mrs. Julian Bullard, Baron and Baroness Wolfgang Bachofen von Echt, Mr. Earl Gilmore, Doktor and Frau Doktor Hugo Hild, Professor Doktor and Frau Doktor Paul Kyrle, Mr. and Mrs. Max Altmann, Frau Witwe Reusser and daughter, Insulinde, Mr. and Mrs. Maurice Firth, Mr. Maarten Schiemer; in Brussels, Mr. Alan B. Urwick; in Palma, Mallorca, Mrs. Claire Cottmann, Mr. and Mrs. Robert Graves; in San Remo, Mr. and Mrs. Stewart Cochrane; in Paris, Mr. Philip Ziegler; in London, Doctor Joan Saunders, Mr. Brian MacDermot, Miss Jennifer Burrows, Mr. and Mrs. Philip Asprey, Mr. and Mrs. Eric Asprey; in Oxford, Mr. and Mrs. F. J. H. Sanders; in Wolverton Park, Captain and Mrs. B. H. Liddell Hart; in America, Miss Luella Pollock, Miss Sarah Gibson Blanding, Miss Sydnor Walker,

Professor Winifred Asprey and Mr. and Mrs. Peter Asprey, Jr., to whom this book is dedicated.

My translations have been reviewed and in many instances repaired by the combined effort of Frau Daisy Sigmund, Oberst Doktor Johann Blumenthal and Mr. John Brenner. While my debt to them is great, I must take full responsibility for all translations that appear in the actual text.

Finally I would like to thank Mr. and Mrs. Peter Asprey, Jr., Doctor Joan Saunders, and Mr. Kurt Hellmer for their critical readings of my manuscript and for their constant encouragement given to me during the long preparation for and the actual writing of this book.

R.B.A.

Cathed Studios
Bermuda

INDEX

Acht, Captain, 167-168, 171, 176
Aehrenthal, Baron von, 157, 182-188, 193
Agram, 103; treason trials, 186-187
Albergo, Count de Alvanti, 201-205
Albrecht, Archduke, 182
Alexander, Crown Prince, 185
America, 102, 135
Anders, Carl von, 18, 41
Annexation Crisis, 182-193
Arna, Duke von, 280
Aston, Sir George, 264
Auffenberg-Komarów, Moritz von, 25, 182, 292-293
Austria-Hungary, 11-12, 18, 23-25, 56, 102, 109, 120, 144, 155, 160, 182-187, 192, 202, 226, 292, 294
    Austrian Parliament, 34, 169, 262, 266, 268, 275-279, 281, 290
    Emperor, *see* Francis Joseph
    Foreign Office, 106, 145, 154, 156-157, 182-187, 193
    General Staff, 11, 33, 35, 38-39, 41, 44, 47, 49, 60, 63, 72, 74, 76-77, 80-84, 101, 103, 106, 108, 130, 132, 138-139, 149, 156-157, 163, 171, 177-179, 182, 192, 200, 206-209, 211-212, 216, 222, 224, 237, 241, 246-247, 261-262, 267-270, 273, 278-283, 286, 291-292, 294
    Chief of the, 12, 14, 78, 85, 94, 97, 102, 105, 111, 131, 133, 154-158, 177, 179, 181-182, 188-190, 209, 224, 233, 252, 269-270, 273, 276, 279-281, 284, 287

Field trips and maneuvers, 83, 102, 151, 177-178, 182, 216, 223-224, 286-287
Intelligence Bureau, 12-13, 82-83, 85-86, 101-109, 120-122, 144, 177-178, 190-191, 208, 219, 225-226, 231, 236, 268, 270, 276-277, 284
    Budget, 106-107, 182, 193, 212, 231
    Cases, 105, 118-123, 141-145, 148-149, 161-168, 173-177, 202-203, 211-212, 214, 236-237; Annexation Crisis, 188-189, 192-194, 218-219
    Chief of the, 12, 83, 86-87, 97, 102-108, 149, 167-168, 182, 190-192, 195, 197, 222-223, 237, 269-270
    Mission, 102-107, 144
    Relations with German Intelligence, 105, 193-194, 226, 236-237, 270, 285
    Techniques, 107-108, 146-148, 164-166, 177, 188-189, 193, 211-212, 237-238, 270
Operations Bureau, 156, 190-191, 285-286
Personnel Bureau, 84, 87-88, 94-96, 179, 222, 281
Railroad Bureau, 74, 77, 81, 285
Telegraph Bureau, 179
War College, 36, 38-39, 44, 48-49, 63-65, 67-75, 79, 81, 199, 206, 220, 255
Germany, relations with, 105, 144, 193-194, 204, 226, 236-237, 270, 282-286, 293

FINE WORKS OF FICTION AND NON-FICTION AVAILABLE IN QUALITY PAPERBACK EDITIONS FROM CARROLL & GRAF

☐ Anderson, Nancy/WORK WITH PASSION
$8.95, Cloth $15.95
☐ Appel, Allen/TIME AFTER TIME   Cloth $17.95
☐ Asch, Sholem/THE APOSTLE $10.95
☐ Asch, Sholem/EAST RIVER $8.95
☐ Asch, Sholem/MARY $10.95
☐ Asch, Sholem/THE NAZARENE
$10.95 Cloth $21.95
☐ Asch, Sholem/THREE CITIES $10.50
☐ Athill, Diana/INSTEAD OF A LETTER
$7.95 Cloth $15.95
☐ Babel, Issac/YOU MUST KNOW EVERYTHING
$8.95
☐ Bedford, Sybille/ALDOUS HUXLEY $14.95
☐ Bellaman, Henry/KINGS ROW $8.95
☐ Bernanos, Georges/DIARY OF A
COUNTRY PRIEST $7.95
☐ Berton, Pierre/KLONDIKE FEVER $10.95
☐ Blanch, Lesley/PIERRE LOTI $10.95
☐ Blanch, Lesley/THE SABRES OF PARADISE$9.95
☐ Blanch, Lesley/THE WILDER SHORES OF LOVE
$8.95
☐ Bowers, John/IN THE LAND OF NYX $7.95
☐ Buchan, John/PILGRIM'S WAY $10.95
☐ Carr, Virginia Spencer/THE LONELY HUNTER: A
BIOGRAPHY OF CARSON McCULLERS $12.95
☐ Chekov, Anton/LATE BLOOMING FLOWERS
$8.95
☐ Conot, Robert/JUSTICE AT NUREMBURG$10.95
☐ Conrad, Joseph/SEA STORIES $8.95
☐ Conrad, Joseph & Ford Madox Ford/
THE INHERITORS $7.95
☐ Conrad, Joseph & Ford Madox Ford/ROMANCE
$8.95

- [ ] Cooper, Lady Diana/AUTOBIOGRAPHY $12.95
- [ ] Cortázar, Julio/A MANUAL FOR MANUEL $9.95
- [ ] Cozzens, James Gould/THE LAST ADAM $8.95
- [ ] de Montherlant, Henry/THE GIRLS $11.95
- [ ] de Poncins, Gontran/KABLOONA $9.95
- [ ] Edwards, Anne/SONYA: THE LIFE OF COUNTESS TOLSTOY $8.95
- [ ] Elkington, John/THE GENE FACTORYCloth $16.95
- [ ] Farson, Negley/THE WAY OF A TRANSGRESSOR $9.95
- [ ] Fennelly, Tony/THE GLORY HOLE MURDERS Cloth $14.95
- [ ] Feutchwanger, Lion/JEW SUSS $8.95 Cloth $18.95
- [ ] Feutchwanger, Lion/THE OPPERMANS $8.95
- [ ] Feutchwanger, Lion/SUCCESS $10.95
- [ ] Fisher, R.L./THE PRINCE OF WHALES Cloth $12.95
- [ ] Ford Madox Ford & Joseph Conrad/ THE INHERITORS $7.95
- [ ] Ford Madox Ford & Joseph Conrad/ROMANCE $8.95
- [ ] Freudenberger, H.J./SITUATIONAL ANXIETY $8.95
- [ ] Fuchs, Daniel/SUMMER IN WILLIAMSBURG $8.95
- [ ] Gold, Michael/JEWS WITHOUT MONEY $7.95
- [ ] Goldin, Stephen & Sky, Kathleen/THE BUSINESS OF BEING A WRITER $8.95
- [ ] Green, Julian/DIARIES 1928–1957 $9.95
- [ ] Greene, Graham & Hugh/THE SPY'S BEDSIDE BOOK $7.95
- [ ] Hamsun, Knut/MYSTERIES $8.95
- [ ] Hawkes, John/VIRGINIE: HER TWO LIVES $7.95
- [ ] Haycraft, Howard (ed.)/ART OF THE MYSTERY STORY $9.95
- [ ] Haycraft, Howard (ed.)/MURDER FOR PLEASURE $10.95
- [ ] Ibañez, Vincente Blasco/THE FOUR HORSEMAN OF THE APOCALYPSE $8.95
- [ ] Jackson, Charles/THE LOST WEEKEND $7.95

- [ ] Lambert, Colin/HERE'S WHY $8.95
- [ ] Lansing, Alfred/ENDURANCE: SHAKLETON'S INCREDIBLE VOYAGE $8.95
- [ ] Linder, Mark/THERE CAME A PROUD BEGGAR Cloth $18.95
- [ ] Macaulay, Rose/CREWE TRAIN $8.95
- [ ] Macmillan, Harold/THE BLAST OF WAR $12.95
- [ ] Martin, Jay/NATHANAEL WEST: THE ART OF HIS LIFE $8.95
- [ ] Maurois, Andre/OLYMPIO: THE LIFE OF VICTOR HUGO $12.95
- [ ] Maurois, Andre/PROMETHEUS: THE LIFE OF BALZAC $11.95
- [ ] Maurois, Andre/PROUST: PORTRAIT OF A GENIUS $10.95
- [ ] McCarthy, Barry & Emily/SEXUAL AWARENESS $9.95
- [ ] McElroy, Joseph/LOOKOUT CARTRIDGE $9.95
- [ ] McElroy, Joseph/A SMUGGLER'S BIBLE $9.50
- [ ] Mizener, Arthur/THE SADDEST STORY: A BIOGRAPHY OF FORD MADOX FORD $12.95
- [ ] Montyn, Jan & Kooiman, Dirk Ayelt/A LAMB TO SLAUGHTER $8.95
- [ ] Mullins, Edwin/THE PAINTED WITCH Cloth $25.00
- [ ] Munro, H.H./THE NOVELS AND PLAYS OF SAKI $8.95
- [ ] Munthe, Axel/THE STORY OF SAN MICHELE $8.95
- [ ] O'Casey, Sean/AUTOBIOGRAPHIES I $10.95 Cloth $21.95
- [ ] O'Casey, Sean/AUTOBIOGRAPHIES II $10.95 Cloth $21.95
- [ ] O'Faolain, Julia/THE OBEDIENT WIFE Cloth $17.95
- [ ] Olinto, Antonio/THE WATER HOUSE Cloth $18.95
- [ ] Ormrod, Richard/UNA TROUBRIDGE: THE FRIEND OF RADCLYFFE HALL Cloth $18.95
- [ ] Pikser, Jeremy/JUNK ON THE HILL Cloth $13.95
- [ ] Plievier, Theodore/STALINGRAD $8.95

- [ ] Poncins, Gontran de/KABIOONA $9.95
- [ ] Prince, Peter/THE GOOD FATHER Cloth $13.95
- [ ] Proffitt, Nicholas/GARDENS OF STONE

                                      Cloth $14.95
- [ ] Proust, Marcel/ON ART AND LITERATURE $8.95
- [ ] Rechy, John/BODIES AND SOULS

                            $8.95 Cloth $17.95
- [ ] Richelson, Hildy & Stan/INCOME WITHOUT TAXES   Cloth $16.95
- [ ] Rowse, A.L./HOMOSEXUALS IN HISTORY $9.95
- [ ] Roy, Jules/THE BATTLE OF DIENBIENPHU $8.95
- [ ] Russel, Robert A./WINNING THE FUTURE

                                        Cloth $16.95
- [ ] Russell, Franklin/THE HUNTING ANIMAL $7.95
- [ ] Salisbury, Harrison/A JOURNEY FOR OUR TIMES

                                          $10.95
- [ ] Scott, Evelyn/THE WAVE $9.95
- [ ] Service, William/OWL $8.95
- [ ] Sigal, Clancy/GOING AWAY $9.95
- [ ] Silverstein, Fanny/MY MOTHER'S COOKBOOK

                                      Cloth $16.95
- [ ] Singer, I.J./THE BROTHERS ASHKENAZI $9.95
- [ ] Sloan, Allan/THREE PLUS ONE EQUALS BILLIONS $8.95
- [ ] Stein, Leon/THE TRIANGLE FIRE $7.95
- [ ] Taylor, Peter/IN THE MIRO DISTRICT $7.95
- [ ] Tolstoy, Leo/TALES OF COURAGE AND CONFLICT $11.95
- [ ] Wassermann, Jacob/CASPAR HAUSER $9.95
- [ ] Wassermann, Jacob/THE MAURIZIUS CASE $9.95
- [ ] Werfel, Franz/THE FORTY DAYS OF MUSA DAGH $9.95
- [ ] Werth, Alexander/RUSSIA AT WAR: 1941–1945

                                        $15.95
- [ ] Zuckmayer, Carl/A PART OF MYSELF $9.95

Available at fine bookstores everywhere

To order direct from the publishers please send check or money order including the price of the book plus $1.75 per title for postage and handling. N.Y. State Residents please add 8¼% sales tax.

Carroll & Graf Publishers, Inc.
260 Fifth Avenue, New York, N.Y. 10001

Hoover Power Max

695 2818 Supreme